CELL AND
TISSUE CULTURE

CELL AND
TISSUE CULTURE

BY

JOHN PAUL

F.R.S.E., M.B., Ch.B., Ph.D., M.R.C.P. Ed., M.C.Path.

Titular Professor in the Department of Biochemistry,
University of Glasgow. Director, Tissue Culture
Association Summer Course, 1957-60

THIRD

EDITION

BALTIMORE

THE WILLIAMS AND WILKINS COMPANY

1965

© 1965. E. & S. Livingstone Ltd.

First Edition .   .   .   1959
Second Edition   .   .   1960
Reprinted   .   .   .   1961
Third Edition   .   .   .   1965

Printed in Great Britain

PREFACE TO THE THIRD EDITION

WHAT might be called the standard techniques of tissue culture have now been worked out and may be regarded as established. By their application a very rich harvest of scientific information has been reaped in the past ten years. Nevertheless, tissue culture is still in its infancy and perhaps the time has come to emphasise its limitations. We are very far indeed from the ideal of being able to take any tissue or cell-type from any species and maintain it for a long time *in vitro*. Although it is clear that the same general techniques are almost universally applicable to those tissues which have been cultured (a principle I have made a particular attempt to emphasise in revising this edition) it is striking that tissues and cells have, in fact, been grown from a rather restricted range of both plant and animal species. Many tissues from these have been made to survive as organ cultures for some days but only a fraction of cells—certainly much less than 1 per cent. from most tissues—have shown themselves capable of giving rise to strains which can be maintained for extended periods. Some of the failures are striking—such as the failure to grow adult hepatocytes. There is much to be done in improving this record. Even when cell strains have been established it has not proved possible to maintain their normal specialised functions *in vitro* except in a very few cases. Still less success has been achieved in manipulating cells so as to regulate their course of development. The few outstanding exceptions are some very interesting studies with plant cells where, for instance, whole plants have been derived from single somatic cells. If the same could be achieved with mammalian cells its value in medicine might be enormous. Nobody could fail to appreciate the potential value of being able to grow renal tissue, for instance, from a biopsy specimen of a patient with renal deficiency. Such speculations are wholly unrealistic at present but who is to say that the concept is not capable of eventual realisation? It has always been a maxim, to which I have wholeheartedly subscribed, that tissue culture should be regarded as a means to an end and not as an end in itself. I believe that this is still the best advice that can be given to a young research worker. However, the time may now have come to

v

try to extend the range of cell and tissue culture techniques by tackling some of the challenges implicit in the limitations I have mentioned.

This edition contains a good deal of new material but few radical changes. Because of increased interest in organ cultures and large-scale cell cultures these each have a chapter devoted to them. Otherwise, some sections have been rearranged to form a rather more logical presentation with a view to emphasising the basic similarities in the methods used for a wide variety of materials. Some old material has been omitted to make way for new and the bibliographies have been extensively revised.

Once again I should like to thank all those who have written to suggest alterations and additions and I should like to repeat my invitation to readers to send me their comments, criticisms and suggestions.

It is my sincere pleasure, once again, to record my gratitude to Mr. R. Callander for his skilled execution of the drawings and to Mrs. Rae Fergusson for her indispensable and conscientious secretarial help. Mr. Charles Macmillan and Mr. James Parker of Messrs. E. & S. Livingstone have, as always, given me their close co-operation and help.

I have continued to glean much of the material for this book from conversations with colleagues and friends in the University of Glasgow, the British Tissue Culture Association and the Tissue Culture Association and have tried to summarise their experience and my own in this book.

JOHN PAUL.

Glasgow, 1965.

PREFACE TO THE FIRST EDITION

THIS book was written in an attempt to provide an up-to-date account of the techniques and applications of tissue culture since, due to the remarkably rapid development of the subject in the last few years, the excellent texts prepared by other authors are already outdated. It is based on the instruction given at the Tissue Culture Association Summer Course and has been written particularly with the needs of participants of that course in mind. The post-doctorate group taking the course represent workers in a wide variety of fields in which the technique is used. Because of their varied backgrounds, there is often a great lack of uniformity in their basic biological knowledge. Thus, mitosis is often a mystery to a biochemist while the Krebs cycle is only a name to an embryologist. For this reason I have included a few chapters which give an elementary outline of fundamental cytology.

I am of the opinion that a textbook should try to create a sense of proportion and that it fails if it treats all subjects with equal emphasis. Consequently, while giving a brief outline of the entire field of tissue culture, I have tried to emphasise standard procedures. For the reader who might require more detailed information I have provided a reasonably selective bibliography, quoting only key references. The Bibliography of the Research in Tissue Culture is available for those who might wish a complete list of publications.

Undoubtedly, many people will disagree with my opinions as to which subjects require emphasis and it is not unlikely that errors in the text will have escaped my notice. I should like to receive any comments, suggestions and criticisms that readers of the book might wish to make.

It has often been said that a man never writes a book alone and this was never more true than in the present case. I particularly owe a debt to Drs. Margaret Murray and Charles Pomerat who taught me most of what I know about the subject and much of whose material is incorporated in the text. It also includes a great deal of material which has been contributed to the Tissue Culture Course instruction by my colleagues and friends, past and present. Drs. Payne, Sidman, Ackermann, Rutter, Algard, Black and McCarty, Miss Marilyn Bozeman and Mrs. Elsa Zitcer will all find small sections of this book very familiar but I know none of them will mind the liberty I have taken. I should like not only to acknowledge their contributions but also to thank them for the enthusiastic co-operation that has made the Tissue Culture Course so enjoyable and so worthwhile. There is, in addition, some material in this book which originated from our predecessors on the staff of the Tissue Culture Course and I should like to acknowledge the contributions made by Drs. Hanks, Leighton, Fawcett, Scherer and Porter. For some information incorporated in the virology section I have to thank Dr. R. G. Sommerville.

In the actual compilation of the book I could not have done without the conscientious and enthusiastic help of Mrs. Patricia Kent and I am deeply grateful to her for her secretarial assistance. To Mr. R. Callander I am also extremely grateful for the meticulous care and outstanding draughtsmanship with which he executed the drawings. I should like too to thank Mr. Charles Macmillan and Mr. James Parker of Messrs. E. & S. Livingstone for their help, patience and co-operation.

Professor J. N. Davidson and Miss E. S. Pearson read the manuscript and made numerous useful suggestions which I greatly appreciate.

I gratefully acknowledge the loan of illustrations and blocks by the following : Adelphi Manufacturing Co. Ltd., London ; Baird & Tatlock (London) Ltd., London ; Becton Dickinson & Company, Rutherford, New Jersey, U.S.A. ; Bellco Glass Inc., Vineland, New Jersey, U.S.A. ; The Biochemical Journal, London, and Professor H. McIlwain, London ; Electro-Mechanical Development Co., Houston, Texas, U.S.A. ; Gallenkamp & Co., Ltd., London ; Hanovia Lamps, Slough ; Kontes Glass Company, Vineland, New Jersey, U.S.A. ; Laboratory Thermal Equipment Ltd., Greenfield ; Merck Sharp & Dohme Ltd., Hoddesdon, and Dr. Charles Pomerat ; Shandon Scientific Co. Ltd., London.

JOHN PAUL.

Glasgow, 1959.

CONTENTS

PART IV

SPECIAL APPLICATIONS OF CELL AND
TISSUE CULTURE METHODS

INTRODUCTION

CHAPTER I

DEVELOPMENT OF TISSUE CULTURE TECHNIQUES

TISSUE culture developed quite naturally from some of the techniques of embryology which were in use last century. Wilhelm Roux's experiment of maintaining the medullary plate of a chick embryo in warm saline for a few days was performed in the year 1885 and is the first recorded instance of a successful explantation. About the same time Arnold (1887) implanted fragments of alder pith into frogs. When these had become invaded by leucocytes he removed them to a dish of warm saline and subsequently observed that they migrated and survived for a short time.

These two experiments were performed ahead of their time and the possibility that excised animal tissues might be kept alive even longer in favourable conditions was not explored until 1898 when Ljunggren demonstrated by reimplantation that human skin could survive *in vitro* for many days if stored in ascitic fluid.

In 1903, Jolly performed experiments which marked the first detailed observations on cell survival and cell division *in vitro*. He maintained leucocytes from the salamander in hanging drops for up to a month. This study was followed three years later, in 1906, by a paper by Beebe and Ewing which recorded a genuine attempt at tissue culture. These authors described the cultivation of an infectious canine lymphosarcoma in blood from resistant and susceptible animals.

Many of these earlier experiments anticipated by 30 or 40 years techniques which are in general use today. At the time they were difficult to repeat since the media used were generally unsatisfactory and there was some doubt whether they demonstrated genuine survival of healthy tissues or merely somewhat delayed death of the cells.

It was because Ross Harrison's experiment in 1907 demonstrated quite unequivocal continuation of normal function *in vitro* and

1   1

offered a reproducible technique that it has been generally accepted as marking the true beginning of tissue culture. Harrison explanted small pieces of tissue from the medullary tube region of frog embryos into clots of frog lymph. When kept in aseptic conditions the fragments survived for some weeks and axones (nerve fibres) grew out from the cells. This helped to settle a current controversy about the origin of these structures and incidentally illuminated the potentialities of experimental methods using surviving tissues *in vitro*.

The 'traditional' techniques of tissue culture were rapidly established thereafter. Burrows, studying with Harrison, introduced the use of a plasma clot in place of a lymph clot. Shortly afterwards Burrows and Carrel undertook investigations into the effects of tissue extracts on growth and Carrel made the discovery that embryo extract had a strong growth-promoting effect on certain cells. The technique of growing tissues in plasma clots supplemented with embryo extract then became standard practice. The culture was usually prepared on a coverslip inverted over the cavity of a depression slide, in the manner originally used by Harrison, and the method, elegant in its simplicity, is still in use.

The greatest difficulty in performing tissue culture at that time was the avoidance of bacterial contamination. Alexis Carrel, already a Nobel prize-winner for his work in experimental surgery, was largely responsible for the development of the method in the next few years. Bringing with him a knowledge of aseptic techniques, he tackled tissue culture as he would a surgical operation. In consequence, he was able to obtain consistently successful results and the measure of his technical genius was his feat of keeping a strain of cells in active multiplication for 34 years by means of the very tedious methods he had available and in the total absence of antibiotics. Carrel's work demonstrated without doubt that animal cells could be grown indefinitely *in vitro*. Unfortunately, the meticulous surgical techniques he employed dissuaded many biologists from using the method and engendered the belief that tissue culture was fantastically difficult—a belief which was only being dispelled when the first edition of this book was written.

One of the main achievements of the Carrel school was the continuous cultivation of rapidly growing and dividing cells over long periods of time. Success in this field suggested the possibility that cells might be grown almost like protozoa or micro-organisms. Such a thought was a particularly intriguing one and the possible use of large amounts of cells in metabolic studies occurred to several investigators. The perfection of our present methods of cell culture owes a very great deal to the group at the National Cancer Institute in the United States, headed by Dr. Wilton Earle. This group was the first to grow cells direct on glass in large numbers, the first to grow cultures from single cells and the first to propagate cells intentionally in suspension.

An entirely different approach to the cultivation of tissues *in vitro* was initiated by Dr. David Thomson in 1914 and later developed by Drs. T. S. P. Strangeways and Honor Fell. Instead of trying to make cells grow as rapidly as possible, their aim was to maintain small fragments of tissue in a state as close as possible to their state *in vivo*. The ' organ culture ' technique, as it is called, is in many ways the most direct descendant of Harrison's original experiment. In the hands of Dame Honor Fell herself and an outstanding group of workers, especially Dr. Gaillard and Dr. and Mme. Wolff, this technique has yielded a great deal of important information in embryogenesis and endocrinology.

At an early stage in the development of animal tissue culture Warren and Margaret Lewis started to investigate the factors in the medium necessary for growth and survival (1911-1912). Baker, in association with Carrel, also undertook investigations into the composition of the medium and attempted, by analytical procedures, to identify the important constituents present in it. This type of work was carried on by Fischer and then, later, by a large body of capable workers, especially Parker, Healy, Morgan, White, Waymouth and Eagle, and resulted in the development of our present-day media.

Plant tissue culture has tended to develop quite separately from animal tissue culture and only in recent years has there been any general exchange of information between the two fields. The idea of the cultivation of plant cells was proposed by Haberlandt but his attempts proved fruitless and in 1902 he abandoned it. First successful attempts were made in 1921 by Molliard and in 1922 by Kotte and Robbins. These workers succeeded in maintaining plant roots for some weeks. Interest in the subject lapsed for a number of years and it was not until White and Gautheret developed suitable media in the mid-1930s that the technique began to appear promising. Subsequently, it advanced very rapidly and synthetic media for the cultivation of plant tissues were developed almost immediately.

The implications of the tissue culture method were not lost, even in the very earliest days, and its potential value in such subjects as morphogenesis, cancer research and virology was immediately recognised, the only discouragement being the difficulties of the technique itself. In spite of these, much valuable information was accumulated by embryologists and histologists from the beginning while experiments in cancer research almost preceded the development of reliable methods. In virology and biochemistry, however, although attempts were made to wrest information from tissue culture material, the technical difficulties proved overwhelming and it was only with the rapid developments of the 1950s that its application in these fields became widespread.

Steinhardt, Israeli and Lambert showed as early as 1913 that the vaccinia virus could survive for several weeks in explanted cornea. No attempt was made to follow up this observation until, in 1925, Parker and Nye demonstrated multiplication of vaccinia virus in tissue cultures of rabbit testis. Similar experiments with vaccinia and also with the Rous sarcoma virus were reported by Carrel and Rivers and Carrel in the next two years.

In 1928 Maitland and Maitland developed a very simple tissue culture method for virus multiplication. This consisted of suspended fragments of tissue in a fluid medium and it led to many interesting studies in the ensuing years. However, it was the observations of Enders and his colleagues in 1948 that gave the subject its great impetus. They showed conclusively that the poliomyelitis virus could be cultivated *in vitro* in the absence of nerve tissue. This observation was made at a time when cell culture techniques had undergone some remarkable developments. With the added practical interest, the number of people in the field increased rapidly and the whole subject evolved with extraordinary speed in the next ten years.

Originally tissue culture was concerned almost entirely with the growth of tissue *in vitro*, *i.e.*, explantation, but since the 1940s there has been a resurgence of interest in transplantation, *i.e.*, the culture of animal tissues *in vivo*, especially in cancer research. The techniques of transplantation originally had much in common with tissue culture *in vitro*, the early pioneer work being done by embryologists such as Born, Harrison and Morgan in the 1890s. Transplantation to different species was first carried out successfully in 1912 by Murphy who developed the technique of chorioallantoic membrane implantation in the hen's egg and later demonstrated that irradiation with X-rays would permit heterografting in rodents. At about the same time a number of workers, mainly Ruben, Hegener and Keysser managed successfully to transplant tissue to the anterior chamber of the eye, a technique which had been tried quite unsuccessfully by many previous investigators. Apart from sporadic experiments there was very little interest in these methods until quite recently. Murphy's technique was developed by Goodpasture in the late 1930s and later by Dagg and Harris. Greene has been responsible for the development of methods for transplantation to the anterior chamber of the eye and most of his work also dates from the late 1930s. The greatest advance in this field has been the relatively recent work of Toolan, in which she has followed up Murphy's use of X-irradiation to suppress host reaction and has introduced the use of cortisone for the same purpose. With this work and a better understanding of the homograft reaction, mainly due to Medawar's studies, the implantation and explantation of animal cells have again become closely related as investigators have begun to explore the behaviour of cultured cells and tissues on reimplantation into the animal.

BIBLIOGRAPHY

ARNOLD, J. (1887). Ueber Theilungsvorgänge an den Wanderzellen, ihre progressiven und retrogressiven Metamorphosen. *Arch. mikr. Anat.* **30,** 205.

BEEBE, S. P. & EWING, J. (1906). A study of the biology of tumour cells. *Brit. med. J.* **2,** 1559.

BURROWS, M. T. (1910). The cultivation of tissues of the chick embryo outside the body. *J. Amer. med. Ass.* **55,** 2057.

BURROWS, M. T. (1911). The growth of tissues of the chick embryo outside the animal body, with special reference to the nervous system. *J. exp. Zool.* **10,** 63.

BURROWS, M. T. (1912). A method of furnishing a continuous supply of new medium to a tissue culture *in vitro. Anat. Rec.* **6,** 141.

CARREL, A. (1912). The permanent life of tissue outside of the organism. *J. exp. Med.* **15,** 516.

CARREL, A. (1913). Artificial activation of the growth *in vitro* of connective tissue. *J. exp. Med.* **17,** 14.

CARREL, A. (1913). Neue Untersuchungen über das selbständige Leben der Gewebe und Organe. *Klin. Wschr.* **5,** 1097.

CARREL, A. & EBELING, A. (1922). Pure cultures of large mononuclear leucocytes. *J. exp. Med.* **36**, 365.

CARREL, A. & BAKER, L. E. (1926). The chemical nature of substances required for cell multiplication. *J. exp. Med.* **44**, 503.

ENDERS, J. F., WELLER, T. H. & ROBBINS, F. C. (1949). Cultivation of the Lansing strain of poliomyelitis virus in cultures of various human embryonic tissues. *Science* **109**, 85.

GAUTHERET, R. J. (1934). Culture du tissu cambial. *C.R. Acad. Sci. (Paris)* **198**, 2195.

GREENE, H. S. N. (1941). Heterologous transplantation of mammalian tumours. I. The transfer of rabbit tumours to alien species. *J. exp. Med.* **73**, 461.

HABERLANDT, G. (1902). Culturversuche mit isolierten Pflanzenzellen. *S.-B. dtsh. Akad. Wiss., Kl. med. Wiss.*, **111**, 69.

HARRISON, R. G. (1907). Observations on the living developing nerve fiber. *Proc. Soc. exp. Biol. (N.Y.)* **4**, 140.

HARRISON, R. G. (1912). The cultivation of tissues in extraneous media as a method of morphogenetic study. *Anat. Rec.* **6**, 181.

HARRISON, R. G. (1928). On the status and significance of tissue culture. *Arch. exp. Zellforsch.* **6**, 4.

JOLLY, J. (1903). Sur la durée de la vie et de la multiplication des cellules animales en dehors de l'organisme. *C.R. Soc. Biol. (Paris)* **55**, 1266.

KOTTE, W. (1922). Kulturversuche mit isolierten Wurzelspitzen. *Beitr. allg. Bot.* **2**, 413.

LEWIS, MARGARET R. & LEWIS, W. H. (1911). The cultivation of tissues from chick embryos in solutions of NaCl, CaCl₂, KCl, and NaHCO₃. *Anat. Rec.* **5**, 277.

LEWIS, MARGARET R. & LEWIS, W. H. (1911). The growth of embryonic chicken tissues in artificial media, agar and bouillon. *Bull. Johns Hopk. Hosp.* **22**, 126.

LEWIS, MARGARET R. & LEWIS, W. H. (1912). The cultivation of sympathetic nerves from the intestine of chicken embryos in saline solutions. *Anat. Rec.* **6**, 7.

LOEB, L. (1902). On the growth of epithelium in agar and blood-serum in the living body. *J. med. Res.* **8**, 109.

MAITLAND, H. B. & MAITLAND, M. C. (1928). Cultivation of vaccinia virus without tissue culture. *Lancet* **215**, 596.

MAXIMOW, A. (1925). Tissue cultures of young mammalian embryos. *Contr. Embryol. Carneg. Instn.* **16**, 47.

MOLLIARD, M. (1921). Sur le développement des plantules fragmentées. *C.R. Soc. Biol. (Paris)* **84**, 770.

MURPHY, J. B. (1913). Transplantability of tissues to the embryo of foreign species. Its bearing on questions of tissue specificity and tumour immunity. *J. exp. Med.* **17**, 482.

PARKER, F. JR. & NYE, R. N. (1925). Studies on filterable viruses. I. Cultivation of vaccine virus. *Amer. J. Path.* **1**, 325.

RIVERS, T. M. & WARD, S. M. (1935). Jennerian prophylaxis by means of intradermal injections of culture vaccine virus. *J. exp. Med.* **62**, 549.

ROBBINS, W. J. (1922). Cultivation of excised root tips and stem tips under sterile conditions. *Bot. Gaz.* **73**, 376.

ROUX, WILHELM (1885). Beiträge zur Entwicklungsmechanik des Embryo. *Z. Biol.* **21**, 411.

STEINHARDT, E., ISRAELI, C. & LAMBERT, R. A. (1913). Studies on the cultivation of the virus of vaccinia. *J. infect. Dis.* **13**, 294.

THOMPSON, D., EBIN, C. E. & CANTAB, D. P. (1914). Some further researches on the cultivation of tissues *in vitro*. *Proc. R. Soc. Med.* **7**, 21.

TOOLAN, HELENE, W. (1954). Transplantable human neoplasms maintained in cortisone-treated laboratory animals: H.S. 1; H.Ep. 1; H.Ep. 2; H.Ep. 3; and H.Emb.Rh. 1. *Cancer Res.* **14**, 660.

WHITE, P. R. (1932). Plant tissue cultures. A preliminary report of results obtained in the culturing of certain plant meristems. *Arch. exp. Zellforsch.* **12**, 602.

CURRENT TECHNIQUES

A wide variety of techniques has become available and the main ones in common use are illustrated in Figure 1. One of the simplest consists of embedding small fragments of tissue in a clot on a coverslip inverted over the concavity of a depression slide and sealed to it with paraffin wax. This technique is very easy and is convenient for short term experiments involving large numbers of cultures of small pieces of tissue. By the use of a growth-stimulating medium and frequent transfer, these cultures may be propagated for many generations and it was by this method that Carrel kept his 'immortal' strain alive for almost 40 years. However, the maintenance of cells in this manner for long periods of time requires a great deal of practice and patience and it is very difficult to keep cultures growing in a slow-growing state, since this requires that the medium be renewed at frequent intervals without disturbing the tissue. The double coverslip method was developed for use where it was desired to keep tissue alive for long periods without transfer. Techniques using slides with a concavity have the disadvantage that it is impossible to use them with some optical systems and therefore numerous modifications, *e.g.* special phase slides and perforated glass or metal slides, have been developed to permit examination by phase contrast or interference microscopy.

Special techniques have been developed for organ culture and in particular Strangeways and Fell developed the watch-glass technique in which the tissue is grown on a clot in a watch-glass which is itself surrounded by wet cotton-wool in a Petri dish to maintain humidity. Other organ culture techniques have stemmed from this, in particular the use of a raft or platform of rayon net or metal gauze on which the tissue is grown.

Ordinary test-tubes are convenient for growing large numbers of cultures when good optical conditions are not essential. Hence they are used for the maintenance of tissues and for virus and biochemical assays. The tubes may be rotated or kept stationary in racks.

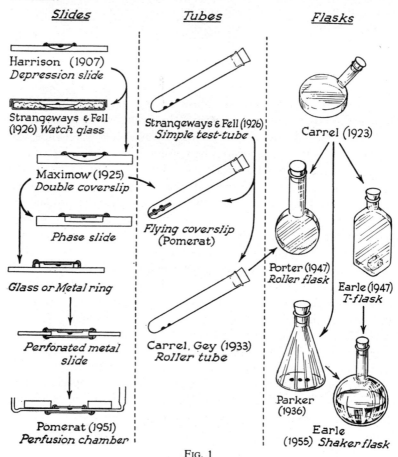

Slides   *Tubes*   *Flasks*

Harrison (1907)
Depression slide

Strangeways & Fell
(1926) *Watch glass*

Strangeways & Fell (1926)
Simple test-tube

Carrel (1923)

Maximow (1925)
Double coverslip

Phase slide

Flying coverslip
(Pomerat)

Porter (1947)
Roller flask

Earle (1947)
T-flask

Glass or Metal ring

*Perforated metal
slide*

Carrel, Gey (1933)
Roller tube

Parker
(1936)

Pomerat (1951)
Perfusion chamber

Earle
(1955) *Shaker flask*

FIG. 1
Vessels used for culturing cells and tissues.

If it is desired to grow large numbers of cultures for subsequent morphological examination, the 'flying coverslip' technique is particularly convenient. Cultures are prepared on narrow coverslips and inserted into roller tubes. It is commonly used in preparing coverslip cultures for subsequent photography or cinemicrographic study.

A large variety of roller tubes of various kinds has been developed for special purposes. For instance, roller tubes have been made with very thin side windows to permit direct application of an end-window Geiger counter. Others have been developed with a micro test-tube at one end so that a chemical analysis of the tissue can be carried out in the same tube after the growth phase is completed.

The original Carrel flask was designed to facilitate the handling of cultures which it was desired to maintain for some time. Very good optical properties were usually insisted upon but nowadays the Carrel flask is used almost entirely to start strains and in this case such good optical qualities are not so necessary. The Carrel flask has otherwise fallen out of use entirely. However, other flasks are used extensively, mainly for growing large quantities of cells. Earle's T flask was designed specifically for this purpose and is specially made to have a very flat surface inside and to have good optical properties. Ordinary Erlenmeyer flasks are also used frequently for growing cells, as are Roux bottles and penicillin culture flasks. Vessels made of polystyrene are now used extensively.

Nowadays cells are often grown in suspension and originally ordinary round-bottomed flasks, agitated in a special shaker, were used for this purpose. Now there are a number of techniques, some employing stirrers and some fast roller tubes.

Besides the techniques described, many others have been employed. Some special vessels have been developed and in particular a number of different perfusion chambers have been described which permit the continuous observation of cells by time-lapse cinemicrography while the medium is being changed.

All of these techniques have been widely applied in biological research. While many of them have been employed especially in particular fields there is no single technique which can be described as useful solely in tackling one kind of problem and most of them have proved valuable in several entirely different sets of circumstances. For instance, Ross Harrison's original method of growing fragments of tissue in a plasma clot proved useful many years later in making the first electron microscopic studies on animal cells. Similarly, organ culture technique, a classical tool of the experimental embryologist, has recently been used to investigate host-parasite relationships in virus studies.

It is this fact, along with the common principles involved in all tissue culture work, that serves to unite the many different techniques as a single branch of biological technology.

BIBLIOGRAPHY

GENERAL AND CLASSICAL TEXTS ON TISSUE CULTURE

BISCEGLIE, V. & JUHASZ-SCHAFFER, A. (1928). *Die Gewebezuchtung in Vitro.* Berlin: Springer.

BUCHSBAUM, R. & LOOSLI, C. G. (1936). *Methods of Tissue Culture in Vitro.* Chicago: University Press.

CARREL, A. & LINDBERGH, C. A. (1938). *The Culture of Organs.* New York: Hoeber.

CAMERON, GLADYS (1950). *Tissue Culture Technique.* 2nd ed. New York: Academic Press.

CRACIUN, E. C. (1931). *La Culture des Tissus en Biologie Experimentale.* Paris: Masson.

EARLE, W. R. (1948). Tissue culture. In *Laboratory Technique in Biology and Medicine.* 2nd. ed. Ed. Cowdry, E. V. Baltimore: Williams & Wilkins.

EPHRUSSI, B. (1932). *La Culture des Tissus.* Paris: Gauthiers-Villars.

FISCHER, A. (1946). *Biology of Tissue Cells.* New York: Hafner.

FISCHER, ILSE (1942). *Grundriss der Gewebezuchtung.* Jena: Fischer.

KIMURA, R. (1953). *Tissue Culture.* Copenhagen: Munksgaard.

LEVI, G. (1928). Gewebezuchtung. In *Methodik der wissenschaftlichen Biologie,* ed. T. Peterfi. Berlin: Springer.

LEVI, G. (1934). Explantation, besonders die Struktur und die biologischen Eigenschaften der *in vitro* gezüchteten Zellen und Gewebe. *Ergebn. Anat. EntwGesch.* **31,** 125.

MERCHANT, D. J., KAHN, R. H. & MURPHY, W. H. (1964). *Handbook of Cell and Organ Culture.* 2nd ed. Minneapolis: Burgess.

MURRAY, MARGARET R. & KOPECH, GERTRUDE (1953). *A Bibliography of the Research in Tissue Culture.* New York: Academic Press.

PARKER, R. C. (1960). *Methods of Tissue Culture.* 3rd ed. New York: Hoeber.

PIGG-STRANGEWAYS, T. S. (1924). *The Technique of Tissue Culture.* Cambridge: Heffer.

POMERAT, C. M. (1951). Tissue culture methods. In *Medical Research,* ed. M. B. Visscher. Chicago: Year Book Publishers.

SCHERER, W. F. (1955). *An Introduction to Cell and Tissue Culture.* Minneapolis: Burgess.

VERNE, J. (1937). *La Vie Cellulaire Hors de l'Organisme.* Paris: Douin.

WHITE, P. R. (1943). *A Handbook of Plant Tissue Culture.* Lancaster, Pa.: Cattell Press.

WHITE, P. R. (1963). *The Cultivation of Animal and Plant Cells.* 2nd ed. London: Thames & Hudson. New York: Ronald Press.

WHITE, P. R. ed. (1957). Decennial Review Conference on Tissue Culture. *J. nat. Cancer. Inst.* **19.**

WILLMER, E. N. (1954). *Tissue Culture; the Growth and Differentiation of Normal Tissues in Artificial Media. Methuen's Monographs on Biological Subjects.* 2nd ed. London: Methuen. New York: Wiley.

WILLMER, E. N. ed. (1964). *The Biology of Cultured Tissues.* New York: Academic Press. (In press.)

PART I
PRINCIPLES OF CELL CULTURE

CHAPTER II

THE CELL

THIS outline of our present knowledge of the structure and function of cells and tissues is essentially elementary. It is intended mainly for the many non-cytologists who are now using tissue cultures.

The cell is the unit of structure of all plants and animals. For example, metazoa consist of aggregates of cells of different types living together to their mutual advantage. This implies a degree of mutual dependency which is not very highly developed in the lowest metazoa but is very highly developed in the highest forms. Thus it is commonplace that the destruction of any one of the vital organs in an animal will result in the death of the whole. With increasing complexity of organisation masses of different cell types tend to become localised and to form recognisable patterns. An aggregation of cells forming a definite pattern in this way is referred to as a tissue. At a still higher level of organisation tissues aggregate in a characteristic way to form organs. The whole animal consists of an orderly arrangement of organs.

With the exception of a very few creatures at the borderline between protozoa and metazoa, it is unlikely that metazoan cells ever survive for any length of time outside the animal except in tissue culture conditions.

Fine cell structure

The animal cell is itself a highly organised structure and in many respects it resembles very closely certain protozoa, especially the amoebae. It is surrounded by a membrane, very thin in some cells, thick in others. Plant cells are distinguished from animal cells by having a cellulose cell-wall, which renders the structure rigid. Within all cells are a number of well-defined structures. These are the nucleus, mitochondria, lysosomes, Golgi apparatus, centrioles,

11

and, in some cases, inclusions. The remainder of the cell is the cytoplasm.

The nucleus is separated from the cytoplasm by a well-defined nuclear membrane, which appears to be double. It can rotate freely within the living cell and it has been suggested that this movement may be due to the secretion of material into the cytoplasm. Within the nucleus there occur one or more nucleoli. These are rich in

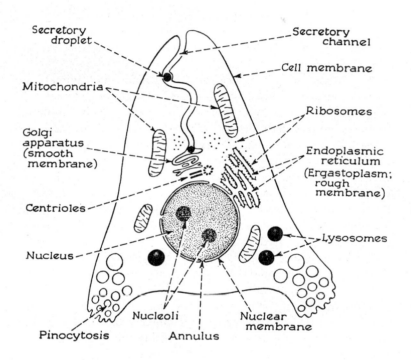

FIG. 2
Diagram of a cell showing its structure.

ribonucleic acid (RNA) and it has been shown that this RNA is metabolically highly active. The remainder of the nucleus normally consists of a structureless basophilic mass, containing a high concentration of deoxyribonucleic acid (DNA) and a characteristic basic protein, nuclear histone. When cell division occurs the structureless material of the nucleus aggregates into a skein of chromatin, containing most of the DNA, and this subsequently forms the chromosomes.

The mitochondria may vary considerably in size and shape. They are frequently long thread-like structures, but may also form small spheres. In the living cell they are constantly in motion. They have a double membrane and a series of internal folds, known as cristae. Most of the oxidative enzymes of the cell and the enzymes of the tricarboxylic acid cycle are concentrated within them. They are the main site of oxidative phosphorylation and therefore are the main energy-producing loci within the cell.

The lysosomes are similar in size to the mitochondria but consist either of solid spheres or thick-walled spheres with a small internal cavity. They do not contain the enzymes characteristic of the mito-chondria but have particularly high concentrations of lytic enzymes, such as proteases and ribonuclease.

The Golgi apparatus has also been referred to as the cell centre. It consists of a series of closely packed membranes along with some vacuoles. It is a region of very intense activity in time-lapse films and is particularly prominent in secreting cells.

The centrosome occurs in the area of the Golgi apparatus. Its precise function is unknown but it may be associated with cell division since it is absent in cells which are known to undergo no further division in the adult animal. Also it is the first structure to divide during cell division in animal cells.

Inclusions within the cells include glycogen granules, fat droplets and secretion droplets. Some of these are responsible for the typical appearance of many cells *in vivo*. They tend to dis-appear in tissue culture conditions, with the exception of lipid droplets. Vacuoles are also frequently seen within cultured cells. These arise from the process of pinocytosis described below.

The cytoplasm itself has a distinct structure, consisting of an intricately folded membrane, called the endoplasmic reticulum or ergastoplasm. Minute granules of ribonucleoprotein, the ribosomes, are dispersed along the folds of the reticulum. These, along with the debris of the reticulum itself, constitute the microsomes. Most of the cytoplasmic ribonucleic acid is located in them. Within the folds of the endoplasmic reticulum lies the cell-sap which is a watery solution of proteins and crystalloids. A variable number of free ribosomes occur in the cell sap.

The cell membrane is extremely thin in most cells. In the red blood cell it is comparatively very thick and consists of oriented layers of lipid and protein. The red cell is not typical of all cells, however, and there is no evidence at present that other cells have a similar membrane.

Nuclear-cytoplasmic relationships

It is now established that genetic information is carried by DNA in the chromosomes. The information is carried by a code made up of the four nucleotides of which DNA is composed. Each amino acid is represented in this code by a sequence of three nucleotides. The information in DNA is transcribed to a molecule of RNA, called messenger RNA. This subsequently becomes associated with ribosomes in the cytoplasm and acts as a template on which amino-acids are assembled in the correct order to form proteins. In this way the information in the genes is translated into the synthesis of protein molecules.

Cellular activity

Animal cells in tissue culture are capable of quite active movement. Rarely is this rapid enough to be observed by the eye, and time-lapse cinemicrography is usually employed to speed up the movements. Time-lapse photography is the technique of taking cine-films at a very slow speed (*e.g.* 8 frames per minute) and projecting them at normal speed (16 frames per second) so that the action is speeded up (in this case 120 times).

The principal movements observed in living cells are pseudo-podial movements, undulation of the membrane, pinocytosis, mitochondrial movements and nuclear rotation.

Pseudopodial movements in cells are similar to those occurring in amoebae. Highly active migratory tips of protoplasm extend out from the cell. Other processes retreat, often leaving characteristic fibrillae or reticula behind them. Frequently these movements are oriented, advance in one direction being accompanied by retreat in the opposite side so that the cell migrates. This behaviour is particularly characteristic of white blood cells of all types. A highly specialised type of process formation is the extension of axones from nerve cells. These may grow in tissue cultures to a length of several millimetres and the advancing axone carries a characteristic migratory tip, sometimes referred to as a growth cone.

Undulation of the cell-membrane, as the term implies, consists of wave-like motions of the membrane, from the outer margin of the cell towards the centre. These undulating movements are closely associated with some other phenomena of the living cell, particularly pinocytosis. Pinocytosis, a word coined by the Lewises, literally means cell-drinking and describes the process very well. It consists essentially of the engulfing of globules of medium by the cell. This description suggests a process similar to phagocytosis (the engulfing of particles of foreign matter) and the processes in animal cells may be essentially the same. Pinocytosis is of particular interest in the light of our concepts of cell-membrane permeability. It is a very prominent feature in certain cultured cells but there is very good evidence that it also occurs in the intact animal, though on a smaller scale.

Movements of mitochondria may be secondary to the general activity of the cell and they are certainly displaced by vacuoles passing towards the cell centre. Some movements are almost certainly characteristic of intrinsic activity, however, particularly the changes in shape and size which occur.

As has been mentioned previously, the nuclei of the cells frequently show active rotating movements, apparently independently of other cell activity. In some cells these movements are very active indeed and it has been suggested that they may be due to the passage of material between the nucleus and cytoplasm.

In addition to these general patterns of activity there are many specific patterns to be observed. For instance, Pomerat (1951) has described rhythmic pumping movements of oligodendroglia (supporting cells of the nervous system). Other cells, such as muscle cells, show contractile activity. Also, injurious stimuli evoke some characteristic patterns of response, for instance vacuolisation of the mitochondria, bubbling of the cytoplasm and fragmentation of cytoplasm.

CELL DIVISION

One of the most fundamental of all cellular processes and one in which the tissue culturist is particularly interested is that of cell division. In fact, the process to be described is nuclear division. The cytoplasm usually follows the nucleus in dividing (but this does not happen invariably).

Three types of nuclear division have been described. Amitosis is a simple division of a nucleus without formation of chromosomes. It is very uncommon and probably not a normal process. Consequently, it will not be discussed further.

Meiosis and mitosis are both characterised by the appearance of chromosomes which are segregated into two groups, one group going to each of the daughter cells. Meiosis is a special case, occurring in the formation of germ cells. During meiosis the normal (diploid) number of chromosomes is halved so that each daughter cell contains a haploid number. In mitosis, on the other hand, the cell at the time of division has material for a double set of chromosomes. On segregation of the chromosomes each daughter cell is left with the normal (diploid) number. This is the normal type of cell division occurring in somatic cells during growth and is almost the only type of cell division seen in tissue cultures. All subsequent discussion will be concerned only with mitotic division.

The early stages of mitosis are characterised by the appearance of the chromosomes. These structures carry the genes, which are mainly responsible for transferring information about hereditary characteristics to the daughter cells. Each cell has a double set of chromosomes and the number is characteristic of the species. The number of chromosome sets is referred to as the 'ploidy' of the cells. Thus, normal cells with two sets are referred to as diploid, cells with three sets are triploid, with four sets tetraploid, and so on. Germ cells with half the diploid amount are referred to as haploid.

The function of mitosis is the distribution of chromosomal material equally between daughter cells during cell division. Since the special function of chromosomes is the storage of genetic information, this process results in the distribution of almost equal amounts of genetic material to each daughter. It has become increasingly apparent in recent years that the genetic information is conveyed by DNA.

The DNA molecule has been shown to consist of a double helical chain of nucleotides, linked together by hydrogen bonds (Fig. 3). Nucleotides have the structure base-sugar-phosphate. In RNA the sugar is ribose and in DNA it is deoxyribose. The bases are either purines or pyrimidines and in DNA the purines are adenine and guanine while the pyrimidines are thymine and

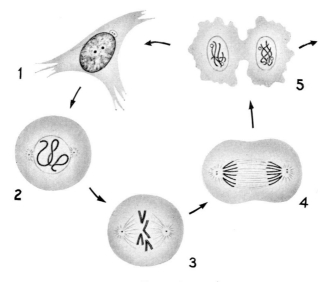

PLATE 1

The main stages during mitosis. 1. Interphase. 2. Prophase. 3. Metaphase. 4. Anaphase. 5. Telophase.

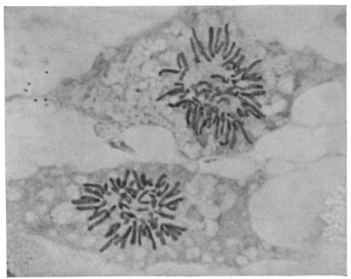

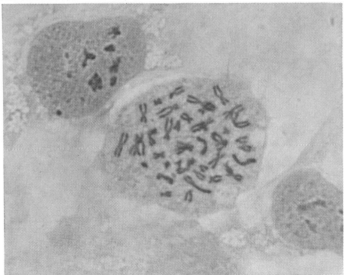

PLATE 2

Cells in mitosis (treated with hypotonic salt solution before fixation).
Top: A cell in late prophase, showing individual chromosomes.
Bottom: A cell in late metaphase showing splitting of the chromo-
somes to form chromatids. (Courtesy of Dr. C. M. Pomerat. From
Seminar International, Vol. IV, No. 1. Published by Merck Sharp
& Dohme, Limited, Hoddesdon, Herts, England.)

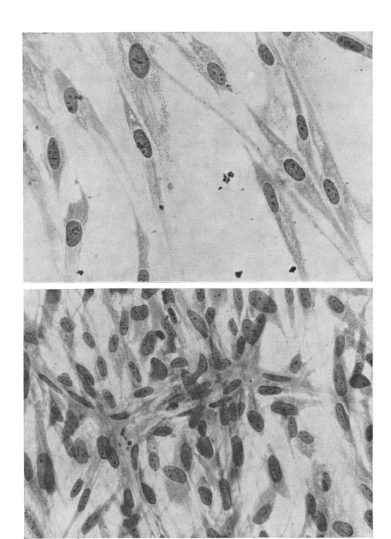

PLATE 3

Cells of fibroblastic type in tissue culture. (Courtesy of Dr. C. M. Pomerat. From *Seminar* International, Vol. IV, No. 1. Published by Merck Sharp & Dohme, Limited, Hoddesdon, Herts, England.)

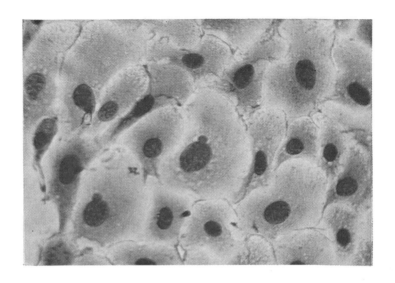

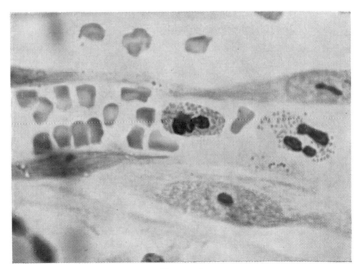

PLATE 4

Top: Cells of epithelial type in tissue culture.   Bottom: Cells from
an explant of bone marrow showing retention of typical morphological elements. (Courtesy of Dr. C. M. Pomerat. From *Seminar*
International, Vol. IV, No. 1. Published by Merck Sharp & Dohme,
Limited, Hoddesdon, Herts, England.)

cytosine. One of the important observations about DNA structure is that the bases in DNA are always paired, adenine with thymine and guanine with cytosine. Thus, we can represent a section of

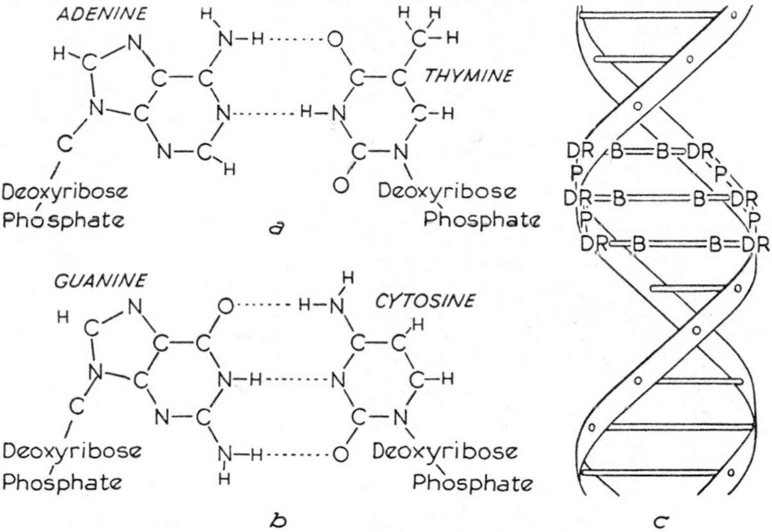

FIG. 3

The chemical structure of DNA. (*a*) Base pairing of the nucleotides deoxyadenosine monophosphate and thymidine monophosphate by means of hydrogen bonds. (*b*) Pairing of the nucleotides, deoxyguanosine monophosphate and deoxycytidine monophosphate. (*c*) The double helix of DNA. DR—deoxyribose; P—phosphate; B—base (adenine, guanine, thymine or cytosine).

the DNA molecule as in Figure 3c. Crick and Watson, who proposed this structure for DNA, have suggested an ingenious mechanism whereby this molecule could reproduce itself exactly. If we assume that during replication the hydrogen bonds break between the two chains in Figure 4a, then we are left with two complementary single strands as in Figure 4b. We know that each base can only be paired with its complementary base and thus, by attaching new nucleotides to the bases in each single strand, as in Figure 4c, we end up with two identical double chains as in Figure 4d. An experiment performed by Meselson and Stahl provided strong evidence for the correctness of this theory. It has also been shown by Taylor and Woods by labelling DNA with radioactive thymidine that the whole chromosome behaves as the DNA molecule would be predicted to behave according to this theory. It should be mentioned in passing that it is difficult at present to envisage a mechanism which would explain this behaviour of the chromosome since it is very much larger than a DNA molecule. It is apparent therefore that other mechanisms must also be involved.

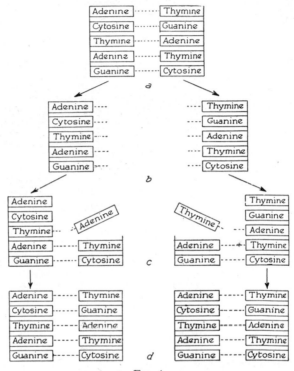

FIG. 4
Scheme for the replication of DNA by pairing of complementary bases.

The stages of division in somatic animal cells are as follows:

1. THE INTERMITOTIC PHASE (INTERPHASE).—This is also, mistakenly, referred to as the resting phase. In growing cells most of the synthesis of new materials proceeds during this period. When the cell contents have been doubled the cell then enters prophase.

2. PROPHASE.—This is, as a rule, the earliest recognisable stage of cell division. Within the nucleus the chromatin condenses into long

filaments which rapidly condense to form chromosomes. Mean-time, the centrosome divides and the two portions move in opposite directions. Between these two poles the structure of the spindle (rather like visualised magnetic lines of force) appears and chromosomes arrange themselves on it. The nucleoli disappear and the nuclear membrane disintegrates. At the end of this phase the cell has the typical appearance of metaphase.

3. METAPHASE.—The chromosomes are arranged in the equator of the cell. By time-lapse cinemicrography they can be seen to be highly active at this stage, often apparently rotating *en masse*. Quite suddenly the cell enters anaphase.

4. ANAPHASE.—The chromosomes split longitudinally and the halves (chromatids) move in opposite directions towards the poles. When they are completely separated they are again regarded as chromosomes. As cytoplasmic division begins the cell enters telophase.

5. TELOPHASE.—The chromosomes at each pole come together and begin to fade and disappear. Simultaneously a new nuclear membrane forms around each nuclear zone. A constriction appears in the cytoplasm between the two new nuclei. It gradually deepens until the two new cells are separated. The cell surface ' bubbles ' very actively indeed at this stage and as the activity decreases the new daughter cells spread out over the surface on which they are growing.

The duration of cell division varies with different cells. With avian fibroblasts it can be quite rapid and can be watched with the eye over a period of about 20 minutes (at 38° C.). The interphase period in rapidly growing cells is of the order of 18 hours or less.

The above description has referred entirely to normal cells. In tissue cultures abnormal cells and abnormal cell divisions are frequently encountered. It is common for cytoplasm to fail to divide when the nucleus divides so that multinucleate giant cells occur. Also, instead of the dipolar division described, multipolar divisions may occur, especially in cancer cells. Thus tripolar divisions are not infrequently seen where the cell divides into three. Cells resulting from such divisions are often very small and fail to divide further.

Other common abnormalities are abnormalities of the population as a whole. In a 'normal' population, all the cells usually have the same number of chromosomes—the diploid number for the species. Occasionally, there may be cells with multiples of this number, tetraploid, octaploid, and so on. In cell strains it is almost the rule to find an unusual chromosome number. Frequently the cells have a triploid or tetraploid number of chromosomes. Occasionally, as in the HeLa cell, there is no modal distribution and the number of chromosomes in the cells seems to be quite random. This condition is referred to as aneuploidy.

This behaviour of animal cells in culture is of considerable interest because, although variations in chromosome number are quite common in plant materials, it was thought until very recently that animal cells always remained strictly diploid. It has now been demonstrated that this is not true and even in man, certain chromosomal imbalances are compatible with survival into adult life. Thus it has been found that Mongolian idiocy is due to the presence of an extra chromosome so that these individuals have 47 instead of 46. Several other less well-known conditions have also been shown to have the same kind of defect. The reason why aneuploid chromosomal complements are uncommon is probably that the imbalance produced is incompatible with survival rather than that the mechanism involved is exceptionally rare. In cells in culture chromosomal imbalance may be less of a handicap than in the developing animal since the cells do not form part of a delicately balanced organism. Indeed there is evidence to suggest that polyploidy and aneuploidy favour the survival of cells in culture conditions. This is probably because the development of unusual combinations of genes improves the chances of survival in the unusual environment. Thus, the occurrence of aneuploidy *in vitro* may be a kind of genetic adaptation.

The actual mechanism involved in the development of aneuploidy is known as 'nondisjunction'. This term implies that due to some accident, both chromatids arising from a parent chromosome migrate to one of the daughter cells. Now since each pair of chromosomes gives rise to a total of four chromatids, this means that one daughter cell has three chromosomes—one derived in the normal fashion by division of one parent chromosome and the other two derived from the same parent. The other daughter is left with only one chromosome and since this is quite likely to carry a number of lethal recessive genes the cell is unlikely to survive. Thus there is a tendency for polyploid, aneuploid cells to predominate eventually.

The frequency and rapidity of occurrence of aneuploidy in cultured cells varies very much from strain to strain and stability is probably affected by genetic factors. Available evidence would tend to suggest that cells derived from tumour tissues are less stable in this respect than cells derived from normal, and especially adult, tissues. It should be emphasised, however, that this generalisation is by no means a strict rule.

CELL-TYPES AND TISSUES

In the organism a very large number of different cell-types can be recognised by morphological and metabolic characteristics. In tissue culture, most of these recognisable differences tend to disappear. Almost certainly important differences remain, but our

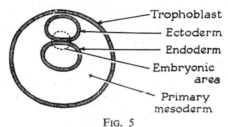

Fig. 5

Diagrammatic cross-section of an early mammalian embryo.

techniques have not yet advanced sufficiently to enable us to recognise them. Undoubtedly criteria will be developed but in the meantime our knowledge of cell-types derives solely from our knowledge of the origin of the cells. The following brief description refers only to animal cells.

All cells in an organism are, of course, derived from a single cell, the fertilised egg. At an early stage in development, the embryonic area consists of three types of cells—ectoderm, mesoderm and endoderm. Mesoderm at a very early stage shows a further development, part of it becoming mesenchyme. All the cells in the adult animal are derived from these.

Ectoderm gives rise to all the epithelia covering the outer surfaces of the body and extending into the mouth and nasal passages. Practically all the nervous system is also ectodermal.

From the same source come the smooth muscle of the iris and a number of other small structures, such as the anterior lobe of the pituitary gland.

The mesoderm gives rise directly to all the body muscles (with a very few exceptions) and to the urogenital system. After differentiation to form the loose mesenchyme, it gives rise to all the connective tissues, the blood and the endothelial linings of body cavities.

The endoderm gives rise to all the epithelia lining the alimentary tract, the respiratory passages and the lower part of the genito-urinary passages, in all cases to the point where it meets with cells of ectodermal origin as mentioned above. It also gives rise to the parenchymal epithelial cells of the liver and pancreas.

The tissues of animals are usually classified in five groups as follows:

1. Epithelial tissue.   3. Muscle tissue.
2. Connective tissue.   4. Nervous tissue.
                5. Blood and lymph.

The epithelial tissues are those which form sheets covering organs and lining cavities. Thus the skin and the linings of the alimentary tract and lungs are typical epithelial tissues. They are classified according to their morphology as squamous, cubical, columnar, ciliated and secretory. Malignant growths arising from these tissues are called carcinomas in general. If they preserve some of their original structure they may receive more precise names, such as adenocarcinoma or epithelioma.

The connective tissues are those whose main function can be regarded as structural, such as bone, fibrous tissue, cartilage, tendon. They are usually characterised by having a specific intercellular material or matrix which they produce. Malignant growths arising from these tissues are called sarcomas, and again they may have more specific names, which usually include the word sarcoma.

Muscle tissue consists of ordinary skeletal muscle, smooth muscle such as occurs in the intestines and heart muscle. Tumours arising from them are classified as sarcomas.

Nervous tissue includes the brain, spinal cord, peripheral nerves and ganglia. It is highly complex and, in addition to the nerve cells, includes many supporting cells, called glial cells, *e.g.* astroglia, microglia, oligodendroglia. Malignant growths rarely arise from the nerve cells, except in infants, but often develop from the glial cells and are named after the cells of origin, *e.g.* glioma, astrocytoma.

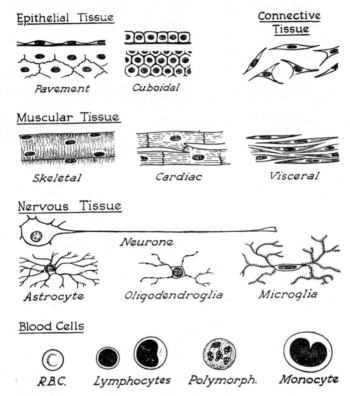

FIG. 6
The principal cell-types of vertebrate tissues.

The blood and lymph tissues include all the cells in the peripheral blood and their precursors in the bone marrow and lymph glands. Malignant growths of these tissues are usually referred to as leukaemias. Some rather rare conditions are referred to as sarcomas.

The reticulo-endothelial system is often classified with the blood. It is not regarded as a tissue by all authorities, but it has particular interest in tissue culture since its cells appear in every organ and may often be the cells which establish themselves in tissue cultures, especially in the early stages of explantation. The characteristic of all the cells in this system is that they are capable of migration and have phagocytic activity, *i.e.* they are capable of taking up foreign particulate matter.

From the above classification, it is apparent that tissues of ectodermal and endodermal origins have close similarities and malignant growths arising from tissues derived from them are called carcinomas. (Nervous tissue is an exception to this generalisation.) On the other hand, tissues of mesodermal origin have a variety of functions and malignant growths from them are usually called sarcomas.

The final point that remains to be made in this general outline is that an organ may consist of many different tissues that intermingle with each other more or less intimately. Thus, for example, a very small piece of liver may contain the following cell-types : Hepatocytes, fibrous tissue cells, blood cells (red cells, basophil, eosinophil and neutrophil leucocytes, large and small lymphocytes, monocytes, plasma cells), blood vessels (endothelium, muscle, elastic tissue), bile ducts (bile-duct epithelium), nerve fibres, reticuloendothelial cells (Kupffer cells). There may be others but, even in this list, there are many different cell-types potentially capable of growing *in vitro*. Liver is a relatively simple organ and it can therefore be seen that with our present non-selective techniques and the loss of morphological characteristics it is virtually impossible to identify with certainty the type of cell that becomes established as a continuous tissue culture.

BIBLIOGRAPHY

ABERCROMBIE, M. & HEAYSMAN, JOAN (1953). Observations on the social behaviour of cells in tissue culture. I. Speed of movement of chick heart fibroblasts in relation to their mutual contacts. *Exp. Cell. Res.* **5,** 111.

ALGARD, THOMAS (1953). Morphology and migratory behaviour of embryonic pigment cells studied by phase microscopy. *J. exp. Zool.* **123,** 499.

APPELMANS, F., WATTIAUX, R. & DE DUVE, C. (1955). The association of acid phosphatase with a special class of cytoplasmic granules in rat liver. *Biochem. J.* **59,** 438.

BOSS, J. (1954). Mitosis in cultures of newt tissues. I. A critical study of the methods and material. II. Chromosome pairing in anaphase. *Exp. Cell Res.* **7,** 215.

BOSS, J. (1954). Mitosis in cultures of newt tissues. III. Cleavage and chromosome movements in anaphase. *Exp. Cell Res.* **7,** 443.

BRACHET, J. (1957). *Biochemical Cytology.* New York: Academic Press.

CHAMBERS, R. & KEMPTON, R. T. (1933). Indications of functions of the chick mesonephros in tissue culture with phenol red. *J. cell comp. Physiol.* **3**, 131.

CHÈVREMONT, M. & FREDERIC, J. (1951). Contribution à l'étude du chondriome par la microscopie et la microcinématographie en contraste de phase. *C.R. Ass. Anat.* **38**, 268.

CHÈVREMONT, M. & FREDERIC, J. (1951). Recherches sur le comportement du chondriome pendant la mitose. *C.R. Soc. Biol. (Paris)* **145**, 1245.

CHU, E. H. Y. & GILES, N. H. (1958). Comparative chromosomal studies on mammalian cells in culture. I. The HeLa strain and its mutant clonal derivatives. *J. nat. Cancer Inst.* **20**, 383.

CLAUDE, A., PORTER, K. R. & PICKELS. E. G. (1947). Electron microscope study of chick tumor cells. *Cancer Res.* **7**, 421.

DAVIDSON, J. N. & LESLIE, I. (1951). Cell number and composition of chick heart explants. *Exp. Cell Res.* **11**, 366.

DEITCH, ARLINE D. & MURRAY, MARGARET R. (1956). The Nissl substance of living and fixed spinal ganglion cells. I. A phase contrast study. *J. biophys. biochem. Cytol.* **2**, 433.

DE DUVE, C., PRESSMAN, B. C., GIANETTO, R. J., WATTIAUX, R., & APPELMANS, F. (1955). Tissue fractionation studies. 6. Intracellular distribution patterns of enzymes in rat-liver tissue. *Biochem. J.* **60**, 604.

FORD, C. E., JACOBS, P. A. & LAJTHA, L. B. (1958). Human somatic chromosomes. *Nature (Lond.)* **181**, 1565.

FORD, C. E., JONES, K. W., MILLER, O. J., MITTWOCH, U., PENROSE, L. S., RIDDLER, M. & SHAPIRO, A. (1959). The chromosomes in a patient showing both mongolism and the Klinefelter syndrome. *Lancet* **1**, 709.

FORD, D. K. & YERGANIAN. G. (1958). Observations on the chromosomes of Chinese hamster cells in tissue culture. *J. nat. Cancer Inst.* **21**, 393.

HOGEBOOM, G. H. & SCHNEIDER, W. C. (1955). The cytoplasm. In *The Nucleic Acids.* Ed. E. Chargaff & J. N. Davidson. New York: Academic Press.

HOGEBOOM, G. H., SCHNEIDER, W. C. & STRIEBICH, MARY J. (1953). Localization and integration of cellular function. *Cancer Res.* **13**, 617.

HOWATSON, A. F. & HAM, A. W. (1957). The fine structure of cells. *Canad. J. Biochem.* **35**, 549.

HSU, T. C. (1952). Mammalian chromosomes *in vitro.* I. The Karyotype of man. *J. Hered.* **4**, 167.

HSU, T. C. (1959). Numerical variation of chromosome in higher animals. In *Development Cytology.* New York: Ronald Press Company.

HSU, T. C. & MOORHEAD, P. S. (1956). Chromosome anomalies in human neoplasms with special reference to the mechanisms of polyploidization and aneuploidization in the HeLa strain. *Ann. N.Y. Acad. Sci.* **63**, 1083.

HSU, T. C. & MOORHEAD, P. S. (1957). Mammalian chromosomes *in vitro.* VII. Heteroploidy in human cell strains. *J. nat. Cancer Inst.* **18**, 463.

HUGHES, A. (1952). *The Mitotic Cycle.* London: Butterworth.

JACOBS, P. A., BAIKIE, A. G., COURT BROWN, W. M. & STRONG, J. A. (1959). The somatic chromosomes in mongolism. *Lancet* **1**, 710.

LEJEUNE, J., GAUTHIER, M. & TURPIN, R. (1959a). Les chromosomes humains en culture de tissus. *C.R. Acad. Sci. (Paris)* **248**, 602.

LEJEUNE, J., GAUTHIER, M. & TURPIN, R. (1959b). Étude des chromosomes somatiques de neuf enfants mongoliens. *C.R. Acad. Sci. (Paris)* **248**, 1721.

LEVAN, A. (1956). Chromosome studies on some human tumors and tissues of normal origin, grown *in vitro* at the Sloan-Kettering Institute. *Cancer (Philad.)* **9**, 648.

LEWIS, W. H. (1931). Pinocytosis. *Bull. Johns Hopk. Hosp.* **49**, 17.

MAZIA, D. & DAN, K. (1952). The isolation and biochemical characterization of the mitotic apparatus of dividing cells. *Proc. nat. Acad. Sci. (Wash.)* **38**, 826.

MELLORS, R. C. (1953). Microscopy. I. A review. *Cancer Res.* **13**, 101.

MOORE, A. E., SOUTHAM, C. M. & STERNBERG, S. S. (1956). Neoplastic changes developing in epithelial cell lines derived from normal persons. *Science* **124**, 127.

MURRAY, MARGARET R. & PETERSON, EDITH R. (1953). Nerve outgrowth and myelinization *in vitro*. *XVe Congr. Soc. int. Chir., Lisbon.*

PALADE, G. E. (1955). A small particulate component of the cytoplasm. *J. biophys. biochem. Cytol.* **1**, 59.

PARKER, R. C. (1932). The races that constitute the group of common fibroblasts. I. The effect of blood plasma. *J. exp. Med.* **55**, 713.

PARKER, R. C. (1933). The races that constitute the group of common fibroblasts. II. The effect of blood serum. *J. exp. Med.* **58**, 97.

PARKER, R. C. (1933). The races that constitute the group of common fibroblasts. III. Differences determined by origin of explant and age of donor. *J. exp. Med.* **58**, 401.

PARKER, R. (1936). The cultivation of tissues for prolonged periods in single flasks. *J. exp. Med.* **64**, 121.

POMERAT, C. M. (1951). Pulsatile activity of cells from human brain in tissue culture. *J. nerv. ment. Dis.* **114**, 430.

PORTER, K. R., CLAUDE, A. & FULLAM, E. F. (1945). A study of tissue culture cells by electron microscopy. Methods and preliminary observations. *J. exp. Med.* **81**, 233.

PORTER, K. R. & KALLMANN, F. L. (1952). Significance of cell particulates as seen by electron microscopy. *Ann. N.Y. Acad. Sci.* **54**, 882.

PORTER, K. R. ed. (1956). Proceedings of conference on tissue fine structure. *J. biophys. biochem. Cytol.* **2** Supplement.

PUCK, T. T. & FISHER, H. W. (1956). Genetics of somatic mammalian cells. I. Demonstration of the existence of mutants with different growth requirements in a human cancer strain (HeLa). *J. exp. Med.* **104**, 427.

SANFORD, KATHERINE K., LIKELY, GWENDOLYN D. & EARLE, W. R. (1954). The development of variations in transplantability and morphology within a clone of mouse fibroblasts transformed to sarcoma-producing cells *in vitro*. *J. nat. Cancer Inst.* **15**, 215.

SCHNEIDER, W. C. & HOGEBOOM, G. H. (1951). Cytochemical studies of mammalian tissues. The isolation of cell components by differential centrifugation. *Cancer Res.* **11**, 1.

SELBY, CECILY C. (1953). Microscopy II. Electron microscopy: A review. *Cancer Res.* **13**, 753.

SWANN, M. M. (1957). The control of cell division—A review. I. General mechanisms. *Cancer Res.* **17**, 727.

SWANN, M. M. (1958). The control of cell division: A review. II. Special mechanisms. *Cancer Res.* **18**, 1118.

THOMSON, R. Y., PAUL, J. & DAVIDSON, J. N. (1958). The metabolic stability of the nucleic acids in cultures of a pure strain of mammalian cells. *Biochem. J.* **69**, 553.

TJIO, J. H. & LEVAN, A. (1956). The chromosome number of man. *Hereditas*, **42**, 1.

WOODS, P. S. & SCHAIRER, MARIE U. (1959). Distribution of newly synthesized deoxyribonucleic acid in dividing chromosomes. *Nature (Lond.)* **183**, 303.

CHAPTER III

THE CELL AND ITS ENVIRONMENT

PRESUMABLY the best environment for growing cells is one providing as nearly as possible the conditions they experience *in vivo*. Before considering the general subject of tissue culture and particularly the topic of cell nutrition, it is desirable, therefore, to consider the various environmental factors affecting tissues. They may be listed as follows:

1. Temperature.
2. Osmotic pressure.
3. Hydrogen ion concentration.
4. Other inorganic ions.
5. Essential metabolites
      (*a*) Carbohydrates.
      (*b*) Dissolved gases.
      (*c*) Amino-acids.
      (*d*) Vitamins.
      (*e*) Proteins and peptides.
6. Supplementary metabolites
      (*a*) Amino-acids.
      (*b*) Vitamins.
      (*c*) Co-enzymes.
      (*d*) Nucleosides.
      (*e*) Peptides.
      (*f*) Intermediary metabolites.
7. Hormones.
8. Other specific factors affecting cell metabolism.
      (*a*) Substrates for adaptive enzymes.
      (*b*) Organisers.
      (*c*) Transforming factors.
9. The matrix in which the cells grow.
10. Interaction between factors.

Temperature

One of the fundamental properties of living matter is the ability to perform complicated chemical reactions at comparatively low temperatures. It is also characteristic of living cells that they are rapidly destroyed by temperatures slightly in excess of those at which they operate best. In the case of most mammalian and avian tissues, the temperature is between 37° and 38·5° C. If the temperature is raised as high as 45° C. the cells are killed within an hour. They stand up to lower temperatures than this for rather longer periods and, for instance, can often survive 42° C. for 12 to 24 hours, but on the whole any slight deviation above the normal temperature for the tissue is lethal to the cells. These figures apply to most fibroblasts and many epithelial types of cells arising from mammalian tissues. There are, nevertheless, some cells which may prefer lower temperatures, even from mammals. Thus, it has often been suggested that human skin epithelial cells grow better at a lower temperature than this. When one considers other species, marked differences become apparent and most fish tissues will not survive at temperatures much in excess of 20° C. Amphibian tissues also survive better at a lower temperature.

On the other hand, most cells will survive cooling to a considerable extent, and cells which normally require a temperature of about 38° C. for rapid growth will continue to grow slowly at a temperature of 20 - 25° C. They may even be cooled to 4° C. and kept at this temperature for some time without apparent harm (other than delayed cell division). It has been suggested that some cell types are sensitive to this cooling process but the majority of cells are apparently unharmed. If cells are cooled below freezing point they are destroyed due to the formation of ice crystals within the cytoplasm. But if a protecting agent such as glycerol is added to the medium and the cells are frozen slowly to a very low temperature ($-70°$ C.) they may be stored for months, and will re-establish themselves after thawing.

Osmotic pressure

The osmotic pressure of the medium is also critical. For mammalian cells the normal osmotic pressure at 38° C. is about 7·6 atmospheres (corresponding to a freezing point depression of about 0·63° C.).

Cells are apparently unaffected by variations of the order of plus or minus 10 per cent. and in fact very much greater variations may be tolerated if they do not take place too quickly. However,

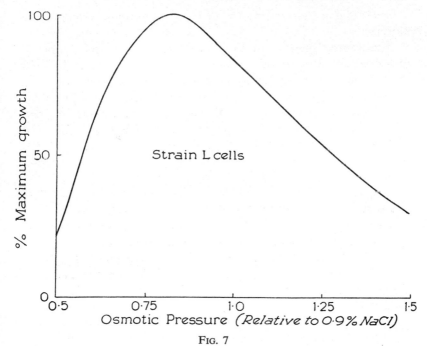

FIG. 7

The effect of osmotic pressure on the rate of growth of strain L cells.

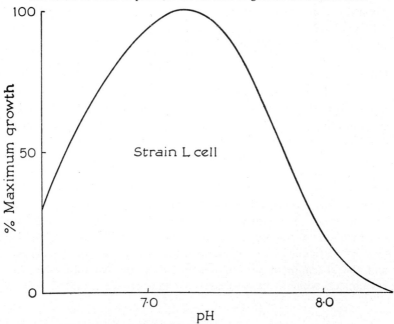

FIG. 8

The effect of *p*H on the rate of growth of strain L cells.

in general it is essential to try to keep within close limits of the normal.

The osmotic pressure in most biological fluids is mainly due to dissolved crystalloids and in mammalian and other animal tissues by far the greater part of it is accounted for by sodium chloride. However, it must not be forgotten that all the other ions contribute substantially and that glucose also accounts for a significant part of the osmotic pressure in the medium so that if the glucose concentration is raised this may affect the osmotic pressure. The larger molecules in the medium contribute relatively little to the osmotic pressure.

Hydrogen ion concentration

The pH of biological fluids has to be very near neutrality to permit survival of the whole animal. However, most isolated tissues will tolerate remarkably wide variations in pH and, for instance, the average mammalian cell will survive indefinitely in the range pH 6·6 to 7·8. There are well authenticated cases of cells growing and differentiating in a pH very much higher than 8 and there are other cases where cells have been maintained for a long time at a pH below 6·6. As a general rule, however, optimal growth is obtained between pH 7·2 and 7·4 and it is undesirable to let the pH deviate outside the limits of pH 6·8 to 7·6. Above pH 7·8, many cell types will die within 24 hours and the same is true in many cases if cells are maintained in a medium more acid than pH 6·8.

Other inorganic ions

All cells require certain inorganic ions in addition to those involved in the regulation of osmotic pressure and hydrogen ion concentration. In the case of most animal cells, the ions required are sodium, potassium, calcium, magnesium, iron, carbonate, phosphate, and probably sulphate. The function of some of these is obscure. The sodium ion is mainly required for the maintenance of osmotic pressure in the medium. The potassium ion may serve a similar purpose within the cell though it probably has some more specific effects also. Calcium and magnesium ions are necessary for the function of some intracellular enzymes while the calcium ion may be particularly associated with the alternation between the sol and the gel state of the cytoplasm. Both the calcium and magnesium ion seem to be necessary for the spreading of cells over a glass surface. Iron is required for some of the respiratory pigments and particularly the cytochromes. The bicarbonate ion is essential for many fundamental biochemical processes in the cell and is also one of the main buffering substances in the medium. The phosphate ion is essential for energy metabolism since most of the energy of the cell is carried in the form of high energy phosphate bonds. It also functions as a buffer substance. It is less certain that the sulphate ion is required by the cell but it seems highly likely since radio-active sulphate is actively incorporated into cellular proteins. In the case of cells which synthesise a sulphonated mucopoly-saccharide the presence of sulphate in the medium must be essential.

Carbohydrates

A source of carbohydrate seems to be almost essential to cultured cells. The most commonly available source is, of course, glucose, although it can be replaced by other substances, notably fructose, mannose, trehalose, turanose, glucose phosphates and possibly galactose. Maltose and a number of disaccharides and polysaccharides can be utilised although they are almost certainly broken down to monosaccharides first. Glucose can be replaced also by simpler molecules and it has been shown, for instance, that lactate and pyruvate will satisfy the cell's energy requirements so long as there is plenty of oxygen available. Some mutant strains have been described which preferentially utilise pentoses, such as xylose and ribose. In some cases, cells may be able to survive without glucose for some considerable time, especially those which possess proteolytic activity, since some cells are capable of deami-nation and the amino-acid residues may then be used as a source of energy.

Gases

Both oxygen and carbon dioxide are probably essential for cell survival. There is evidence to suggest that a few cell types may be able to survive for a considerable time in the complete absence of oxygen and they may be able to obtain all their energy by the process of anaerobic glycolysis. However, it seems unlikely that any animal cell will survive indefinitely in the absence of oxygen since some of the by-products of the Krebs cycle are necessary for the synthesis of various cell components and unless these are supplied in the medium the cells are bound to die when their stores are used up.

The need for carbon dioxide in the medium is slightly controversial. This is because it is virtually impossible to exclude carbon dioxide completely from the cells since it is a product of metabolism and is immediately fixed by kations present in the medium. However, the experiments of Harris very strongly suggest that for some cell types the bicarbonate ion is absolutely essential. Apart from its requirement in tissue metabolism, the bicarbonate ion is the most important buffering ion in most culture media and most systems require some control of the carbon dioxide tension in the gas phase and in the medium. This is achieved either by adding a special gas phase to the culture vessel or by sealing it tightly so that the carbon dioxide produced by metabolism is retained.

Amino-acids

It has now been established that most animal cells have a specific requirement for 12 amino-acids. These are—arginine, cystine, histidine, isoleucine, leucine, lysine, methionine, phenylalanine, threonine, tryptophane, tyrosine and valine. It is almost certain that there are a few cells in which the requirements are slightly different. In some organ cultures, fewer amino-acids are required. (Although in this case it is possible that there is re-utilisation of breakdown products from other parts of the tissue.)

Some interesting observations may be made about the above list of amino-acids. In addition to all the so-called essential amino-acids for mammals, it includes cystine and tyrosine. In the intact animal, cystine and methionine can replace each other and cystine is, therefore, not considered essential but in cultured cells cystine is required for growth and survival irrespective of the presence of methionine. Similarly, in the intact animal phenylalanine is quite readily transformed to tyrosine, but it has been shown recently that in most of the cells commonly cultured this transformation does not take place, or at least not to a degree adequate for cell survival. Consequently, tyrosine has to be considered an essential amino-acid for cell cultures.

In addition to the amino-acids already mentioned, it has been shown that most cells have a high requirement for glutamine. This appears intact in the cell protein but the explanation of the rather high requirement is at present obscure in view of the demonstration by Levintow *et al.* that the α-amino groups of other amino-acids are not derived from it. However, it has a number of other important functions in metabolism and in particular it can be utilised in the synthesis of the nucleic acids.

Vitamins

Several vitamins of the B group are necessary for cell growth and multiplication. Most of them are known to form essential parts of co-enzymes involved in metabolism and, therefore, a requirement for them is readily understood. Those which have been shown to be necessary are para-aminobenzoic acid, biotin, choline, folic acid, nicotinic acid, pantothenic acid, pyridoxal, riboflavin, thiamine, and inositol. Nicotinic acid can be replaced by nicotinamide and pyridoxal can be replaced by pyridoxine. It is interesting that the other vitamins do not appear to be essential for cell survival.

Proteins and peptides

It has not yet been satisfactorily established to what extent proteins and peptides are essential for the growth and survival of cells. It seems unlikely that proteins *per se* are essential for cell growth, but, on the other hand, few satisfactory media have been produced in which cells will grow rapidly in the total absence of protein or a similar polypeptide. In the few cases where growth in protein-free media has been achieved, it is considerably stimulated by the addition of a trace of serum. This may be due to the presence in the serum of some trace substances bound tightly to protein, but until this has been proved, a need for protein or peptide cannot be excluded. One particular peptide, glutathione, improves cell survival but this is almost certainly because it is highly specialised to act as an oxidation-reduction buffer by virtue of its SH groups which can be oxidised to give S-S linkages. Kent and Gey (1957) have shown that α-globulin disappears from the medium in which some cells are grown. It is of interest that the substance fetuin is associated with this fraction since it has been suggested by Puck *et al.* that this substance is necessary for the spreading of cells on glass surfaces. Liebermann *et al.* (1959) have made a similar observation, although they present evidence that the flattening factor and fetuin are distinct.

Supplementary metabolites

So far, we have been considering the environmental factors essential for the survival of the cell. However, in a great many studies we are interested not in the survival of the cell but in the full development of its potentialities and this may require the addition of many other factors to the environment. From the point of view of nutrition several supplementary factors may be considered.

Although the cells will make do with the essential amino-acids mentioned above, it seems certain that they grow much better in the presence of adequate amounts of the other amino-acids commonly used in the synthesis of proteins. In particular, the cells like to have one general source of amino groups and amino-acid residues. For this purpose glycine is a useful addition to the medium. Also, when a very dilute cell inoculum is used serine, and possibly proline, seem to be required for survival although they can be synthesised. Certain vitamins other than those already mentioned are essential in some tissues performing specialised functions. This aspect of metabolism has not been thoroughly investigated as yet but, as an example, it has been shown that vitamin A is essential for the differentiation of ciliated columnar epithelium since, in its absence, it changes to keratinised epithelium. Moreover, it has been claimed that cells often grow better if the B group vitamins are added as co-enzymes rather than as the vitamins themselves, and for this reason some media have contained such substances as diphosphopyridine nucleotide, triphosphopyridine nucleotide, co-enzyme A, cocarboxylase, flavine adenine dinucleotide and uridine triphosphate. In this same context, it has been shown quite conclusively that while cultured cells will readily synthesise nucleic acids from simple molecules such as glycine, carbon dioxide and sodium formate, they will, nevertheless, preferentially use nucleosides when these are available in the medium.

The possibility that cells may use peptides has been mentioned above. Indeed, it has been shown that cells will utilise amino-acids present in dipeptides when the amino-acids themselves are omitted from the medium. However, it is by no means certain, and from other studies it seems unlikely, that these dipeptides are incorporated intact into the cell proteins. Nevertheless, it has been persistently reported in the tissue culture literature that cells benefit from the addition of peptides to the medium, and there is some suggestion that their presence may in some way counteract some of the ill-effects caused by an imbalance of amino-acids.

Hormones

Very little is known as yet about the action of hormones on cells *in vitro*. Tissue cultures would seem to provide an ideal tool for the study of hormone action and our present lack of knowledge is disappointing. It seems quite certain that the presence of hormones is not essential for cell survival but in view of their great importance in the intact animal, it is likely that they are required for the full development and function of differentiated cells.

Other specific factors

Theoretically, there are a number of other factors which may affect the behaviour of differentiated cells and, although similar factors have been demonstrated to operate on bacteria, it must be stated that at the time of writing there is no definite evidence for the existence of these mechanisms in animal cells.

First in this respect it is necessary to mention substrates and inducers for adaptive enzymes. Since there is now fairly good evidence that adaptive enzymes exist in animals as well as bacteria, it seems almost certain that the presence of substrates for these enzymes is essential for the full development of the cell's potentialities. Jones, Featherstone and Bonting (1956) claim to have demonstrated adaptation of cholinesterase in cultured cells. Another apparent example of adaptive enzyme formation in cultured cells has been demonstrated in the case of glutamyl transferase by De Mars (1958) and this has been confirmed by ourselves.

There is no evidence at all at present for the existence of transforming factors (as such) in animal cells, but there is very good evidence for the existence of so-called organisers in early embryonic development and there is some evidence to suggest that these may be of the nature of nucleic acids and therefore very similar indeed to the transforming factors in bacteria. The diffusible factors which Grobstein has demonstrated to be necessary for the development of tissue structure at a fairly late stage of embryonic growth, may be of a similar nature.

The matrix

It is well known that the morphological appearances of tissue culture cells have very little relationship in most cases to the morphology of the same types of cells *in vivo* and it has been shown that to a large extent this is due to the fact that the cells grow on a two-dimensional substrate in which there are no lines of force for orientation. In order to reproduce the morphological and possibly the functional characteristics of cells, it may be necessary to grow them in specially oriented three-dimensional substrates. This has been done with many cell types by growing them on cellulose sponges by Leighton's technique which produces morphological pictures very similar to those existing *in vivo*.

Balance among factors

At the present time we know very little about the importance of the balance among factors in cultured cells. We know that in the intact animal alterations in the levels of amino-acids or other metabolites in the body may produce profound changes in the organism. Similarly, in cell cultures, competitive relationships exist among certain essential amino-acids and consequently an unbalanced medium may lead to inhibition of growth.

The above considerations apply particularly to mammalian and avian cells. Very little is known about the metabolic requirements of other animal cells. However, the metabolic requirements of plant cells have been investigated quite thoroughly and their general requirements are known fairly well. Again, there is a need for certain ions, namely calcium, potassium, magnesium, manganese, zinc, copper, molybdenum, iron and possibly others such as sodium, titanium and nickel. A source of carbohydrate is essential and sucrose is the one usually supplied. Plants on the whole have much less exacting amino-acid requirements than animal cells and it is usually sufficient to add some glycine to the medium. A number of vitamins are needed, particularly nicotinic acid and pyridoxine, although some tissues require pantothenic acid, biotin and inositol. In addition to these it seems that some individual plant tissues have specific requirements.

BIBLIOGRAPHY

AUERBACH, R. & GROBSTEIN, C. (1958). Inductive interaction of embryonic tissues after dissociation and reaggregation. *Exp. Cell Res.* **15**, 384.

BARSKI, G., MAURIN, J., WIELGOSZ & LÉPINE, P. (1951). Conditions de nutrition cellulaire *in vitro* en culture sans support plasmatique. Rôle des fractions micro- et macro-moléculaires. *Ann. Inst. Pasteur* **81**, 9.

BIGGERS, J. D., RINALDINI, L. M. & WEBB, M. (1957). The study of growth factors in tissue culture. *Symp. Soc. exp. Biol. XI.* The Biological Action of Growth Substances, p. 264.

BISCEGLIE, V. (1928). La transformazione oncogena sperimentale delle cellule normali coltivate fuori dell'organismo. *Arch. exp. Zellforsch.* **6**, 161.

BLOOM, W. (1937). Cellular differentiation and tissue culture. *Physiol. Rev.* **17**, 589.

BORGHESE, E. (1950). The development *in vitro* of the submandibular and sublingual glands of the Mus musculus. *J. Anat. (Lond.)* **84**, 287.

BORGHESE, E. (1950). Explantation experiments on the influence of the connective tissue capsule on the development of the epithelial part of the submandibular gland of the Mus musculus. *J. Anat. (Lond.)* **84**, 303.

CAILLEAU, RELDA, HOARD, DOROTHY & ZITCER, ELSA M. (1957). Chemical composition of some sera and cells used in tissue cultures. Fatty acid and lipid phosphorus content. *Tex. Rep. Biol. Med.* **15**, 250.

CARREL, A. & BAKER, L. E. (1926). The chemical nature of substances required for cell multiplication. *J. exp. Med.* **44**, 503.

CHEN, J. M. (1952). Studies on the morphogenesis of the mouse sternum. II. Experiments on the origin of the sternum and its capacity for self-differentiation *in vitro. J. Anat. (Lond.)* **86**, 387.

CHEN, J. M. (1954). The effect of insulin on embryonic limb-bones cultivated *in vitro. J. Physiol.* **125**, 148.

DAVENPORT, H. W. & CHAVRE, V. J. (1951). Acid secretion and acetoacetate utilization in mouse stomachs *in vitro. Fed. Proc.* **10**, 33.

DAVIDSON, J. N. & WAYMOUTH, C. (1943). Factors influencing nucleoprotein content of fibroblasts growing *in vitro. Biochem. J.* **37**, 271.

DAVIDSON, J. N., LESLIE, I. & WAYMOUTH, CHARITY (1949). The nucleoprotein content of fibroblasts growing *in vitro.* 4. Changes in the ribonucleic acid phosphorus (RNAP) and deoxyribonucleic acid phosphorus (DNAP) content. *Biochem. J.* **37**, 271.

DOLJANSKI, L. (1930). Sur le rapport entre la prolifération et l'activité pigmentogène dans les cultures d'épithélium de l'iris. *C.R. Soc. Biol. (Paris)* **105**, 343.

EAGLE, H. (1955). The specific amino acid requirements of mammalian cells (strain L) in tissue culture. *J. biol. Chem.* **214**, 839.

EAGLE, H. (1955). The specific amino-acid requirements of a human carcinoma cell (strain HeLa) in tissue culture. *J. exp. Med.* **102**, 37.

EAGLE, H. (1955). The minimum vitamin requirements of the L and HeLa cells in tissue culture, the production of specific vitamin deficiencies and their cure. *J. exp. Med.,* **102**, 595.

EAGLE, H. (1955). Nutrition needs of mammalian cells in tissue culture. *Science* **122**, 501.

EAGLE, H. (1955). Utilization of dipeptides by mammalian cells in tissue culture. *Proc. Soc. exp. Biol. (N.Y.)* **89**, 96.

EAGLE, H. & PIEZ, K. A. (1960). The utilization of proteins by cultured human cells. *J. biol. Chem.* **235**, 1095.

EAGLE, H., BARBAN, S., LEVY, MINA & SCHULZE, H. O. (1958). The utilization of carbohydrates by human cell culture. *J. biol. Chem.* **233**, 551.

EAGLE, H., OYAMA, V. I., LEVY, M. & FREEMAN, A. (1956). Myo-inositol as an essential growth factor for normal and malignant human cells in tissue culture. *Science* **123**, 845.

EAGLE, H., OYAMA, V. I., LEVY, M., HORTON, C. L. & FLEISCHMAN, R. (1956). The growth response of mammalian cells in tissue culture to L-glutamine and L-glutamic acid. *J. biol. Chem.* **218**, 607.

EAGLE, H., OYAMA, V. I. & LEVY, M. (1957). Amino-acid requirements of normal and malignant human cells in tissue culture. *Arch. Biochem.* **67**, 432.

EAGLE, H., OYAMA, VANCE I., LEVY, MINA & FREEMAN, AARON E. (1957). Myo-inositol as an essential growth factor for normal and malignant human cells in tissue culture. *J. biol. Chem.* **226**, 191.

EHRENSVÄRD, G. A., FISCHER, A. & SJERNHOLM, R. (1949). Protein metabolism of tissue cells *in vitro*. VII. The chemical nature of some obligate factors of tissue cell nutrition. *Acta physiol. scand.* **18**, 218.

FELL, HONOR B. (1953). The effect of vitamin A on organ cultures of skeletal and other tissues. In *Connective Tissue*. Ed. C. Rogan. New York: Macy.

FELL, HONOR B. (1954). The effect of hormones and vitamin A on organ cultures. *Ann. N.Y. Acad. Sci.* **58**, 1183.

FELL, HONOR B. (1956). Effect of excess vitamin A on organized tissues cultivated *in vitro*. *Brit. med. Bull.* **12**, 35.

FELL, HONOR B. & MELLANBY, E. (1952). The effect of hypervitaminosis A on embryonic limb-bones cultivated *in vitro*. *J. Physiol.* **116**, 320.

FELL, HONOR B. & MELLANBY, E. (1953). Metaplasia produced in cultures of chick ectoderm by high vitamin A. *J. Physiol.* **119**, 470.

FELL, HONOR B. & MELLANBY, E. (1955). The biological action of thyroxine on embryonic bones grown in tissue culture. *J. Physiol.* **127**, 427.

FELL, HONOR B. & MELLANBY, E. (1956). The effect of 1-triiodothyronine on the growth and development of embryonic chick limb-bones in tissue culture. *J. Physiol.* **133**, 89.

FELL, HONOR B., MELLANBY, E. & PELC, S. R. (1954). Influence of excess vitamin A on the sulphate metabolism of chick ectoderm grown *in vitro*. *Brit. med. J.* **2**, 611.

FISCHER, A. (1921). Growth of fibroblasts and hydrogen ion concentration of the medium. *J. exp. Med.* **34**, 447.

FISCHER, A. (1948). Amino-acid metabolism of tissue cells *in vitro*. *Nature* (*Lond.*) **161**, 1008.

FISCHER, A. (1948). Nutrition of animal tissue cells. *Scientia* **83**, 170.

FISCHER, A. (1948). Amino-acid metabolism of tissue cells *in vitro*. *Biochem. J.* **4**, 491.

FISCHER, H. W., PUCK, T. T. & SATO, G. (1958). Molecular growth requirements of single mammalian cells. The action of Fetuin in promoting cell attachment to glass. *Proc. nat. Acad. Sci.* (*Wash.*) **44**, 4.

GAILLARD, P. J. (1955). Parathyroid gland tissue and bone *in vitro*. I. *Exp. Cell Res.* **3**, 154.

GEYER, R. P. & CHANG, R. S. (1958). Bicarbonate as an essential for human cells *in vitro*. *Arch. Biochem.* **73**, 500.

GIFFORD, G. E. (1963). Some effects of anaerobiosis on the growth and metabolism of HeLa cells. *Exp. Cell Res.* **31**, 113.

GROBSTEIN, C. (1952). Effect of fragmentation of mouse embryonic shields on their differentiative behavior after culturing. *J. exp. Zool.* **120**, 437.

GROBSTEIN, C. (1953). Epithelio-mesenchymal specificity in the morphogenesis of mouse sub-mandibular rudiments *in vitro. J. exp. Zool.* **124**, 383.

GROBSTEIN, C. (1953). Morphogenetic interaction between embryonic mouse tissues separated by a membrane filter. *Nature (Lond.)* **172**, 869.

GROBSTEIN, C. (1953). Analysis *in vitro* of the early organization of the rudiment of the mouse sub-mandibular gland. *J. Morph.* **93**, 19.

GROBSTEIN, C. (1955). Tissue interaction in the morphogenesis of mouse embryonic rudiments *in vitro.* In *Aspects of Synthesis and Order in Growth.* Ed. Dorothea Rudnick. Princeton: University Press.

GROBSTEIN, C. (1956). Trans-filter induction of tubules in mouse metanephrogenic mesenchyme. *Exp. Cell Res.* **10**, 424.

HANKS, J. H. (1949). Inorganic aging of the plasma layer of tissue cultures. *Proc. Soc. exp. Biol. (N.Y.)* **71**, 313.

HARRIS, M. & KUTSKY, P. (1953). Utilization of added sugars by chick heart fibroblasts in dialyzed media. *J. cell comp. Physiol.* **42**, 449.

HARRIS, M. (1954). The role of bicarbonate for outgrowth of chick heart fibroblasts *in vitro. J. exp. Zool.* **125**, 85.

HULL, W. & KIRK, P. (1950). The effect of medium constituents on nucleic acids and uptake of P^{32}. *J. gen. Physiol.* **34**, 81.

JONES, M., FEATHERSTONE, R. M. & BONTING, S. L. (1956). The effect of acetyl-choline on the cholinesterases of chick embryo intestine cultured *in vitro. J. Pharmacol. exp. Therap.* **116**, 114.

KENT, H. N. & GEY, G. O. (1957). Changes in serum proteins during growth of malignant cells *in vitro. Proc. Soc. exp. Biol. (N.Y.)* **94**, 205.

KUTSKY, R. (1953). Stimulating effect of nucleoprotein fraction of chick embryo extract on homologous heart fibroblasts. *Proc. Soc. exp. Biol. (N.Y.)* **83**, 390.

LASNITZKI, I. (1954). The effect of estrone alone and combined with 20-methyl cholanthrene on mouse prostate glands grown *in vitro. Cancer Res.* **14**, 632.

LASNITZKI, I. (1955). The effect of testosterone propionate on organ cultures of the mouse prostate. *J. Endocr.* **12**, 236.

LEIGHTON, J. (1951). A sponge matrix method for tissue culture. Formation of organized aggregates of cells *in vitro. J. nat. Cancer Inst.* **12**, 545.

LEIGHTON, J. (1954). The growth patterns of some transplantable animal tumors in sponge matrix tissue culture. *J. nat. Cancer Inst.* **15**, 275.

LESLIE, I. & DAVIDSON, J. N. (1951). The effect of insulin on cellular composition and growth of chick-heart explants. *Biochem. J.* **49**, 41.

LESLIE, I. & PAUL, J. (1954). The action of insulin on the composition of cells and medium during culture of chick heart explants. *J. Endocr.* **11**, 110.

LESLIE, I., FULTON, W. C. & SINCLAIR, R. (1956). The influence of the medium on the insulin response of two unrelated human cells grown in tissue culture. *Biochem. J.* **63**, 18P.

LESLIE, I., FULTON, W. C. & SINCLAIR, R. (1957). The metabolism of human embryonic and malignant cells and their response to insulin. *Biochim. biophys. Acta* **24**, 365.

LEWIS, MARGARET R. & LEWIS, W. H. (1926). Transformation of mononuclear blood-cells into macrophages, epithelioid cells, and giant cells in hanging-drop blood-cultures from lower vertebrates. *Contr. Embryol. Carneg. Instn* **18**, 95.

LIEBERMAN, I. & OVE, R. (1957). Purification of a serum protein required by a mammalian cell in tissue culture. *Biochim. biophys. Acta* **25**, 449.

LIEBERMAN, I. & OVE, P. (1958). A protein growth factor for mammalian cells in culture. *J. biol. Chem.* **233**, 637

LIEBERMAN, I., LAMY, F. & OVE, P. (1959). Nonidentity of fetuin and protein growth (flattening) factor. *Science*, **129**, 43.

DE MARS, R. (1958). The inhibition by glutamine of glutamyl transferase formation in cultures of human cells. *Biochim. biophys. Acta* **27**, 435.

MORGAN, J. F. (1958). Tissue culture nutrition. *Bact. Rev.* **22**, 20.

MORGAN, J. F. & McCRONE, M. A. (1957). A study of protein synthesis in tissue culture. *J. nat. Cancer Inst.* **19**, 393.

MORTON, H. J., PASIEKA, A. E. & MORGAN, J. F. (1956). The nutrition of animal cells cultivated *in vitro*. III. Use of a depletion technique for determining specific nutritional requirements. *J. biophys. biochem. Cytol.* **2**, 589.

MOSCONA, A. (1956). Development of heterotypic combinations of dissociated embryonic chick cells. *Proc. Soc. exp. Biol. (N.Y.)* **92**, 410.

MOSCONA, A. (1957). The development *in vitro* of chimeric aggregates of dissociated embryonic chick and mouse cells. *Proc. nat. Acad. Sci. (Wash.)* **43**, 184.

MOSCONA, A. (1961). Environmental factors in experimental studies on histogenesis. *Colloq. int. Cent. nat. Rech. Sci.* **101**, 155.

MOSCONA, A. & MOSCONA, H. (1952). The dissociation and aggregation of cells from organ rudiments of the early chick embryo. *J. Anat. (Lond.)* **86**, 287.

NEUMANN, R. E. & McCOY, T. A. (1958). Growth-promoting properties of pyruvate, oxalacetate and α-ketoglutarate for isolated Walker carcinosarcoma 256 cells. *Proc Soc. exp. Biol. (N.Y.)* **98**, 303.

NIU, M. C. (1956). VII. New approaches to the problem of embryonic induction. In *Cellular Mechanisms in Differentiation and Growth*. Ed. Dorothea Rudnick. Princeton: University Press.

NIU, M. C. & TWITTY, V. C. (1953). The differentiation of gastrula ectoderm in medium conditioned by axial mesoderm. *Proc. nat. Acad. Sci. (Wash.)* **39**, 985.

OWENS, OLGA V. H., GEY, MARGARET K. & GEY, G. O. (1958). The effect of calcium and magnesium on the growth and morphology of mouse lymphoblasts (MBIII, de Bruyn) in tissue culture. *Cancer Res.* **18**, 968.

PARKER, R. C. (1931). Structural and functional variations of fibroblasts in pure cultures. *Science* **73**, 401.

PARKER, R. C. (1932). The races that constitute the group of common fibroblasts. I. The effect of blood plasma. *J. exp. Med.* **55**, 713.

PARKER, R. C. (1932). The functional characteristics of nine races of fibroblasts. *Science* **76**, 219.

PARSHLEY, M. S. & SIMMS, H. S. (1946). Conditions favoring the growth of adult skin epithelium *in vitro*. *Anat. Rec.* **94**, 42.

PAUL, J. (1959). Environmental influences on the metabolism and composition of cultured cells. *J. exp. Zool.* **142**.

PAUL, J. (1962). The cancer cell *in vitro*: a review. *Cancer Res.* **22**, 431.

PAUL, J. & PEARSON, E. S. (1957). Metabolism of chick embryonic heart explants during transition from *in vivo* to *in vitro* conditions. *Exp. Cell Res.* **12**, 212.

PAUL, J. & PEARSON, E. S. (1957). Metabolism of chick embryonic liver explants during transition from *in vivo* to *in vitro* conditions. *Exp. Cell Res.* **12**, 223.

PEDERSEN, K. O. (1944). Fetuin, a new globulin isolated from serum. *Nature (Lond.)* **154**, 575.

PIKOVSKI, MARY A. (1954). Differentiated mammary gland tumor tissue grown in an alkaline medium *in vitro*. *Exp. Cell Res.* **7,** 52.

RUECKERT, R. R. & MUELLER, G. C. (1960). Effect of oxygen tension on HeLa cell growth. *Cancer Res.* **20,** 944.

SEAMAN, ARLENE R. (1956). The *in vitro* cultivation of the prostate gland of the adult mouse in alkaline fluid medium. *Exp. Cell Res.* **11,** 283.

SEVASTIKOGLOU, J. (1957). A study of endochondral osteogenesis in tissue culture. *Exp. Cell Res.* **12,** 80.

SCHABERG, A. (1955). Regeneration of the adrenal cortex *in vitro*. *Anat. Rec.* **122,** 205.

SIDMAN, R. L. (1956). The direct effect of insulin on organ cultures of brown fat. *Anat. Rec.* **124,** 723.

STRANGEWAYS, T. S. P. & FELL, HONOR B. (1926). Experimental studies on the differentiation of embryo tissues growing *in vivo* and *in vitro*. I. *Proc. R. Soc.* **B99,** 340.

STRANGEWAYS, T. S. P. & FELL, HONOR B. (1926). Experimental studies on the differentiation of embryo tissues growing *in vivo* and *in vitro*. II. *Proc. R. Soc.* **B100,** 273.

SWIM, H. E. & PARKER, R. F. (1956). The amino acid requirements of human uterine fibroblasts, strain U12. *Anat. Rec.* **124,** 499.

SWIM, H. E. & PARKER, R. F. (1958). Vitamin requirements of uterine fibroblasts, strain U12-79; their replacement by related compounds. *Arch. Biochem.* **78,** 46.

WEISS, L. P. & FAWCETT, D. W. (1953). Cytochemical observations on chicken monocytes, macrophages and giant cells in tissue culture. *J. Histochem. Cytochem.* **1,** 47.

WEISS, P. (1952). "Attraction fields" between growing tissue cultures. *Science* **115,** 293.

WEISS, P. & GARBER, B. (1952). Shape and movement of mesenchyme cells as functions of the physical structure of the medium. Contributions to a quantitative morphology. *Proc. nat. Acad. Sci. (Wash.)* **38,** 264.

WESTFALL, B. B., EVANS, V. J., PEPPERS, E. V., HAWKINS, N. M. & EARLE, W. R. (1956). Effect of glutamine on the growth and metabolism of liver cells *in vitro*. *J. nat. Cancer Inst.* **17,** 131.

WILLMER, E. N. (1926). Studies on the influence of the surrounding medium on the activity of cells in tissue culture. *Brit. J. exp. Biol.* **4,** 280.

WILLMER, E. N. (1954). Tissue culture; the growth and differentiation of normal tissues in artificial media. Methuen, *Monographs on Biological Subjects*. 2nd ed. London: Methuen. New York: Wiley.

WINNICK, P. & WINNICK, T. (1953). Utilization of amino acids, peptides and protein by cultures of embryonic heart. *J. nat. Cancer Inst.* **14,** 519.

WOLFF, E. M. (1953). Sur la croissance et la différenciation en milieu synthétique de la syrinx de l'embryon le poulet. *C.R. Soc. Biol. (Paris)* **147,** 864.

WOLFF, E. T. & WOLFF, E. M. (1952). Le déterminisme de la differenciation sexuelle de la syrinx du canard cultivée *in vitro*. *Bull. biol.* **86,** 325.

CHAPTER IV

THE GROWTH AND METABOLISM OF CULTURED CELLS

THERE are few features of the metabolism of cultured cells which are peculiar to them and the general descriptions of metabolic pathways to be found in any biochemical textbook apply equally to avian and mammalian cells *in vitro*. This account will, therefore, be confined to a brief summary of the general principles involved in metabolism with emphasis on a few points of particular interest in relation to cells grown *in vitro*.

All living cells perform work. This work consists, on the one hand, of synthetic activity (such as the production of new cytoplasm) and on the other hand of functional activity (such as contraction). In order to perform this work they require energy and this is provided by the combustion of carbohydrates, especially glucose, or fats. It is well known that in the absence of living matter carbohydrates and fats can be oxidised and will release large amounts of energy if they are heated in the presence of oxygen to a temperature where combustion occurs spontaneously. In these circumstances, it is necessary to put a large amount of energy into the system before getting energy out. In living cells exactly the same consideration applies but due to the presence of highly efficient catalysts, the enzymes, the amount of energy which has to be put into the system is relatively small and its subsequent release is regulated so that the reactions take place at low temperatures.

As energy is produced it has to be transmitted to the chemical reactions for which it is required. In living systems this is done by the creation of ' high energy phosphate bonds '. These are chemical bonds which release a large amount of energy when they are broken.

Finally, the degradation of glucose, etc., proceeds, not in one large step but in a series of small stages, each mediated by a single enzyme. The oxidative stages involved do not permit direct combination with molecular oxygen. Instead, most of the oxidative reactions are performed by the removal of hydrogen, which ultimately combines with molecular oxygen to form water.

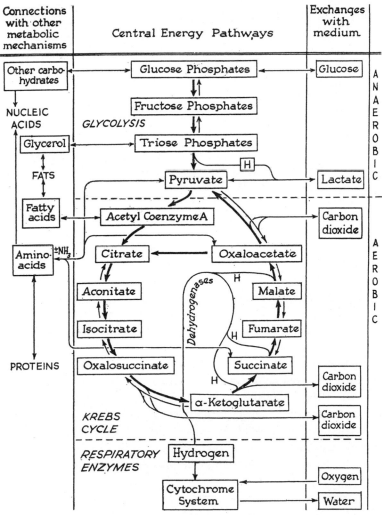

Anaerobically 1 mole glucose → 2 moles lactate + 2 high energy phosphate bonds (= 23,000 cal.).

Aerobically 1 mole glucose + 3 moles O_2 → 6 moles CO_2 + 6 moles H_2O + ca 40 high energy phosphate bonds (= 460,000 cal.)

FIG. 9

Interrelationships between the main metabolic pathways in animal cells.

Carbohydrate metabolism

With these points in mind, it is now possible to examine two of the standard energy-producing pathways in living systems—the glycolysis, or Embden-Meyerhof, pathway and the tricarboxylic acid, or Krebs, cycle (Fig. 9). It should be noted that although the principal pathways, these are not the only energy-producing mechanisms in living cells.

Two points are particularly noteworthy in these systems. In the first place, glucose can be converted to lactic acid without utilising any oxygen whatsoever, and some energy is released in the process. On the other hand, the oxidation of pyruvic acid to carbon dioxide and water requires large amounts of oxygen. Secondly, the oxidation of glucose to carbon dioxide and water releases much more energy from a given amount of material than the conversion of glucose to lactic acid.

In cultured cells the metabolism of glucose proceeds by way of glycolytic and Krebs pathways, as in the tissues of the intact organism. However, many cells show a marked tendency to accumulate lactic acid and keto acids in the medium. It has been suggested that this is a peculiarity of malignant cells *in vitro*, but in fact a high level of aerobic glycolysis (as this is called) is even more typical of healthy embryonic cells and can be demonstrated in some normal adult cells.

Most cultured cells exhibit a marked Pasteur effect. That is to say, when the air in the vessel is replaced by nitrogen so that the cells are grown anaerobically, the amount of glucose which is converted to lactic acid is greatly increased. Virtually all the glucose can be accounted for as lactic acid in these conditions whereas in aerobic conditions the amount of glucose accounted for as lactic acid varies from 5 or 10 per cent. up to about 70 per cent. depending on the cell type and the conditions of cultivation.

It is clear that cultured cells have very variable needs for oxygen and that a considerable part of the energy requirements can be met by the breakdown of six-carbon carbohydrates such as glucose to three-carbon compounds such as lactic acid and pyruvic acid, a process which requires no oxygen. The question arises whether cells require to use oxidative pathways at all. Unfortunately, the information available is by no means precise. That cells can be grown in the complete absence of oxygen for rather short periods of time was originally demonstrated by Laser and this observation has been verified repeatedly. There can be no doubt that many cells will survive briefly in very low oxygen tensions and for long periods of time in fairly low concentrations of oxygen. Further evidence that oxidative pathways may not play an essential role in the metabolism of cultured cells arises from the observations of Swann and Pomerat that carbon monoxide and cyanide do not affect cell metabolism or mitosis (for the first cycle at least), whereas inhibitors of glycolysis such as iodoacetate, azide and fluoride inhibit respiration and prevent cell division almost immediately. Direct inhibition of the Krebs cycle by means of malonate or fluoroacetate does not seem to affect cultured cells adversely either. In assessing this evidence it becomes clear that in none of the experiments was the inhibition maintained for very long. It can therefore only be stated that these inhibitors are not immediately lethal to cultured cells and it remains to be seen whether they can survive continuous inhibition. There is some evidence to suggest that over a longer time period respiration is intimately related to growth. Thus, Fulton, Sinclair and Leslie (1956) have shown that the amount of glucose oxidised is proportional to the total nucleic acid phosphorus in growing cultures and Gifford, Robertson and Syverton have indicated that the rate of oxygen utilisation can be correlated with growth. These findings, however, are not entirely in agreement with those of Westfall et al. (1955) who found glucose consumption and lactic acid accumulation to parallel cell number. Studies performed in the author's laboratory indicated that both glycolysis and respiration can vary very greatly and that many cells grow satisfactorily irrespective of which pathway is predominant.

The above remarks apply only to cell cultures and explants of embryonic material because Trowell has shown that high oxygen tensions are necessary for the survival of some adult tissues in organ culture. He, in fact, used 95 per cent. oxygen in a gas phase to which organ fragments were directly exposed. Such high oxygen tensions are, in fact, lethal to embryonic tissues and cell strains grown as monolayers on glass or in suspension. For cell strains Cooper and his colleagues (1958) have suggested that an oxygen tension rather lower than atmospheric is optimum and Danes and Kieler also have found normal atmospheric oxygen tension to be about the optimum. The reason for this discrepancy is not very clear. It may well be that the oxygen requirements of adult or differentiated tissues on the one hand and embryonic or undifferentiated tissues on the other are completely different. In this connection Krebs has shown that the oxygen requirements of the tissues of large animals are relatively less than the requirements of similar tissues from small animals while there are great differences in the oxygen requirements of embryonic and adult tissues. Since many of the cells in permanent culture originated from embryonic or malignant tissues they may therefore have radically different requirements from 'normal' cells.

While carbon dioxide is an end-product of the metabolism of glucose, it should be observed that it can also be taken up and condensed with pyruvic acid to form oxaloacetic acid in the tricarboxylic acid cycle. In this way it may be said to prime the tricarboxylic acid cycle. Kieler and Danes have found that the respiration of cultured cells is affected by carbon dioxide tension and suggest that this mechanism provides the explanation. Carbon dioxide seems to be necessary for prolonged survival of cultured cells and this process of 'fixation' of carbon dioxide may be the reason although M. Harris has adduced evidence that its essential function is the regulation of intracellular pH.

Synthetic mechanisms

The building of complex molecules from simple ones usually requires energy. Growing cells very rapidly produce new molecules of many kinds and hence a constant supply of energy is needed. This is employed in synthetic processes in a fairly standard manner. The small molecules to be linked together to form large molecules are first 'activated'. This usually means that they have a high-energy phosphate bond joined on to them. An 'activated' molecule may then be linked to another molecule by the loss of a phosphate ion from the 'activated' molecule and a hydrogen ion from the other, the hydrogen ion and the phosphate ion forming 'low-energy' inorganic phosphate. Some of the energy released is incorporated into the new chemical bond linking the two molecules. This process operates in the synthesis of proteins, fatty acids, nucleic acids and many other substances.

Protein metabolism

Proteins are large molecules consisting of chains of small molecules, amino-acids, linked together. The number of amino-acids occurring in nature is quite small and in the proteins of avian and mammalian cells about 20 different ones are found. About 12 of these are essential for most cultured cells. The others can be synthesised by the transfer of amino-groups to organic acid molecules (transamination).

TRANSAMINATION

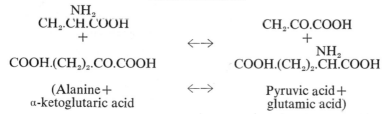

$$NH_2$$
$$CH_2.CH.COOH$$
$$+$$
$$COOH.(CH_2)_2.CO.COOH$$

$\longleftrightarrow$

$$CH_2.CO.COOH$$
$$+$$
$$NH_2$$
$$COOH.(CH_2)_2.CH.COOH$$

(Alanine+ $\longleftrightarrow$ Pyruvic acid+
α-ketoglutaric acid   glutamic acid)

Amino-acids can also act as an energy source for metabolism since after removal of the amino-group (deamination) the residue is treated as a carbohydrate by the cell.

HYDROLYTIC DEAMINATION

$$NH_2$$
$$R.CH.COOH + H_2O = R.CH.OH.COOH + NH_3$$
(Amino-acid + water = Hydroxy-acid + ammonia)

OXIDATIVE DEAMINATION

$$NH_2$$
$$R.CH.COOH + \tfrac{1}{2}O_2 = R.CO.COOH + NH_3$$
(Amino-acid + oxygen = Keto-acid + ammonia)

Although direct evidence is lacking, it seems probable from our knowledge in other fields that cell proteins are directly synthesised from amino-acids and intact proteins or peptides are not incorporated into the cell proteins.

As is discussed in the previous chapter, most mammalian cells so far examined require the same 12 essential amino-acids. The fact that these are essential suggests that they cannot be synthesised from other amino-acids by the processes described above. Using

[14]C-labelled amino-acids, Harris and Jahnz (1961) have confirmed this, inasmuch as leucine, isoleucine, valine, phenylalanine, arginine, lysine, histidine, tryptophan, methionine and cystine can apparently not arise from any of the other amino-acids. A little synthesis of tyrosine from phenylalanine was obtained in these experiments (with rat heart) but Gerarde, Jones and Winnick (1952) did not find any conversion of phenylalanine to tyrosine in chick heart or lung explants. On the other hand, threonine, which was found essential for many cell-types by Eagle et al. (1957), was found to be produced from a number of other amino-acids and glucose by Harris and Jahnz.

The rôle of glutamine in amino-acid metabolism is not clear. In a number of established mammalian strains it has been shown by several workers that there is a rather high requirement for glutamine (although this does not seem to be the case in freshly explanted avian tissues, according to Pasieka et al. (1958). An obvious function for glutamine in the cell is as a donor of amide nitrogen in transamination, but Levintow et al. have shown that this does not occur at all and glutamine is actually incorporated intact into protein. It does not even give rise to free ammonia in these cells. The only transfer reaction that seems to take place is between the amide nitrogen of glutamine and asparagine.

Glutamic acid can give rise to glutamine but in the mammalian cell strains investigated by Eagle et al. this only happened when extremely high concentrations of glutamic acid were used. In the cells investigated by Pasieka et al., on the other hand, synthesis of glutamine appeared to occur readily. It is possible that cells adapted to different types of media may have slightly different absolute requirements. In fact, De Mars was able to demonstrate clearly that some cultured cells can undergo adaptation in respect of some of the enzymes involved in glutamine metabolism when they are grown for a time in media rich in glutamic acid.

Some cells apparently cannot use protein added to the medium and this is probably because they lack proteolytic enzymes. Other cell types equally certainly do use proteins in the medium and in these cases proteolytic enzymes probably break the proteins down to their constituent amino-acids which can be utilised.

Lipid metabolism

Tissue culture cells can synthesise lipids from simple chemical substances such as acetate. It is not known whether fats themselves can be taken up from the medium and stored, and most of the fat that appears in tissue culture cells is probably synthesised *de novo*. It has been suggested that cholesterol in the medium is essential but some cells are certainly capable of synthesising it since labelled acetate in the medium gives rise to labelled cholesterol.

Nucleic acids

Cultured cells can build nucleic acids readily from simple compounds in the medium (such as formate, glycine and bicarbonate) ; they must therefore possess all the enzymes necessary for this purpose. However, when intact nucleosides or other intermediary metabolites, such as 4-amino-5-imidazole-carboxamide riboside, are present in the medium they are used preferentially. This indicates both that these materials can gain entry to the cell and that they are almost certainly on the direct pathways of nucleic acid metabolism.

Structural elements

The synthesis of a few structural elements has been shown *in vitro,* and particularly it has been shown that certain cultured cells can synthesise large amounts of mucopolysaccharides.

KINETICS OF CELL GROWTH

Animal cells in culture display very much the same type of growth pattern as micro-organisms. In particular, they show the classical growth kinetics demonstrated by cultures of bacteria, yeasts and protozoa. When cells are taken from a stationary culture there is at first a *lag phase* of some hours to some days before growth commences. Growth then proceeds steadily with the population doubling every 15 to 20 hours in the case of fast growing cells. This is known as the *logarithmic phase.* At the end of it the maximum population is reached and the cells enter *stationary phase.* During the logarithmic phase the cell population increases according to the formula $N = N_o 2^{kt}$

$$i.e., \log N = \log N_o + kt \log 2$$

(where N_o=initial inoculum, N=cell number at t hrs. and k is a

4

regression constant). The mean generation time (T), the time taken for the cell population to double, is the inverse of k (*i.e.*, T=1/k).

Cell growth stops due to exhaustion of a nutrient or accumulation of toxic products (notably hydrogen ions). The lag phase encountered on reinoculation into fresh medium may be due to many factors. The most obvious one is the accumulation of intermediary metabolites in intracellular pools which have become exhausted. The situation may not always be as simple as this, however, and, for instance, time may be required for the readaptation of some enzymes.

This type of growth curve is particularly observed in suspension cultures or when the inoculum is very dilute. In other conditions the classical cycle may not occur. Thus, Harris (1956) found that rat heart fibroblasts grown on cover slips never entered a true logarithmic phase but had a constantly decreasing growth rate from the outset. He suggested that this was related to oxygen tension in the medium but the main reason is probably the progressive *p*H change. A similar kind of observation was made by Klein and Revesz (1953) who demonstrated that the kinetics of growth of ascites tumours in mice were those of a solid tumour rather than of a suspension of cells. That is to say, they increased at a rate described by the formula

$$\sqrt[3]{N} = b(t - t_o) + \sqrt[3]{N_o}$$

(where N=no. of cells, t=hrs. after inoculation, N_o=no. of cells inoculated, t_o=time when N=N_o, and b=a regression coefficient). Several reasons can be advanced for this discrepancy. In the first place, a percentage of the cells in an ascites tumour suspension may be exudative cells and not tumour cells. Furthermore a high proportion of the tumour cells may be non-viable and the non-multiplying cells in the population may therefore distort the kinetics. Moreover, when the cell population is high the effective concentration of metabolites such as glucose and oxygen tends to fall progressively while toxic products accumulate more rapidly than they can be removed. Many cases can undoubtedly be explained by factors of this kind but it must be mentioned that in animal cells there is also evidence to suggest that a specific mechanism exists whereby growth diminishes when the population becomes dense.

The growth rate of cultured cells is not necessarily always the same. It may vary to some extent from one cell strain to another but in particular it varies considerably with environmental conditions such as pH, temperature and osmotic pressure.

The optimum pH for many cell strains can be quite precisely defined. It usually lies between pH 7·2 and 7·4 for mammalian cells and growth rate diminishes as the pH diverges from the optimum value. This is due to a decrease in the rate of cell doubling which occurs independently of any prolongation of lag phase or decrease in the maximum population reached during stationary phase. Osmotic pressure, too, affects growth rate and for most cells the optimum osmotic pressure is about that obtaining within the animal. On either side of this optimum the rate of growth falls off.

With regard to temperature it is a general rule that the rate of growth increases with increasing temperature until a maximum is reached and thereafter it begins to decline very sharply due to cell death. The optimum temperature varies from species to species but is about 37·5 for mammalian and avian tissue.

Relation of metabolism to growth.

The metabolism and composition of cultured cells may vary considerably from one growth phase to another. RNA tends to accumulate just before logarithmic phase begins. During the logarithmic phase RNA, DNA and protein values increase at the same steady rate until the maximum population is approached when synthetic processes slow down, RNA decreasing first, rapidly followed by protein.

During different phases of growth radical changes occur in the pattern of carbohydrate metabolism. Both in suspension cultures and in monolayer cultures on glass the glycolytic rate is very high during lag phase and the earlier part of the logarithmic phase. At that time 90 to 100 per cent. glucose may be converted to lactic acid. However, as the cells enter stationary phase the amount of lactic acid produced progressively decreases, often to zero, whereas the utilisation of glucose continues. That is to say, glycolysis is initially high but it falls to very low values until practically all the glucose utilised can be accounted for by oxidation. It has been found that two independent factors account for this change.

In the first place, the pattern of carbohydrate metabolism varies greatly with changes in pH. In alkaline conditions cells have a high rate of aerobic glycolysis whereas in more acid conditions glucose metabolism is almost entirely oxidative. Thus the accumulation of acid during growth in part accounts for the shift from glycolytic to oxidative metabolism during the growth cycle.

The other factor is the leakage of tricarboxylic acids from newly inoculated cells into the medium. In some cells this causes the oxygen uptake of the cells to fall to very low values initially (about 10^{-6} μl O_2/hr/cell). In a day or two, the actual time depending on such factors as the cell/medium ratio, intermediates accumulate and respiration increases to about $5 - 10 \times 10^{-6}$ μl O_2/hr/cell. Hence the amount of glucose oxidised is considerably greater after some days' growth than it is immediately after inoculation.

Fluctuations of a more specific nature also occur. Of special interest are the variations in some of the enzymes associated with DNA synthesis, which increase to much higher levels during rapid growth.

Relation of metabolism to mitosis

It has been established that the synthesis of cellular components does not proceed at a steady rate during the growth cycle of the cells but that certain components are synthesised in a stepwise fashion. In particular it has been shown that in cultured mammalian and avian cells with a mean generation time of about 20 hours the synthesis of DNA occurs for a period of about 6 hours only. Immediately after cell division there is a period, lasting about 10 hours, during which no DNA synthesis occurs. This is called the G_1 period. The period of DNA synthesis, called the S period, follows and it lasts 6-8 hours. After this DNA synthesis again stops for about 4 hours prior to mitosis. This is called the G_2 period. Mitosis itself lasts for a very short time, usually less than an hour. The synthesis of other cellular components, especially RNA and protein, proceeds at a much steadier rate throughout mitosis.

SPECIAL FACTORS INFLUENCING GROWTH AND METABOLISM

The feature which distinguishes animal cells from protozoa is, of course, the ability of the germ cell to give rise to an enormous variety of specialised cells which live together as mutually dependent members of a community. Two of the greatest problems of biology stem from these characteristics, the first being the mechanism of cyto-differentiation and the second the mechanisms whereby the functions of all the cells in an organism are harmonised. Little is known about either of these processes at the present time and nothing constructive can be written about cyto-differentiation in a chapter on cell metabolism. On the other hand, there is some information about the effects of certain environmental influences such as nutritional factors and hormones on cell growth and metabolism. In Chapter III many of these have already been discussed generally. Only a little precise information remains to be added at the present time about the effects of hormones on cell growth and metabolism.

The hormone that has been most intensively investigated in cell and tissue cultures is insulin. Gey and Thalhimer were the first to report that insulin had a growth stimulatory effect on tissue cultures and several other investigators confirmed this. Leslie and his colleagues showed that an increase in nucleic acid synthesis accompanied insulin treatment. However, Paul and Pearson (1957) found that increased growth as a result of insulin treatment did not invariably occur whereas increased glycolysis did. They suggested that increased synthesis of cell components only occurs in response to insulin when the supply of energy-rich compounds is limiting—a condition which rarely occurs with the use of modern culture methods and media.

They also concluded that insulin has a primary effect in stimulating glycolysis and that all other phenomena, such as increased phosphorus turnover, increased synthesis and fluctuations in pyruvic acid level can be attributed to this. The increased glycolysis may actually be secondary to an increased rate of entry of glucose to the cell.

The only other hormones that have been demonstrated to have a definite metabolic effect on cultured cells are the thyroid hormones. Thyroxine and triiodoacetic acid have been shown to increase the uptake of glucose.

Studies of the direct effects of other hormones on tissue culture metabolism have, on the whole, been disappointing. Attempts to demonstrate an action of steroid hormones have been unsuccessful except with very high concentrations when an inhibition of growth, probably non-specific, has occurred. It should be emphasised that this statement applies only to cell culture studies. As has already been mentioned, some quite dramatic effects have been produced by steroid hormones in organ cultures. Pituitary hormones have also been found to demonstrate some activity in organ cultures but no general effect on the metabolism of cultured cells has yet been found.

BIBLIOGRAPHY

ABERCROMBIE, M. & AMBROSE, E. J. (1958). Interference microscope studies of cell contacts in tissue culture. *Exp. Cell Res.* **15**, 332.

AUERBACH, V. H. & WALKER, D. L. (1959). Further studies in the enzymic pattern of a cultured cell line from liver. *Biochem. biophys. Acta* **31**, 268.

BARBAN, S. & SCHULTZ, H. O. (1956). Metabolism of tissue culture cells. The presence in HeLa cells of the enzymes of the citric acid cycle. *J. biol. Chem.* **222**, 665.

BARBAN, S. & SCHULTZE, H. O. (1958). Transamination reactions of mammalian cells in tissue culture. *J. biol. Chem.* **234**, 829.

BENSCH, K. G., KING, D. W. & SOCOLOW, E. L. (1961). The source of lipid accumulation in L cells. *J. biophys. biochem. Cytol.* **9**, 135.

BERENBLUM, I., CHAIN, E. & HEATLEY, N. G. (1939). The study of metabolic activities of small amounts of surviving tissues. *Biochem. J.* **33**, 68.

BERLINER, D. L., SWIM, H. E. & DOUGHERTY, T. F. (1958). Synthesis of cholesterol by a strain of human uterine fibroblasts propagated in vitro. *Proc. Soc. exp. Biol. (N.Y.)* **99**, 51.

BONTING, S. L. & JONES, M. (1954). Some investigations on the relation between growth and carbohydrate metabolism. *Anat. Rec.* **118**, 445.

BROSEMER, R. W. & RUTTER, W. J. (1961). The effect of oxygen tension on growth and metabolism of a mammalian cell. *Exp. Cell Res.* **25**, 101.

CARPENTER, E., BEATTIE, J. & CHAMBERS, R. D. (1954). The uptake of I[131] by embryonic chick thyroid glands *in vivo* and *in vitro*. *J. exp. Zool.* **127**, 249.

COMAN, D. R. (1961). Adhesiveness and stickiness: two independent properties of the cell surface. *Cancer Res.* **21**, 1436.

COOPER, P. D., BURT, A. M. & WILSON, J. N. (1958). Critical effect of oxygen tension on rate of growth of animal cells in continuous suspended culture. *Nature (Lond.)* **182**, 1508.

COX, R. P. & MACLEOD, C. M. (1962). Alkaline phosphatase content and the effects of prednisolone on mammalian cells in culture. *J. gen. Physiol.* **45**, 439.

DANES, BETTY (1955). Metabolism of the embryonic chick heart fibroblast grown in tissue culture. *Exp. Cell Res.* **8**, 543.

DANES, BETTY & LEINFELDER, P. J. (1951). Cytological and respiratory effects of cyanide on tissue cultures. *J. cell. comp. Physiol.* **37**, 427.

DANES, B. S. & PAUL, J. (1961). Environmental factors influencing respiration of strain L cells. *Exp. Cell Res.* **24**, 344.

DAVIDSON, J. N. (1947). Some factors influencing the nucleic acid content of cells and tissues. *Cold Spr. Harb. Symp. quant. Biol.* **12**, 50.

DAVIDSON, J. N., LESLIE, I. & WAYMOUTH, C. (1949). The nucleo-protein content of fibroblasts growing *in vitro*. 4. Changes in the ribonucleic acid phosphorus (RNAP) and deoxyribonucleic acid phosphorus (DNAP) content. *Biochem. J.* **44,** 5.

DEMUTH, F. (1931). Energiestoffwechsel in vitro lebender Gewebezellen. *Arch. exp. Zellforsch.* **11,** 98.

DEMUTH, F. & MEIER, R. (1929). Milchsäurebildung in Gewebekulturen. *Biochem. Z.* **212,** 399.

EAGLE, H. (1955). The specific amino acid requirements of mammalian cells (strain L) in tissue culture. *J. biol. Chem.* **214,** 839.

EAGLE, H. (1955). The specific amino-acid requirements of a human carcinoma cell (strain HeLa) in tissue culture. *J. exp. Med.* **102,** 37.

EAGLE, H. (1955). The minimum vitamin requirements of the L and HeLa cells in tissue culture, the production of specific vitamin deficiencies and their cure. *J. exp. Med.* **102,** 595.

EAGLE, H. (1955). Nutrition needs of mammalian cells in tissue culture. *Science* **122,** 501.

EAGLE, H. (1955). Utilization of dipeptides by mammalian cells in tissue culture. *Proc. Soc. exp. Biol. (N.Y.)* **89,** 96.

EAGLE, H., OYAMA, V. I., LEVY, M. & FREEMAN, A. (1956). Myoinositol as an essential growth factor for normal and malignant human cells in tissue culture. *Science* **123,** 845.

EAGLE, H., OYAMA, V. I., LEVY, M., HORTON, C. L. & FLEISCHMAN, R. (1956). The growth response of mammalian cells in tissue culture to L-glutamine and L-glutamic acid. *J. biol. Chem.* **218,** 607.

EAGLE, H., OYAMA, V. I. & LEVY, M. (1957). Amino-acid requirements of normal and malignant human cells in tissue culture. *Arch. Biochem.* **67,** 432.

EAGLE, H., PIEZ, K. A. & FLEISCHMAN, R. (1957). The utilization of phenylalanine and tyrosine for protein synthesis by human cells in tissue culture. *J. biol. Chem.* **288,** 847.

EARLE, W. R. (1962). Some morphologic variations of certain cells under controlled experimental conditions. *Nat. Cancer Inst. Monograph* No. 7, 213.

FISCHER, A. (1941). Die Bedeutung der Aminosaüren fur die Gewebezellen *in vitro*. *Acta physiol. scand.* **2,** 143.

FISCHER, A. (1948). Amino-acid metabolism of tissue cells *in vitro*. *Biochem. J.* **43,** 491.

FISCHER, A. (1953). On the protein metabolism of tissue cells *in vitro*. *J. nat. Cancer Inst.* **13,** 1399.

FRANCIS, M. D. & WINNICK, T. (1953). Studies on the pathway of protein synthesis in tissue culture. *J. biol. Chem.* **202,** 273.

FULTON, W. C., SINCLAIR, R. & LESLIE, I. (1956). Changes in glucose utilization and the growth of tissue cultures of HeLa cells. *Biochem. J.* **63,** 18p.

GEMMILL, G. L., GEY, G. O. & AUSTRIAN, R. (1940). The metabolism of tissue cultures of Walker rat sarcoma 319. *Johns Hopk. Hosp. Bull.* **66,** 167.

GERARDE, H. W., JONES, M. & WINNICK, T. (1952). Protein synthesis and amino-acid turnover in tissue culture. *J. biol. Chem.* **196,** 51.

GEYER, R. P. & NEUMARK, J. M. (1958). Response of CO_2-deficient cells *in vitro* to normal cell extracts. *Proc. Soc. exp. Biol. (N.Y.)* **99,** 599.

GOTHOSKAR, B. P., RATNAM, S. & RAMAKRISHNAN, C. V. (1958). Nonrequirement of glutamine for proliferation of chick embryonic heart fibroblasts in a synthetic medium. *Ind. J. med. Res.* **46,** 576.

GRAHAM, A. F., & SIMINOVITCH. L. (1957). Conservation of RNA and DNA phosphorus in strain L (Earle mouse cells). *Biochim. biophys. Acta* **26**, 427.

GREEN. H. & GOLDBERG, B. (1963). Kinetics of collagen synthesis by established mammalian cell lines. *Nature (Lond.)* **200**, 1097.

GROSSFELD, H. (1957). Production of hyaluronic acid in tissue culture by fibroblasts growing from intestinal, stomach, liver and kidney explants. *Proc. Soc. exp. Biol. (N.Y.)* **96**, 144.

GROSSFELD, H., MEYER, K., GODMAN, G. & LINKER, A. (1957). Mucopolysaccharides produced in tissue culture. *J. biophys. biochem. Cytol.* **3**, 391.

GRUNBAUM. B. W., SCHAFFER, F. L. & KIRK, P. L. (1955). Lipides of chick heart fibroblasts. Effect of vitamin B_{12} and folic acid. *Proc. Soc. exp. Biol. (N.Y.)* **88**, 459.

HALEVY, S. & AVIVI, LIDIA (1958). The effect of thyroid hormones on carbohydrate metabolism in tissue culture. *Biochim. biophys. Acta* **30**, 198.

HARRIS, H. (1956). The relationship between the respiration and multiplication of rat connective tissue cells in vitro. *Brit. J. exp. Path.* **37**, 512.

HARRIS, H. & JAHNZ, MARIANNE (1957). The synthesis of protein in the rat connective tissue cell. *Brit. J. exp. Path.* **38**, 525.

HARRIS. H. & WATTS, J. W. (1958). Turnover of protein in a non-multiplying animal cell. *Nature (Lond.)* **18**, 1582.

HARRIS, M. (1954). The role of bicarbonate for outgrowth of chick heart fibroblasts *in vitro. J. exp. Zool.* **125**, 85.

HARRIS, M. (1957). Quantitative growth studies with chick myoblasts in glass substrate cultures. *Growth* **21**, 149.

HARRIS, M. (1959). Selective uptake and release of substances by cells. In *Symposium on The Chemical Basis of Development.* Ed. W. D. McElroy, B. Glass. Maryland: Johns Hopkins Press.

HARRIS, M. & KUTSKY, P. B. (1953). Utilization of added sugars by chick heart fibroblasts in dialyzed media. *J. cell. comp. Physiol.* **42**, 449.

HEALY, G. M., SIMINOVITCH, L., PARKER, R. C. & GRAHAM, A. F. (1956). Conservation of deoxyribonucleic acid phosphorus in animal cells propagated *in vitro. Biochim. biophys. Acta* **20**, 425.

JACKSON, SYLVIA & SMITH, R. H. (1957). Studies on the biosynthesis of collagen. I. The growth of fowl osteoblasts and the formation of collagen in tissue culture. II. The conversion of ^{14}C-L-Proline to ^{14}C-Hydroxyproline by fowl osteoblasts in tissue culture. *J. biophys. biochem. Cytol.* **3**, 897.

JACOBSON, W. & WEBB, M. (1952). The two types of nucleoproteins during mitosis. *Exp. Cell Res.* **3**, 163.

JONES, M. & BONTING, S. L. (1956). Some relations between growth and carbohydrate metabolism in tissue cultures. *Exp. Cell Res.* **10**, 631.

JONES, M. & GERARDE, H. W. (1953). Sulfate fixation by embryonic chick lung in tissue culture. *Proc. soc. exp. Biol. (N.Y.)* **84**, 310.

JORDAN, H. C. & SCHMIDT, P. A. (1961). Constant protein turnover in mammalian cells during logarithmic growth. *Biochem. biophys. res. Commun.* **4**, 313.

KLEIN, G. & REVESZ, L. (1953). Quantitative studies on the multiplication of neoplastic cells *in vivo*. I. Growth curves of the Ehrlich and MCIM Ascites tumors. *J. nat. Cancer Inst.* **14**, 229.

LASER, H. (1932). Eine Methode zur manometrischen Messung des Stoffwechsels von Gewebekulturen während des Wachstums. *Biochem. Z.* **251**, 2.

LASER, H. (1933). Der Stoffwechsel von Gewebekulturen und ihr Verhalten in der Anaerobiose. *Biochem. Z.* **264**, 72.

LASER, H. (1934). Weitere Untersuchungen über Stoffwechsel und Anaerobiose von Gewebekulturen. *Biochem. Z.* **268**, 451.

LEVINTOW, L., EAGLE, H. & PIEZ, K. A. (1957). The role of glutamine in protein biosynthesis in tissue culture. *J. biol. Chem.* **227**, 929.

LIEBERMAN, I. & OVE, P. (1958). Catalase requirement for mammalian cells in culture. *J. exp. Med.* **108**, 631.

LIEBERMAN, I. & OVE, P. (1958). Enzyme activity levels in mammalian cell cultures. *J. biol. Chem.* **233**, 634.

LIPPMANN, F. (1932). Versuche zur methodik der Messung des Zuwachses *in vitro* wachsender Gewebe durch Messung des Umsatzanstiegs. *Biochem. Z.* **244**, 177.

LIPPMANN, F. (1933). Stoffwechselversuche an Gewebekulturen, insbesondere über die Rolle des Glykolyse im Stoffwechsel embryonaler Zellen. *Biochem. Z.* **261**, 157.

LIPPMANN, F. & FISCHER, A. (1932). Proliferationsgrösse von Gewebezellen *in vitro* und Stoffumsatz. *Biochem. Z.* **244**, 187.

LU, K. H., WINNICK, T. (1954). The correlation of growth with incorporation of radioactive metabolites into nucleic acids in embryonic tissue culture. *Exp. Cell Res.* **7**, 238.

LUCY, J. A. & RINALDINI, L. M. (1959). The amino acid metabolism of differentiating skeletal myoblasts *in vitro*. *Exp. Cell Res.* **17**, 385.

DE MARS, R. (1958). The inhibition by glutamine of glutamyl transferase formation in cultures of human cells. *Biochim. biophys. Acta* **27**, 435.

MEIER, R. (1931). Zur Methodik der Stoffwechseluntersuchungen an Gewebekulturen. I. Atmungsmessung an Gewebekulturen. *Biochem. Z.* **231**, 247.

MEIER, R. (1931). Zur Methodik der Stoffwechseluntersuchungen an Gewebekulteren. II. Gewichtsbestimmung an einzelnen Gewebekulturen. Gewichtszunahme und Flächenzunahme. *Biochem Z.* **231**, 253.

MOON, H. D., JENTOFT, V. L. & LI, C. H. (1962). Effect of human growth hormone on growth of cells in tissue culture. *Endocrinology* **70**, 31.

MORGAN, J. F. & McCRONE, M.A. (1957). A study of protein synthesis in tissue culture. *J. nat. Cancer Inst.* **19**, 393.

MORGAN, J. F., MORTON, HELEN J. & PASIEKA, A. E. (1958). The arginine requirement of tissue cultures. 1. Interrelationships between arginine and related compounds. *J. biol. Chem.* **233**, 664.

MORGAN, J. F. & MORTON, H. J. (1956). Studies on the sulfur metabolism of tissues cultivated *in vitro*. II. Optical specificities and interrelationships between cystine and methionine. *J. biol. Chem.* **221**, 529.

MORTON, HELEN J. & MORGAN, J. F. (1959). Studies on the dual requirement for phenylalanine and tyrosine in tissue culture. *J. biol. Chem.* **234**, 2698.

MUNYON, W. H. & MERCHANT, D. J. (1959). The relation between glucose utilization, lactic acid production and utilization and the growth cycle of L strain fibroblasts. *Exp. Cell Res.* **17**, 490.

MURRAY, MARGARET R., DE LAM, HELENA H. & CHARGAFF, E. (1951). Specific inhibition by meso-inositol of the colchicine effect on rat fibroblasts. *Exp. Cell Res.* **11**, 165.

MURRAY, M. R., PETERSON, E. R. & BUNGE, R. P. (1962). Some nutritional aspects of myelin sheath formation in cultures of central and peripheral nervous system. *Inter. Cong. Neuropathol.* **2**, 267.

NEUMAN, R. E. & McCOY, T. A. (1956). Dual requirement of Walker carcinomsarcoma 256 *in vitro* for asparagine and glutamine. *Science* **124,** 124.

NEWTON, A. A. & WILDY, P. (1959). Parasynchronous division of HeLa cells. *Exp. Cell Res.* **16,** 624.

PASIEKA, A. E. & MORGAN, J. F. (1959). Glutamine metabolism of normal and malignant cells cultivated in synthetic media. *Nature (Lond.)* **183,** 1201.

PASIEKA, A. E., MORTON, HELEN J. & MORGAN, J. F. (1956). The metabolism of animal tissues cultivated *in vitro*. I. Amino acid metabolism of chick embryonic heart fibroblasts cultivated in synthetic medium M 150. *J. nat. Cancer Inst.* **16,** 995.

PASIEKA, A. E., MORTON, HELEN J. & MORGAN, J. F. (1958). The metabolism of animal tissues cultivated *in vitro*. I. Amino acid metabolism of chick embryonic kidney, chick embryonic liver and monkey kidney cortex cultures. *Canad. J. Biochem.* **36,** 171.

PASIEKA, A. E., MORTON, HELEN J. & MORGAN, J. F. (1958). The metabolism of animal tissue cultivated *in vitro*. III. Amino acid metabolism of strain L cells in completely synthetic media. *Canad. J. Biochem.* **36,** 771.

PAUL, J. (1959). Environmental influences on the metabolism and composition of cultured cells. *J. exp. Zool.* **142.**

PAUL, J. (1962). Mechanisms of metabolic control in cultured mammalian cells. In *New Development in Tissue Culture*. Ed. J. W. Green. New Brunswick, New Jersey: Rutgers University Press.

PAUL, J. & PEARSON, E. S. (1957). Metabolism of chick embryonic heart explants during transition from *in vivo* to *in vitro* conditions. *Exp. Cell Res.* **12,** 212.

PAUL, J. & PEARSON, E. S. (1957). Metabolism of chick embryonic liver explants during transition from *in vivo* to *in vitro* conditions. *Exp. Cell Res.* **12,** 223.

PHILLIPS, H. J. & FELDHAUS, R. J. (1956). Respiration and glycolysis of Earle's Strain L cells. *Proc. Soc. exp. Biol. (N.Y.)* **92,** 478.

POMERAT, C. M. (1951) Pulsatile activity of cells from the human brain in tissue culture. *J. nerv. ment. Dis.* **114,** 430.

POMERAT, C. M. & WILLMER, E. N. (1939). Studies on the growth of tissues *in vitro*. VII. Carbohydrate metabolism and mitosis. *J. exp. Biol.* **16,** 232.

SALZMAN, N. P. (1959). Systematic fluctuations in the cellular protein, RNA and DNA during growth of mammalian cell cultures. *Biochim. biophys. Acta* **31,** 158.

SCHABERG, A. & DE GROOT, C. A. (1958). The influence of the anterior hypothesis on the morphology and function of the adrenal cortex *in vitro*. *Exp. Cell Res.* **15,** 475.

SIDMAN, R. L. (1956). The direct effect of insulin on organ cultures of brown fat. *Anat. Rec.* **124,** 723.

SIEGEL, B. V. & CAILLEAU, RELDA (1956). Effect of metabolic inhibitors on the respiration of Earle Strain L cells. *Arch. Biochem.* **60,** 506.

SIMINOVITCH, L. & GRAHAM, A. F. (1956). Significance of ribonucleic acid and deoxyribonucleic acid turnover studies. *J. Histochem. Cytochem.* **4,** 508.

STEWARD, F. C. (1963). The control of growth in plant cells. *Science* **209,** 104.

STREET, H. E. (1950). The role of high-energy phosphate bonds in biosynthesis. *Sci. Progr.* **38,** 43.

SWIM, H. E. & PARKER, R. F. (1958). The role of carbon dioxide as an essential nutrient for six permanent strains of fibroblasts. *J. biophys. biochem. Cytol.* **4**, 525.

TERASIMA, T. & TOLMACH, L. J. (1963). Growth and nucleic acid synthesis in synchronously dividing populations of HeLa cells. *Exp. Cell Res.* **30**, 344.

THOMSON, R. Y. & PAUL, J. (1957). The metabolic stability of nucleic acids in cells grown in tissue culture. *Biochem. J.* **67**, 16P.

THOMSON, R. Y., PAUL, J. & DAVIDSON, J. N. (1956). Metabolic stability of DNA in fibroblast cultures. *Biochim. biophys. Acta* **22**, 581.

THOMSON, R. Y., PAUL, J. & DAVIDSON, J. N. (1958). The metabolic stability of the nucleic acids in cultures of a pure strain of mammalian cells. *Biochem. J.* **69**, 553.

WARBURG, O. & KUBOWITZ, F. (1927). Stoffwechsel wachsender Zellen (Fibroblasten, Herz, Chorion). *Biochem. Z.* **189**, 242.

WATCHORN, E. & HOLMES, B. E. (1927). Studies in the metabolism of tissues growing *in vitro*. II. Effect of glucose upon the ammonia and urea production of kidney tissues. *Biochem. J.* **21**, 1391.

WELLINGS, S. R. & MOON, H. D. (1961). Morphological and functional effects of hydrocortisone in tissue culture. *Lab. Invest.* **10**, 539.

WESTFALL, B. B., EVANS, VIRGINIA J., SHANNON, J. E. & EARLE, W. R. (1953). The glycogen content of cell suspensions prepared from massive tissue culture: Comparison of cells derived from mouse connective tissue and mouse liver. *J. nat. Cancer Inst.* **14**, 655.

WESTFALL, B. B., PEPPERS, E. V. & EARLE, W. R. (1955). The change in concentration of certain constituents of the medium during growth of the strain HeLa cells. *Amer. J. Hyg.* **61**, 326.

WHITFIELD, J. F. & RIXON, R. H. (1961). The effect of dilution and carbon dioxide on the metabolic properties of suspension cultures of strain L mouse cells. *Exp. Cell Res.* **24**, 177.

WILLMER, E. N. (1942). Carbohydrate metabolism of chick fibroblasts *in vitro*. *J. exp. Biol.* **18**, 237.

WILSON, HILDEGARD, JACKSON, ELIZABETH B. & BRUES, A. M. (1942). The metabolism of tissue cultures. I. Preliminary studies on chick embryos. *J. gen. Physiol.* **25**, 689.

ZWARTOUW, H. T. & WESTWOOD, J. C. N. (1958). Factors affecting growth and glycolysis in tissue culture. *Brit. J. exp. Path.* **39**, 529.

CHAPTER V

MEDIA FOR CULTURING CELLS AND TISSUES

I. NATURAL MEDIA

THE medium is by far the most important single factor in culturing cells and tissues.

The function of this medium is to provide (1) the physical conditions of pH, osmotic pressure etc. required for survival and (2) the complicated chemical substances required by the tissue, which it cannot synthesise itself. These latter include amino-acids, carbohydrates and vitamins. Some micro-organisms can synthesise all their component chemicals from simple inorganic substances (*i.e.* they are auxotrophic) but all tissues from multicellular organisms require ready-made molecules to some degree (*i.e.* they are heterotrophic). In general, plant tissues are much less demanding than animal tissues.

Ideally, the medium should be an accurately defined mixture of chemical substances. For the culture of plant cells this ideal was achieved many years ago, but at the time of writing we are only approaching it for animal cells, although already there are one or two synthetic mixtures which will support indefinitely the growth of one or two special strains of cells.

On the whole, animal cells need either a completely natural medium or a medium supplemented with some natural product, usually serum. Although improved synthetic media will be produced in increasing numbers in the next few years, it seems certain that natural media will form the cheapest and most convenient materials for the maintenance of cells for some time to come. Also, it is highly likely that natural media will remain essential for growing newly isolated tissues and highly demanding cells for very many years.

The natural materials used to promote cell growth fall into three general categories : coagula, such as plasma clots ; biological fluids, such as serum, and tissue extracts, of which the commonest type is embryo extract.

PLASMA

In the traditional methods of tissue culture, the tissue fragment is grown in a coagulum. In his original experiments, Ross Harrison grew a small piece of tissue from near the neural tube in a clot of frog lymph. Later, Carrel and Burrows introduced plasma for the same purpose and plasma clots have been in general use since. Although most of the newer techniques of tissue culture do not employ a plasma clot and the vast majority of cells are now grown without one, some tissues can only be grown in the presence of a supporting matrix. The usual one is fowl plasma. It is now available commercially from several sources and can be bought either as liquid plasma in siliconed ampoules or as lyophilised plasma, to be reconstituted by the addition of distilled water saturated with carbon dioxide.

Some people prefer to prepare their own plasma and in certain circumstances it is more suitable to do so. Any animal can provide plasma, but the fowl is generally used since fowl plasma gives a more solid clot than most mammalian plasmas and, in addition, is easily obtained. The male bird is usually employed because the blood calcium level is more constant and in certain procedures, such as bleeding from the carotid artery, it is easier to operate on the male. A young bird is preferred and it is usually stated that it should be less than one year old.

When collecting plasma, it is essential to prevent coagulation of the blood. This can be done either by preventing the initiation of coagulation or by interfering with the coagulation process. Coagulation is initiated either by contact of the plasma with a water-wettable glass surface or by the release of products of tissue damage into the blood. By avoiding tissue damage and by coating the glass vessel with a water-repellent material such as a silicone or paraffin wax, coagulation can be prevented without the addition of anti-coagulant. In most circumstances, however, it is impossible to prevent tissue damage and coagulation is therefore retarded by one of several methods. Heparin is the most commonly used anti-coagulant. It has been shown that in high concentrations it can be inhibitory to the growth of tissue cells and may produce morphological abnormalities, but if the concentration of heparin is kept at such a level that it just inhibits coagulation (0·2 mg. per cent.) it seems to be relatively harmless. The onset of coagulation may also be inhibited by cooling and this is very commonly used as an additional measure, the blood being collected in tubes cooled in ice. In blood transfusion practice, coagulation is commonly prevented by inhibiting the ionisation of calcium by the addition of sodium citrate to the blood, but this is not employed in collecting plasma for tissue culture purposes.

There are three methods of removing blood conveniently from a bird—wing bleeding, heart bleeding, and bleeding from the carotid artery. Where there is no objection to the addition of an anti-coagulant to the blood, wing or heart bleeding may be employed. However, when it is desirable to avoid the addition of an anti-coagulant it is advisable to resort to one of the more complicated procedures such as carotid bleeding where the contamination of blood by tissue material can be kept to a minimum.

BLEEDING   FROM   THE   WING

Bleeding from the wing of a young bird requires a certain amount of knack but when this is learned it is a fairly easy procedure. It is advisable to treat the syringe, needle and tubes for blood with heparin. This is added to the tubes as a 25 mg. per

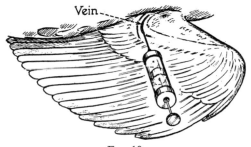

Fig. 10
Bleeding from the wing.

cent. solution in amounts such that the final concentration will be 0·2 mg. per cent. in the blood. It is also advisable to cool them in ice while the blood is being collected. A 20 ml. syringe may be used with an 18 or 19 gauge needle.

The bird is placed on its side or back and the wing is fanned out with the underside uppermost. The feathers are then plucked from the region of the ' elbow '. On clearing this area a large vein can be seen to pass across it, as shown in the diagram. The area is swabbed with alcohol and when this has evaporated, the needle is inserted. This should be done with great care as it is very easy to go right through the vein and cause a large haematoma which will make subsequent exploration futile. When the vein is entered blood can be withdrawn gently. If too much suction is applied, the wall of the vein may be sucked into the lumen of the needle and the flow of blood will stop. When sufficient blood has been collected in this way, it is transferred to a prepared centrifuge tube and spun down as soon as possible.

BLEEDING FROM THE HEART

As a routine procedure, heart puncture is probably the easiest method of obtaining a fairly large quantity of heparinised blood from a fowl and it will therefore be described in detail.

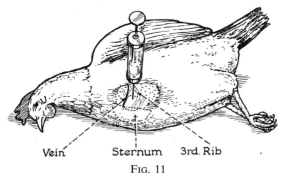

Vein   Sternum   3rd. Rib

Fig. 11
Heart puncture ; first method.

1. Prepare a number of centrifuge tubes by coating them with silicone (Repelcote, Hopkins and Williams). Stopper with cotton-wool or cover with aluminium foil and sterilise by dry heat. To each add 0·1 ml. of a 25 mg. per cent. solution of heparin. Before bleeding the cockerel place the tubes in a bath of crushed ice.
2. Similarly, prepare a 25 ml. syringe and two or three No. 2 serum needles (at least 2 in. long, by treating with silicone and sterilising.
3. If the bird is to be anaesthetised, pluck a few feathers from one thigh and inject into the muscle a solution of sodium nembutal (25 mg. per kilogram body weight).
4. When it is no longer responsive to stimuli, place the bird on its right side. It can be secured to the board by a tape round the neck

and another round the legs and the wings may be crossed over each other to prevent flapping. Instead of securing the bird to a board, it can be steadied by an assistant who should face the operator, grasping the legs in his left hand and restraining the wings with his right hand while the head is held under his right elbow.

5. Pluck the small feathers over the cardiac region and press the larger ones aside. The first landmark to be seen is a large vein running dorsally. Behind this a soft area can be felt and the dorsal

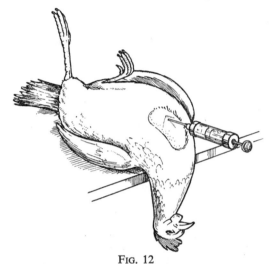

FIG. 12
Heart puncture ; second method.

edge of the breast muscle can be located crossing it. Swab the skin with alcohol and insert the needle at this point. If it strikes the sternum withdraw it partially and re-enter slightly further back. The angle of syringe and needle should be almost vertical. When the needle has been inserted one to one and a half inches the pulsation of the heart should be felt. Advance the needle a little further, applying gentle suction until blood enters it, then aspirate fairly rapidly.

6. Immediately transfer the blood to a cooled tube and centrifuge (5 - 10 minutes at 1,800 g., 2,500 r.p.m. in the ordinary clinical type centrifuge). After centrifugation transfer the plasma layer to clean, sterile, siliconed tubes and store in the refrigerator. Take a sample for sterility testing at the same time. (When centrifuging, the

cotton-wool plugs must be fastened in position by turning some of the cotton over the lip of the tubes and securing with an elastic band. This is not necessary when the tubes are capped with foil.)

Note: In order to obtain clear plasma, the bird should be deprived of food for at least eight hours before bleeding. It should, however, receive a plentiful supply of drinking water. After bleeding it can be fed once more and must have plenty of water since it will be very thirsty. It is unusual to remove more than 25 ml. of blood at a time by this method but up to 75 ml. can be taken if desired. A practised operator can dispense with heparin but unless the bleeding can be carried out with virtually no tissue damage its use is recommended.

An alternative way to bleed a chicken is to place the bird on its back with its head lying over the end of the table. The area at the base of the neck is then swabbed with alcohol and the small feathers plucked as before. A syringe with a 2-in. needle is inserted just behind the sternum and passed back horizontally until it enters the heart. Blood can then be withdrawn as required.

BLEEDING FROM THE CAROTID ARTERY

If it is desired to remove blood without the addition of an anti-coagulant, it is usually necessary to bleed from the carotid artery. This requires an operation which is quite simple although it needs some practice. The bird is placed on its back on an operating board with its head falling over the end of the table. It is anaesthetised either with ether or by injection of sodium nembutal into the thigh muscle some time in advance (25 mg./Kg. body weight). An incision is made down the middle line of the throat and a raphé is then seen in the mid-line. The muscles are separated from this on either side and underneath them the two carotid arteries are found running side by side. A curved needle is inserted behind these to clear them from the surrounding tissues. One artery is freed from the other and a double ligature is passed under it. The distal ligature is tied. Now one of two procedures may be adopted. In the first, some sterile olive oil or liquid paraffin is poured over the area and a small incision made in the wall of the artery (without cutting right through). When this incision is made, blood begins to spurt forth and may be collected in prepared siliconed tubes. This procedure is satisfactory, but many people prefer to insert a silver cannula into the proximal end of the artery

5

after making an incision and to direct blood into the siliconed centrifuge tubes by this means. The bird may be bled to death or the artery ligated and the skin incision repaired. It will then be able to provide another supply of blood in a few weeks from the other artery.

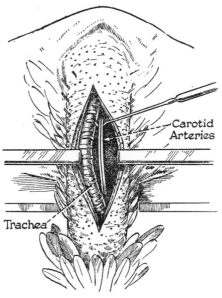

FIG. 13
General anatomical relationships of the carotid arteries in the fowl.

COLLAGEN

There is little doubt that many newly isolated tissues grow better on a physiological substrate such as plasma. Unfortunately fibrin substrates tend to liquefy. As an alternative Ehrmann and Gey (1956) suggested reconstituted rat-tail collagen. It has proved particularly useful for some morphological studies and has been adapted for both test-tube and coverslip cultures.

Rat tails are sterilised in 95 per cent. alcohol and then fractured, the broken pieces being removed to expose the tendons. The tendons from one tail are submerged in 150 ml. of 1:100 acetic acid solution and left, sealed, in the refrigerator for 48 hours. Prolonged centrifugation (one hour at 2,500 g.) is then required to separate the residue from the acetic acid solution of collagen. A further two extractions may be performed. The material can be stored for some months in the refrigerator. Before use it is dialysed against several changes of distilled water. During dialysis the viscosity of the solution increases. Ultimately it becomes too viscous to handle and dialysis should be stopped before this stage, according to whether a thin or thick collagen layer is required. Usually the minimum time of dialysis is 24 hours and the maximum 48 hours. For use the solution is spread over the surface of the vessel and collagen precipitated as a thin tough film by exposure to ammonia vapour. Finally the ammonia is removed by washing with distilled water and then balanced salt solution (p. 84). The tissue is grown direct on the collagen, as on a glass surface.

BIOLOGICAL FLUIDS

Despite the many advances in our knowledge of the nutrition of tissue cultures in the past few years, the basis of most media is still one or other of a number of biological fluids. The traditional biological fluid and the one most commonly used is serum. There seems to be no advantage in using autologous or homologous serum except possibly in the case of a few adult tissues. Primate and human cells seem to survive better in human serum; this may be because it suppresses the growth of human viruses which frequently infect these cells. A percentage of sera are always toxic but autologous sera may be just as toxic as heterologous ones and the rule is that a serum is either toxic or non-toxic irrespective of its origin. Serum is most commonly obtained from human adult or placental cord blood, horse blood, or calf blood. Human placental cord serum and foetal calf serum seem to be particularly satisfactory.

Preparation of serum

The preparation of serum is a straightforward procedure. It consists of permitting whole blood or plasma to coagulate and sinerese and thereafter removing the exuded serum. Serum thus collected has usually to be filtered before use. Filtration of serum through Seitz filter pads seems to result in some loss of growth-promoting activity; better results are obtained when Millipore filters are used. It is advisable to test it for sterility before incorporating it in culture medium. While waiting for the result of the sterility test it is, of course, necessary to store the serum and it is recommended that this should be done at low temperature, preferably in the deep freeze. Opinions differ as to the value of storing serum in very cold conditions but in view of the established importance of glutamine as a nutrient and its known instability, it would seem desirable to freeze serum when it is to be kept for any length of time.

It is recommended that the serum should be tested for toxicity and this is best done by incorporating it in a growth medium and determining the plating efficiency (p. 325) of a standard cell strain when this is used. A given serum may give a high plating efficiency with some cell strains and not with others. Fibroblastic strains seem to be particularly exacting. The toxicity of sera can be avoided to some extent by using pooled material. Some authors claim that the toxicity of serum is reduced by heat inactivation, e.g. heating to 65°C. for thirty minutes, but many other workers feel that such treatment is ineffective.

Placental cord serum

Placental cord serum is strongly recommended by some authorities, in particular Dr. Gey and Dr. Margaret Murray. If possible, the attendants should have been requested not to strip the cord at the time of birth since this is apt to cause haemolysis. The blood is allowed to drip from the umbilical cord into a receiving vessel. The placental blood thus collected is allowed to clot and the serum is pipetted off. It is usually necessary to centrifuge it in order to remove red blood cells. This serum may be filtered but a common practice is to leave it at room temperature for two or three weeks during which time it tends to be self-sterilising. If any bacterial growth occurs during this time it should be rejected. This serum is considered to be particularly good for the growth of tissues which are otherwise very difficult to culture and is said never to be toxic.

Amniotic fluid

Amniotic fluid from various sources has been used in many tissue culture media. The most conveniently obtained amniotic fluid is bovine. A pregnant uterus is obtained from the local slaughterhouse. It is carefully washed on the outside and then hung from a hook. An area near the base is swabbed with iodine and after this has dried a trocar and cannula with tube attached is inserted into the uterus and the amniotic fluid allowed to drain off into suitable vessels. After sterility testing this material is ready for use.

Ascitic and pleural fluid

Ascitic and pleural fluid have both been described as useful culture media and ascitic fluid from patients with peritoneal carcinomatosis is particularly recommended. As a general rule these materials will be obtained from a hospital unit and they can be used as soon as their sterility has been verified. It is advisable to test them for toxicity since many of the patients producing these fluids are receiving heavy medication and some of the drugs may be present in toxic concentrations in the fluids.

Aqueous humour

Aqueous humour from the eye has been suggested as a good nutrient for cultures since *in vivo* it is the sole source of nutrients for the corneal epithelium. The best source of aqueous humour is the ox eye. These can be obtained in large quantities from the local slaughter-house but of course the collection of sizeable amounts is tedious and probably aqueous humour is desirable only for rather small-scale work.

Serum ultrafiltrates

It has been established fairly satisfactorily that the most important components of serum are the large molecules, that is to say, the proteins and protein-bound materials. These are apparently irreplaceable except in a very few instances. However, the ultrafiltrate of serum is a very useful supplementary nutrient. It was developed by Simms to prevent the accumulation of fat in tissue during cultivation. Its preparation requires special apparatus and is somewhat tedious but serum ultrafiltrate is available commercially and may be found a useful supplement in growing some highly demanding tissues.

Dialysed serum

As already mentioned, only a very few cell strains will grow in completely defined media. However, most will grow in defined media supplemented with dialysed serum; in these media the small molecular component is precisely defined.

To prepare dialysed serum its volume is first measured and it is then dialysed against distilled water for 48 hours. At the end of this time 1/5 volume of $10 \times$ stock balanced salt solution (p. 84) is added. The volume is then made up with distilled water to twice the original volume. After filtration through a Millipore filter this material constitutes 50 per cent. dialysed serum.

Insect haemolymph

Haemolymph is used as the basis for many media for insect tissue culture. It is obtained by cutting off the last two or three segments from a large pupa and expressing the fluid. All haemolymph tends to darken when it is exposed to air and this is associated with the development of toxic properties. In order to inhibit tyrosinase and thus prevent this darkening, a number of expedients have been employed. Commonly the haemolymph is saturated with phenylthiourea. This method is successful for many purposes, but Wyatt has found that phenylthiourea is inhibitory to the growth of cells and finds that better results are obtained when tyrosinase is precipitated from haemolymph by heat treatment. This consists of raising the haemolymph to 60°C. for five minutes, deep freezing for 24 hours and then centrifuging at 6,000 g. for 10 minutes, the supernatant being used.

Coconut water (coconut milk)

This is used as a supplement in the culture of plant tissues and it has also been tried for animal tissues (without much success). It is prepared from ordinary coconuts. The water is removed from a number of coconuts, each sample being tested for freshness by taste. Any which are not fresh are rejected. The pooled material can be stored in the deep freeze till required. It is then autoclaved at 15 lb./sq. in. for 15 minutes and filtered while hot through Whatman No. 1 filter paper. The material is then ready for use.

TISSUE EXTRACTS

Almost all media used for the cultivation of tissues until very recently contained some sort of tissue extract, usually embryo extract. In the past few years, effective substitutes for embryo extracts have been developed so that it is less used than previously, and it seems certain that its use will diminish progressively. It has, of course, been known for many years that cells will grow without embryo extract and some tissues have been cultivated quite successfully in serum and balanced salt solution alone. It has been found that the most important components of embryo extract are in the small molecular fraction and that they can be effectively replaced by synthetic supplements which are usually mixtures of amino-acids.

There are, however, exceptions and, especially in the case of differentiated tissues, there may be factors in embryo extracts which cannot be adequately replaced. Harris and Kutsky (1954) have demonstrated that, while the small molecular fraction constitutes the essential component of embryo extract, there is also a nucleo-protein fraction which greatly improves the growth of newly-isolated cells.

The preparation of embryo extract

Broadly speaking, there are two different kinds of extract. There are those prepared with the minimum of damage to the tissue and others which involve complete destruction and are really homo-genates. These two extracts produce quite different effects on cells. For instance, the homogenate type has to be used with care since in high concentrations it can be quite toxic.

Preparation of chick embryo extract

This preparation provides an example of a simple extract from relatively intact cells. Embryos of different ages may be used. If they are young, that is to say, incubated up to 10 days, a simple embryo juice may be prepared by placing two or three of them in the barrel of a sterile 20 ml. syringe and expressing them into a suitable receiver. This juice is diluted with balanced salt solution to 50 per cent. and after centrifugation the supernatant constitutes EE_{50}. The procedure is detailed below.

Preparation of embryo extract from young embryos (Fig. 14)

1. Wipe the eggshell with alcohol.
2. Crack the blunt end of the shell by repeated small taps with a scalpel or heavy forceps.
3. Remove the shell over the air space to expose the membrane.
4. Loosen and remove the membrane with a second pair of forceps.
5. Slip a third (curved) pair of forceps under the embryo's neck, taking care not to apply any pressure. Extract it very slowly from the egg and deposit it in a Petri dish.

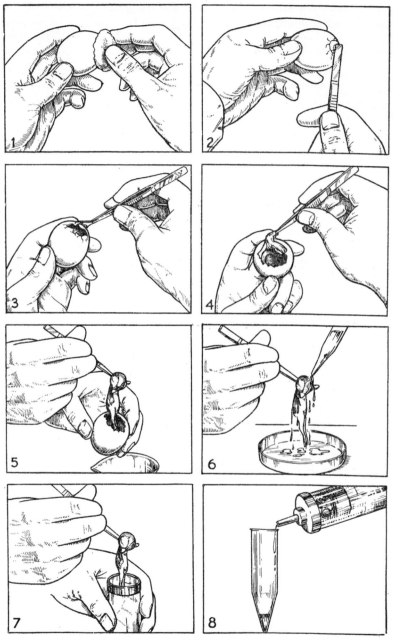

FIG. 14
Preparation of embryo extract (see text).

6. When all the embryos have been removed rinse each three times in balanced salt solution to remove all blood and yolk.

7. Drop them into the barrel of a syringe. Insert the plunger gently.

8. Insert the tip of the syringe into a centrifuge tube and express the embryos.

9. Add an equal volume of balanced salt solution to the pulp and stir with a sterile glass rod. Leave for 30 minutes at room temperature and then centrifuge for 20 minutes at 2,000 g.

10. Remove the supernatant (EE_{50}) and distribute to small test tubes. Stopper. Make a sterility test by adding the last 10 drops to one broth tube. Incubate this tube.

11. Store in the refrigerator if the extract is to be used the same day. For longer storage (up to six weeks) use the deep freeze. Before use, thaw slowly and recentrifuge for 10 minutes at 2,000 g.

The preparation of bovine embryo extract

This provides an example of the homogenate type of extract. A pregnant uterus is obtained from the slaughterhouse and the foetus is palpated. A uterus should be selected which appears to contain an embryo from 4 to 6 in. long. The outside is carefully washed and swabbed with iodine. It is best first to remove the amniotic fluid by means of trocar and cannula. After this the uterus can be placed in a large sterile tray. A long incision is then made and the wall folded back. The embryo presents itself and can be removed quite easily. It is chopped into fairly small pieces and placed in a Waring blender with approximately the same volume of balanced salt solution. After homogenising at high speed for two to five minutes the resulting pulp is transferred to centrifuge bottles and spun down. The supernatant fluid, which is usually cloudy in this case, constitutes EE_{50}. Bryant, Earle and Peppers (1953) have developed a considerable refinement of this technique. They suggest that the product described should be treated with hyaluronidase and then ultracentrifuged in the Spinco to remove all solid matter. Thereafter it can be filtered through a sintered glass filter and the filtrate provides an excellent growth-promoting substance.

Ultrafiltrates of embryo extract

It has been shown by Earle's group that ultrafiltrates of embryo extract have the same growth-promoting potency as the embryo extract itself. After trying embryos of different ages and finding very little difference in growth-promoting potency this group finally prepared an ultrafiltrate of whole infertile egg and found it equally useful.

Other tissue extracts

Although embryo extracts are most commonly employed, extracts from other tissues have been used by other workers. Thus, active extracts have been prepared from adult tissues, such as spleen, liver, bone marrow, leucocytes and tumours. However, in some cases these have had inhibitory effects on growth.

For the culture of tissues from cold-blooded animals extracts of tadpoles (for amphibia) and fish fry (for fish) have been used. However, it is questionable whether these have any special properties and it is not unlikely that media of the type used for mammalian tissues will prove more satisfactory.

All tissue extracts tend to deteriorate rapidly at room temperatures and even at refrigerator temperatures they will lose a great deal of their growth-promoting potency within a week. They can, however, be stored satisfactorily at $-20°C$. and it is best to store them in this way in small quantities. On thawing the extracts a precipitate will be found to have formed and it is necessary therefore to recentrifuge immediately before use.

Other media of biological origin

Since the major nutritional requirements of cultured cells are likely to resemble those of many micro-organisms, it is natural that attempts have been made to employ bacteriological media for their growth. These attempts have met with some success though most bacteriological media are inadequate for prolonged maintenance of animal cells by themselves. As supplements to simple basic media, such as 10 per cent. serum in BSS, they are, however, very useful.

The most useful supplements of this sort are lactalbumin hydrolysate (Nutritional Biochemicals) used at a concentration of 0·1-0·5 per cent. and Difco bactopeptone, which is usually used at 0·5 per cent. These can replace the amino-acid components of defined media. Dehydrated yeast extract (0·1 per cent.) can be used as a source of vitamins and co-enzymes.

A medium commonly used for the maintenance of cell-stocks in virology laboratories contains 0·5 per cent. lactalbumin hydrolysate, 0·1 per cent. yeast extract and 5-10 per cent. calf or human serum.

Other supplements, such as yeast extract, tryptic meat broth, skimmed milk and Filde's medium have been found partly useful.

BIBLIOGRAPHY

ALBRINK, W. S. & WALLACE, A. C. (1951). Aqueous humor as a tissue culture nutrient. Proc. Soc. exp. Biol. (N.Y.) 77, 754.

BAKER, L. E. (1929). The chemical nature of the substances required for cell multiplication. II. The action of glutathione, hemoglobin, and ash of liver on the growth of fibroblasts. J. exp. Med. 49, 163.

BAKER, L. E. (1933). The cultivation of monocytes in fluid medium. J. exp. Med. 58, 575.

BAKER, L. E. & CARREL, A. (1926). Action on fibroblasts of the protein fraction of embryonic tissue extract. J. exp. Med. 44, 387.

BAKER, L. E. & CARREL, A. (1926). Effect of the amino acids and hydrolyzable constituents of embryonic tissue juice on the growth of fibroblasts. J. exp. Med. 44, 397.

BAKER, L. E. & CARREL, A. (1928). The effects of digests of pure proteins on cell proliferation. J. exp. Med. 47, 353.

BORNSTEIN, M. B. (1958). Reconstituted rat-tail collagen used as a substrate for tissue cultures on coverslips in Maximow slides and roller tubes. Lab. Invest. 7, 134.

BRYANT, J. C., EARLE, W. R. & PEPPERS, E. V. (1953). The effect of ultracentrifugation and hyaluronidase on the filtrability of chick embryo extract for tissue culture. J. nat. Cancer Inst. 14, 189.

CAILLEAU, RELDA & KIRK, P. L. (1954). The influence of various culture media on the growth of Earle's Strain L cells and chick heart fibroblasts in vitro. J. nat. Cancer Inst. 15, 295.

CAILLEAU, RELDA & KIRK, P. L. (1957). Some factors affecting the growth promoting properties of serum in tissue culture. Tex. Rep. Biol. Med. 15, 237.

CARREL, A. (1913). Artificial activation of the growth in vitro of connective tissue. J. exp. Med. 17, 14.

CARREL, A. & EBELING, A. H. (1923). Action on fibroblasts of extracts of homologous and heterologous tissues. J. exp. Med. 38, 499.

DOLJANSKI, L. & HOFFMAN, R. S. (1943). The growth activating effect of extract of adult tissue on fibroblast colonies in vitro. III. Cultivation for prolonged periods. Growth 7, 67.

DOLJANSKI, L., HOFFMAN, R. S. & TENENBAUM, E. (1944). The effect of tumor extracts on growth of cells in vitro. Growth 8, 13.

DOLJANSKI, L. & WERNER, H. (1945). Studies on growth-promoting factors of adult tissue extracts; precipitation with alcohol; action of lipid solvents. Growth 9, 229.

DREW, A. H. (1927). The action of tumour extracts on tissues in vitro. Brit. J. exp. Path. 8, 176.

EHRMANN, R. L., & GEY, G. O. (1956). The growth of cells on a transparent gel of reconstituted rat-tail collagen. *J. nat. Cancer Inst.* **16**, 1375.

ENDERS, J. F. (1953). Bovine amniotic fluid as tissue culture medium in cultivation of poliomyelitis and other viruses. *Proc. Soc. exp. Biol. (N.Y.)* **82**, 100.

FISCHER, A. (1939). Nature of the growth-accelerating substance of animal tissue cells. *Nature (Lond.)* **144**, 113.

FISCHER, A. (1941). The nature of the growth-promoting substances in embryonic tissue juice. *Acta physiol. scand.* **3**, 54.

GINSBURG, H. S., GOLD, E. & JORDAN, W. S. Jr. (1955). Tryptose phosphate broth as supplementary factor for maintenance of HeLa cell tissue cultures. *Proc. Soc. exp. Biol. (N.Y.)* **89**, 66.

HANKS, J. H. (1949). Calcification of cell cultures in the presence of embryo juice and mammalian sera. *Proc. Soc. exp. Biol. (N.Y.)* **71**, 328.

HARRIS, M. (1952). Growth factors in alcoholic extracts of chick embryos. *Growth* **16**, 215.

HARRIS, M. (1952). The use of dialyzed media for studies in cell nutrition. *J. cell. comp. Physiol.* **40**, 279.

HARRIS, M. (1952). Growth factors in alcoholic extracts of chick embryos. *Growth* **16**, 215.

HARRIS, M. (1953). Partial purification of growth factors in the dialyzable fraction of chick embryo extract. *Growth* **17**, 147.

HARRIS, M. & KUTSKY, R. J. (1954). Synergism of nucleoprotein and dialysate growth factors in chick embryo extract. *Exp. Cell Res.* **6**, 327.

HETHERINGTON, D. C. (1944). Frozen-dried serum as a medium constituent for tissue cultures. *Proc. Soc. exp. Biol. (N.Y.)* **57**, 196.

HETHERINGTON, D. C. & CRAIG, J. S. (1939). Effect of frozen-dried plasma and frozen-dried embryo juice on tissue cultures. *Proc. Soc. exp. Biol. (N.Y.)* **42**, 831.

HOFFMAN, R. S. & DOLJANSKI, L. (1939). The growth activating effect of extracts of adult tissue on fibroblasts colonies *in vitro*. Experiments with chicken heart extracts. *Growth* **3**, 61.

HOFFMAN, R. S., DINGWALL, J. & ANDRUS, W. (1951). Growth effects on chick fibroblast cultures of fractions of adult and embryonic tissue extracts following differential centrifugation. *Science* **113**, 268.

JACOBY, F. (1936). Migratory and mitotic activity of chick fibroblasts under the influence of dialysate of embryo juice. *Arch. exp. Z.* **19**, 241.

JACQUEZ, J. & BARRY, E. (1951). Tissue culture media. The essential non-dialyzable factors in human placental cord serum. *J. gen. Physiol.* **34**, 765.

KUTSKY, R. J. (1953). Stimulating effect of nucleoprotein fraction of chick embryo extract on homologous heart fibroblasts. *Proc. Soc. exp. Biol. (N.Y.)* **83**, 390.

KUTSKY, R. J. & HARRIS, M. (1954). Growth promoting agents in cell fractions of chick embryos. *J. cell. comp. Physiol.* **43**, 193.

KUTSKY, R. J., TRAUTMAN, R., LIEBERMAN, M. & CAILLEAU, RELDA (1956). Nucleoprotein fractions from various embryonic tissues. A comparison of physicochemical characteristics and biological activity in tissue culture. *Exp. Cell. Res.* **10**, 48.

LEWIS, MARGARET R. (1928). A simple method of drawing blood from the heart of a fowl. *Arch. exp. Z.* **7**, 82.

LU, K. H. & WINNICK, T. (1955). The roles of the nucleic acids and free nucleotides in chick embryonic extract on the growth of heart fibroblasts. *Exp. Cell Res.* **9**, 502.

MALHERBE, H. (1954). Cultivation of human tissues in media containing bovine allantoic and amniotic fluids. *Proc. Soc. exp. Biol. (N.Y.)* **86**, 124.

PORTER, K. R. (1947). The culture of tissue cells in clots formed from purified bovine fibrinogen and thrombin. *Proc. Soc. exp. Biol. (N.Y.)* **65**, 309.

ROSENBERG, S. & KIRK, P. L. (1953). Isolation of a dialyzable growth factor for chick tissue culture. Identification of the ninhydrin reactive band. *Arch. Biochem.* **44**, 226.

SACERDOTE DE LUSTIG, E. (1951). Action of human cerebrospinal fluid on *in vitro* fibroblasts cultures. *Rev. Soc. argent. Biol.* **27**, 114.

SANFORD, KATHERINE K., WALTZ, HELEN K., SHANNON, J. E., EARLE, W. R., EVANS, VIRGINIA J. (1952). The effect of ultrafiltrates and residues of horse serum and chick embryo extract on proliferation of cells *in vitro*. *J. nat. Cancer Inst.* **13**, 121.

SANFORD, KATHERINE K., WESTFALL, B. B., FIORAMONTI, MARY C., McQUILKIN, W. T., BRYANT, J. C., PEPPERS, E. V., EVANS, VIRGINIA J. & EARLE, W. R. (1955). The effect of serum fractions on the proliferation of Strain L mouse cells *in vitro*. *J. nat. Cancer Inst.* **16**, 789.

SIMMS, H. S. & SANDERS, M. (1942). Use of serum ultrafiltrate in tissue cultures for studying deposition of fat and for propagation of viruses. *Arch. Path. (Chicago)* **33**, 619.

WAYMOUTH, CHARITY & WHITE, P. R. (1954). Filtration of embryo extract for tissue culture. *Science* **119**, 321.

WESTFALL, B. B., PEPPERS, E. V., SANFORD, KATHERINE K. & EARLE, W. R. (1954). The amino acid content of the ultrafiltrate from horse serum. *J. nat. Cancer Inst.* **15**, 27.

WILLMER, E. N. & KENDALL, L. P. (1932). The utilisation of proteoses by chicken heart fibroblasts growing *in vitro*. *J. exp. Biol.* **9**, 149.

WOLKEN, J. J. (1952). Fractionation of embryo extract by ultracentrifugation. I. Analysis of fractions. *J. cell. comp. Physiol.* **40**, 243.

CHAPTER VI

MEDIA FOR CULTURING CELLS AND TISSUES

II. DEFINED MEDIA

WHILE tissue culture media obtained from natural sources are still widely used for many purposes, especially for growing tissue freshly isolated from the organism, they suffer from obvious disadvantages. In particular, since their composition is unknown and variable, it is virtually impossible to reproduce conditions exactly from one experiment to another. For this reason attempts have been made from the very earliest days to develop media composed entirely of defined components. The problem was tackled in two different ways—the so-called 'analytical' and 'synthetic' approaches. In the first, attempts were made to analyse the medium and identify essential components. On the whole this has given disappointing results and more has been achieved by the 'synthetic' method in which metabolites shown to be essential or valuable for the survival and development of the intact organism, were combined to form media which were tested for their ability to keep cells alive. It is readily apparent that the division is an artificial one since the two methods of approach are mutually dependent.

With our present knowledge of metabolism it is obvious that there will never be a universal medium for all cell-types. Thus, the requirements for plant cells and animal cells have many things in common but are, on the whole, quite different. Among animals, it is not surprising that the requirements for insect tissues should be different from those for mammalian tissues. And although most media for mammalian cells seem to be equally effective for different cell-types, it must not be forgotten that different absolute requirements exist between different animals. For instance, ascorbic acid is an essential dietary constituent for man, the higher apes and the guinea-pig, but it is not required by other mammals and one might expect such differences to be reflected at some level in the cells. Within the same organism it would also prove surprising if all

78

cells had precisely the same requirements. Thus, cells with strong proteases might be able to use intact protein while cells with no proteases would require the constituent amino-acids. Also for full function we would expect specialised tissues such as thyroid epithelium to have special requirements (in this case iodine and rather large quantities of tyrosine). While these possibilities must be kept in mind, it has to be realised that at the present moment we are at an early stage in the development of special media and most recent achievements have been in producing media of general use.

A substance added to a medium may be beneficial, harmless or harmful. If the effect is beneficial it may be because the substance is essential for the cells or because it has a supplementary value, and it is important to distinguish between these. If it is harmless it may be because it does not enter into the metabolism of the cell or because it is present in an insufficient amount to produce an effect. If it is harmful it may be because it is intrinsically poisonous to the cell or because it is present in an unsuitable concentration. Very few studies have been done to define the precise value, in quantitative terms, of the metabolites added to defined media for mammalian cells.

MEDIA FOR TISSUES FROM WARM-BLOODED VERTEBRATES

Most media consist of mixtures of substances which have proved essential, generally beneficial or harmless. Keeping in mind that our knowledge is incomplete and that most ' synthetic media ' have been derived empirically, we will now consider the different types, in relation to the culture of mammalian and avian cells.

Media can conveniently be classified in four groups.

1. Media essential for immediate survival.
2. Media essential for prolonged survival.
3. Media essential for indefinite growth.
4. Media essential for specialised functions.

The components essential for the immediate survival of cells and tissues have been precisely defined. It is essential to control osmotic pressure and pH, while a source of energy and certain inorganic ions are necessary for all but the briefest survival. These requirements are met by a combination of salts and glucose. A simple medium of this sort is referred to as a *balanced salt solution*. These salt solutions are the basis of all culture media except the very simplest of natural media.

Cells and tissues will survive for a brief time in a balanced salt solution but for more prolonged survival other factors are necessary. These factors, normally present in whole serum, can be replaced by a synthetic mixture. For survival for long periods of time mammalian cells require, in addition to a balanced salt solution, all the essential amino-acids, oxygen, vitamins and serum protein. If the serum protein is not exhaustively dialysed, this mixture may support good growth almost indefinitely but mixtures containing exhaustively dialysed serum will not do this as a rule. In the complete absence of protein the cells do not survive long except in a very few instances of cells which have been specially adapted. The best example of such a medium is the one developed by Eagle (1955) (Table IX).

Recent years have witnessed rapid progress in the development of entirely synthetic media. At present, however, very few cell strains can be grown in media from which serum has been entirely omitted and greatest success has been achieved with the strain L cell. Medium 1066, developed by Parker and his colleagues (1954) and medium NCTC 109 developed in Earle's laboratory were the first media in which prolonged multiplication of the strain L cell was observed. These media resemble each other closely and are distinguished by their complexity. Some of the components used, especially certain of the co-enzymes are relatively impure and therefore some unknown components are almost certainly present. Waymouth's medium 752/1 represents a considerable advance since it is very much simpler than the other two and contains fewer components of dubious purity. HERT 1 medium (Paul, 1959) is capable of maintaining indefinite survival of a subline of strain L cells and is almost as simple as Eagle's medium. Certain cell strains are highly selected for their ability to grow in rigorously defined media and Merchant has even obtained a subline of the L strain which will grow well in Eagle's medium alone. It should be re-emphasised that at the present time most other cell-strains will fail to survive in media containing no serum. Some intermediary media, containing peptone are, however, capable of supporting growth of some of these more exacting strains.

The fourth type of medium—that essential for specialised function—has hardly reached the earliest stage of development. It seems likely that such media are best based on one of the complex defined media mentioned in the previous paragraph. Requirements for each organ will have to be defined as a result of planned investigations. Certain facts are known. Among the best established is that vitamin A is an essential component of media for the growth of ciliated epithelia. Similarly, the survival of many tissues is dependent on the presence of appropriate hormones. For example, adrenal cortex will survive only in the proximity of pituitary tissue and probably requires adrenocorticotrophic hormone. Also some female sex organs are dependent on oestrogens in the medium. Many such requirements can be deduced from a knowledge of the behaviour of the tissues *in vivo*. However, the application of this knowledge to the maintenance of cells and tissues *in vitro* in defined media is still at such an early stage that no medium of this sort has been established.

Before proceeding to consider special examples of the above classes of media some chemical factors will be mentioned which must be taken into account in preparing them.

Solubility of materials.—Many chemicals used in synthetic media are very sparingly soluble and it is essential to prepare them in such a way that they will come into solution. Thus tyrosine is only soluble in acid solution and even then only to a limited extent. Therefore it has to be made up in a special acid stock solution and mixed in with the other materials at a late stage in preparation when the addition of acid will do no harm. Lipids are particularly difficult to dissolve and they have to be taken up in alcoholic solutions. These have to be sufficiently concentrated that the alcohol will be greatly diluted when added to the rest of the medium. Also a non-toxic detergent (Tween 80) has to be added to stabilise the solution. One of the most elementary difficulties concerns calcium phosphate which is highly insoluble, particularly in alkaline solutions. Therefore, in making up salt solutions it is essential that calcium and phosphate should not meet until the solution is quite dilute and that it should not be made alkaline until the last minute.

Compatibility of components.—In combining certain materials it must be remembered that they may react together to produce quite different substances. This does not readily happen at incubator

6

temperature but may occur on heating solutions. Thus, if ascorbic acid and cystine are autoclaved together in the same solution the ascorbic acid will be oxidised and destroyed. Both glucose and ascorbic acid are liable to be destroyed if heated in the presence of alkali.

Purity of materials.—Needless to say, only materials of the highest purity should be used in the preparation of defined media. It is necessary, however, to realise that even the purest chemicals have traces of impurities which may be important. Heavy metals are particularly toxic to cells and thus care must be taken with materials which may have been purified by lead or mercury precipitation. On the other hand, very small traces of certain substances may be essential to the cells and probably the supply of some metals necessary for cell survival (*e.g.* zinc, manganese and cobalt) comes from minute amounts present in other salts. Some of the rarer components of many media are only obtainable in purities of about 85 per cent. and the impurities may not be the same from batch to batch. Thus, in assessing how highly defined a medium is, it is essential to keep this matter of purity in mind.

Chemical instability.—Several of the components added to synthetic media are rather unstable and the only way to store them effectively for long periods of time is in the dry state, preferably in the cold. A particular example of such a substance is glutamine which has an important place in cell metabolism. In solution, glutamine can be stored for a considerable time if it is kept frozen. This is true of most labile compounds so that it is important to prepare media fresh or if they are stored it should be at very low temperatures.

Stock solutions.—From the above considerations, it is apparent that if large amounts of media are to be made up for use and stored for any length of time difficulties are likely to be encountered and only extensive deep freezing facilities permit the long-term storage of large amounts of medium. This requirement can be overcome by making up media as a series of stock solutions which are combined to make the complete medium. The stock solutions can be stored separately in whatever conditions are necessary for the individual components. Incompatible substances can likewise be kept separate until they are mixed together to make the medium.

Table I

BALANCED SALT SOLUTIONS FOR WARM-BLOODED ANIMALS

(Grams per litre)

Substance	Locke	Ringer	Tyrode 1910	Glucosol	Gey 1936	Simms 1941	Earle 1943	Gey 1945	Hanks 1946
NaCl	9·00	9·00	8·00	8·00	7·00	8·00	6·80	8·00	8·00
KCl	0·42	0·42	0·20	0·20	0·37	0·20	0·40	0·375	0·40
$CaCl_2$	0·24	0·25	0·20	0·20	0·17	0·147	0·20	0·275	0·14
$MgSO_4.7H_2O$			0·10	0·10	0·07	0·20	0·10		0·10
$MgCl_2.6H_2O$			0·05	0·05	0·21			0·210	0·10
$NaH_2PO_4.H_2O$							0·125		
$Na_2HPO_4.2H_2O$					0·15	0·21		0·150	0·06
KH_2PO_4					0·03			0·025	0·06
Glucose			1·00	1·00	1·00	1·00	1·00	2·00	1·00
Phenol Red						0·05	0·05		0·02
$NaHCO_3$	0·20		1·00		2·27	1·00	2·20	0·250	0·35
Gas phase	Air	Air	Air	Air	5% CO_2 In air	2% CO_2 In air	5% CO_2 In air	Air	Air

BALANCED SALT SOLUTIONS

All media used in tissue culture have a basis of a synthetic mixture of inorganic salts known as a ' physiological ' or balanced salt solution (BSS). The function of this salt solution is to maintain the pH and osmotic pressure in the medium and also to provide an adequate concentration of essential inorganic ions. All physiological salt solutions have been derived from the salt solution originally described by Ringer. The first one to be developed specifically for supporting the metabolism of mammalian cells was Tyrode

TABLE II

KREBS' BALANCED SALINE SOLUTIONS

	Medium I	Medium II	Medium III
1. 0·9% NaCl (0·154 M)	80 parts	83 parts	95 parts
2. 1·15% KCl (0·154 M)	4 parts	4 parts	4 parts
3. 0·11 M Ca Cl$_2$	3 parts		3 parts
4. 2·11% KH$_2$PO$_4$ (0·154 M)	1 part	1 part	1 part
5. 3·82% MgSO$_4$.7H$_2$O	1 part	1 part	1 part
6. 1·3% NaHCO$_3$ (0·154 M); treated with CO$_2$ until P$_H$ is 7·4 in Medium I	21 parts	3 parts	3 parts
7. Na-phosphate buffer (100 parts of 0·1 M NA$_2$HPO$_4$ (1·78%Na$_2$ HPO$_4$.H$_2$O) and 25 parts of 0·1 M Na H$_2$PO$_4$ (1·38% Na H$_2$PO$_4$.H$_2$O))		18 parts	3 parts
*8. 0·16 M Na-pyruvate (or L-lactate in Mediums I and II)	4 parts	4 parts	4 parts
*9. 0·1 M Na-fumarate	7 parts	7 parts	7 parts
*10. 0·10 M Na-L-glutamate	4 parts	4 parts	4 parts
*11. 0·3 M (5·4%) glucose	5 parts	5 parts	5 parts

* Prepared by neutralising a solution of the acids with M NaHCO$_3$ solution. Solutions 8 - 11, unless sterilised, cannot be kept at room temperature.
The mixture must be saturated with a gas mixture containing about 5 per cent. CO$_2$. The stock solutions are approximately isotonic.

solution, and many other balanced salt solutions have been produced since. Most of them were devised with the object of preventing calcium deposition in the cultures or in order to obtain better buffering conditions in the medium (Tables I and II). In practice, none of these seems to have any demonstrable advantage over any other from the point of view of the maintenance of cell growth. Some of them, however, do have advantages in ease of general handling. For instance, one disadvantage of the original Tyrode solution is that its preparation requires considerable care in order to avoid precipitation of calcium carbonate. The same criticism applies to one or two other salt solutions.

Salt solutions can be divided into two types, those intended to equilibrate with air and those which are designed to equilibrate with a gas phase containing a high carbon dioxide tension of the order of 5 per cent. In the author's opinion the most useful type of the former is Hanks' balanced salt solution and the best example of the latter is Earle's balanced salt solution. Both of these have the great advantage that they are very easy to prepare by autoclaving of different parts. The best buffered salt solution is undoubtedly Earle's solution but the fact that it requires a special gas mixture is sometimes a disadvantage.

Some attempts have been made to buffer the medium with buffering systems other than phosphate and bicarbonate. The most successful have used sodium phosphite (Gifford) or Tris (tris-(hydroxymethyl)-aminomethane). In the author's laboratory several cell-strains (L, Hela, HLM, BHK21) have been kept in active proliferation for up to three years in media containing tris-citrate as the buffer. The composition of " Tris-citrate BSS " is shown in Table III. It has the advantage that cells can grow in media based on it in vessels open to the atmosphere. It has been used successfully for cloning. Gwatkin and Siminovitch have similarly cloned cells in a tris-buffered medium to which was added 1-2 mM. oxaloacetic acid.

The salt solutions developed by Krebs (1950) are also shown in Table II since these were evolved empirically to give the best results in metabolic studies although they have not been employed to any extent in tissue culture work. Their most interesting feature is the inclusion of Krebs cycle intermediates.

TABLE III

TRIS-CITRATE BUFFERED BSS

Substance	g/l	Millimoles
NaCl	5·27	90
KCl	0·26	3·5
CaCl$_2$	0·11	1
MgSO$_4$.7H$_2$O	2·47	10
Na$_2$H PO$_4$.2H$_2$O	0·04	0·23
KH$_2$PO$_4$	0·04	0·29
Tris (hydroxy-methyl)-amino-methane	1·92	16
Citric acid (1H$_2$O)	1·05	5
* Na fumarate	0·16	1
* Oxaloacetic acid	0·13	1
Glucose	1·80	10
Phenol red	0·02	—

* Na fumarate and oxaloacetic acid are required only with a few cell-strains at low inoculum density.

Materials

In making up salt solutions, it is advisable to use double glass distilled water or water which has been "deionised", by passage through a mixed-bed resin, and then distilled once in glass. Ordinary tap water frequently contains a large number of ions, many of which are quite harmless but some of which, such as lead, are toxic to the cells. In addition, it may contain endotoxins released by the growth of gram-negative bacteria, and double distillation from a glass vessel is desirable to remove these materials. It is a common practice to store glass distilled water in polythene bottles to prevent the reaccumulation of metallic salts from glass, as has been shown to occur by Healy. Many metallic ions are also introduced as impurities of the salts used in the solutions. The salts should, therefore, be of the highest analytical purity and special bottles should be kept aside for making up balanced salt solution since, particularly in a chemical laboratory, it is possible for them to be contaminated by other materials weighed simultaneously. Phenol red is added to many salt solutions as a pH indicator since it has been found to be non-toxic in concentrations up to 0·005 per cent if serum is present in the medium. In the absence of serum it may be slightly toxic.

Preparing a balanced salt solution

The main difficulty encountered in preparing a balanced salt solution is the formation of a precipitate of calcium and magnesium carbonate and phosphate. Certain salt solutions are more prone to do this than others and the author prefers Earle's and Hanks' solutions since they give little trouble of this kind. The avoidance of precipitation constitutes the only special art involved in preparing a salt solution.

1ST METHOD.—The calcium and magnesium salts are weighed and dissolved in about 100 ml. water. All other components are weighed and dissolved in about 800 ml. water. While this large amount of solution is stirred vigorously, the calcium and magnesium salt solution is slowly added. The volume is adjusted to one litre and the solution filtered.

2ND METHOD.—The salt solution is made up as before but sodium bicarbonate is omitted: 1·4 per cent. sodium bicarbonate is prepared separately. These two solutions are sterilised by autoclaving. After cooling the volume of the main solution is adjusted with distilled water if necessary and bicarbonate solution added to complete it. Note that when sodium bicarbonate is autoclaved, carbon dioxide is evolved and sodium carbonate remains. If the bottle is sealed tightly before autoclaving the carbon dioxide is, of course, retained. Otherwise, sodium bicarbonate can be reconstituted if desired by bubbling sterile carbon dioxide through the solution after it has been cooled.

USE OF STOCK SOLUTIONS.—It is convenient to prepare stock solutions of salt mixtures. A solution is made up with ten times the concentration of all components except sodium bicarbonate, which is omitted. This is stored in a polythene bottle. If it is subsequently to be autoclaved it can be preserved with a little chloroform (which will be driven off during sterilisation). To reconstitute the BSS, distilled water is added to dilute the stock solution ten times. To adjust the pH after sterilisation 1·4 per cent. sodium bicarbonate is used, as above.

PARTIALLY COMPLETE AND COMPLETE 'SYNTHETIC' MEDIA

The nutritional requirements of cultured cells, so far as they are known, have already been discussed, as have also the factors that have to be taken into account in making up a mixture. A few of the established media illustrated in the accompanying tables will now be considered before the manufacture of an actual synthetic medium is illustrated by a practical example.

TABLE IV

FISCHER'S SUPPLEMENTARY MEDIUM, V-605*
(Fischer *et al.*, 1948)

	Milligrams per 1000 ml.		Milligrams per 1000 ml.
Glucose	800	Riboflavin	0·2
Mannose	100	Pyridoxine	0·3
Galactose	100	Choline	10·0
Inositol	20	Pantothenic acid	0·07
Adenosinetriphosphate	200	Biotin	0·007
Fructose diphosphate	100	*p*-Aminobenzoic acid	1·0
α-Glycerophosphate	100	Ascorbic acid	2·0
Inosinic acid	30	Methylnaphthahydro-	
L-Lysine	15	quinone	0·005
L-Arginine	5	Nicotinic acid	0·3
L-Histidine	2	Cozymase	5·0
DL-Valine	14	Glutathione	5·0
L-Leucine	9	Creatine	10·0
DL-Isoleucine	10	Hypoxanthine	100·0
DL-Threonine	12	Sodium succinate	10·0
DL-Phenylalanine	7	Sodium fumarate	10·0
L-Tryptophan	2	Sodium malate	10·0
DL-Methionine	6	Sodium oxaloacetate	10·0
Cystine	5	Glutamine	250·0
Thiamine	3·0		

* This medium also included dialyzed plasma, dialyzed EE (embryonin) and certain inorganic salts.

Attempts to prepare a synthetic medium were made in the earliest years of tissue culture but the first systematic studies were initiated by Albert Fischer (1941) who, using dialysed plasma as a basal medium, showed that the small molecular fraction could be adequately replaced by a mixture of amino-acids similar to those found in fibrin. His first papers were published in 1941 and culminated in the publication of his medium V-605 in 1948. White independently proposed a similar type of medium in 1946 and these media can be recognised as precursors of the defined media used today. Fischer's medium is shown here mainly for historical interest (Table IV).

Following in the Fischer tradition Morgan, Morton and Parker produced medium 199 in 1950. This medium is still widely used, particularly in the maintenance of tissue for virus production in

TABLE V

WHITE'S MEDIUM (1949) FOR CHICK HEART MUSCLE

	Milligrams per 1000 ml.		Milligrams per 1000 ml.
Glucose	8,500	DL-Valine	130·0
NaCl	7,000	DL-Isoleucine	104·0
KCl	375	DL-Phenylalanine	50·0
Ca(NO₃)₂H₂O	210	Glycine	100·0
MgSO₄	275	Cystine HCl	1·0
Na₂HPO₄12H₂O	145	Glutathione	1·0
KH₂PO₄	26·0	Thiamine	0·1
NaHCO₃	550·0	Pyridoxine HCl	0·5
Fe(NO₃)₃9H₂O	1·3	Niacin	0·5
L-Lysine HCl	156·0	Riboflavin	0·1
L-Arginine HCl	78·0	Biotin	0·4
L-Histidine HCl	26·0	Inositol	0·5
L-Aspartic acid	60·0	Choline	1·0
L-Glutamic acid	140·0	Carotene	0·1
L-Leucine	156·0	Vitamin A	0·1
L-Tryptophan	40·0	Ascorbic acid	0·5
L-Proline	50·0	Calcium pantothenate	0·1
L-Cystine	15·0	Folic acid	0·05
DL-Threonine	130·0	β-Alanine	0·05
DL-Methionine	130·0	Phenol red	5·0

vaccine manufacture. As can be seen from Table VI, it is very complex, containing many substances in addition to those which have been proved to be essential. Despite its complexity this medium is unable to maintain cells for more than a day or two by itself. However, if serum is added it can maintain many cell strains indefinitely. Morgan has subsequently produced a modification of 199, known as M150. The essential differences are the use of Hanks' BSS instead of Earle's BSS as a basis for the medium, replacement of xanthine by monosodium xanthine and of the barium salt of ATP by the sodium salt, addition of glucose, glutamine and bicarbonate immediately before sterilisation by filtration and the addition of antibiotics.

Following the introduction of medium 199 many media of increasing complexity have been produced and two of these, medium 858 and medium NCTC 109, are illustrated because they

TABLE VI

MORGAN, MORTON AND PARKER'S
MEDIUM No. 199* (1950)

	Milligrams per 1000 ml.		Milligrams per 1000 ml.
L-Arginine	70·0	Riboflavin	0·010
L-Histidine	20·0	Pyridoxine	0·025
L-Lysine	70·0	Pyridoxal	0·025
L-Tyrosine	40·0	Niacin	0·025
DL-Tryptophan	20·0	Niacinamide	0·025
DL-Phenylalanine	50·0	Pantothenate	0·01
L-Cystine	20·0	Biotin	0·01
DL-Methionine	30·0	Folic acid	0·01
DL-Serine	50·0	Choline	0.50
DL-Threonine	60·0	Inositol	0·05
DL-Leucine	120·0	p-Aminobenzoic acid	0·05
DL-Isoleucine	40·0	Vitamin A	0·10
DL-Valine	50·0	Calciferol (Vit. D).	0·10
DL-Glutamic acid	150·0	Menadione (Vit. K)	0.01
DL-Aspartic acid	60·0	α-Tocopherol phosphate	
DL-Alanine	50·0	(Vit. E)	0·01
L-Proline	40·0	Ascorbic acid	0·05
L-Hydroxyproline	10·0	Glutathione	0·05
Glycine	50·0	Cholesterol	0·2
Cysteine	0·1	Tween 80 (oleic acid)	20·0
Adenine	10·0	Sodium acetate	50·0
Guanine	0·3	L-Glutamine	100·0
Xanthine	0·3	Adenosine triphosphate	10·0
Hypoxanthine	0·3	Adenylic acid	0·2
Thymine	0·3	Ferric nitrate	0·1
Uracil	0·3	Ribose	0·5
Thiamin	0·010	Deoxyribose	0·5

* This medium also contains a balanced salt solution.

are both capable of supporting the growth of certain cell strains in the total absence of added serum or other biological fluids. According to Dr. Raymond Parker, the cell strains involved are not normal cell strains but have adapted themselves to grow in these media. The media are even more complex than medium 199

TABLE VII

SYNTHETIC MEDIUM No. 858—PARKER AND HEALY
1955

	Milligrams per 1000 ml.		Milligrams per 1000 ml.
AMINO-ACIDS		LIPID SOURCES	
L-Arginine	70·0	Tween 80* (oleic acid)	5·0
L-Histidine	20·0	Cholesterol	0·2
L-Lysine	70·0		
L Tyrosine	40·0	NUCLEIC ACID	
L-Tryptophan	20·0	DERIVATIVES	
L-Phenylalanine	50·0	Adenine deoxyriboside	10·0
L-Cystine	20·0	Guanine deoxyriboside	10·0
L-Methionine	30·0	Cytosine deoxyriboside	10·0
L-Serine	50·0	5-Methylcytidine	0·1
L-Threonine	60·0	Thymidine	10·0
L-Leucine	120·0		
L-Isoleucine	40·0	MISCELLANEOUS	
L-Valine	50·0	Sodium acetate	50·0
L-Glutamic acid	150·0	D-Glucuronic acid	3·6
L-Aspartic acid	60·0	L-Glutamine	100·0
L-Alanine	50·0	D-Glucose	1,000·0
L-Proline	40·0	Phenol red	
L-Hydroxyproline	10·0	(pH indicator)	20·0
Glycine	50·0	Ethanol	
L-Cysteine	260·0	(as an initial solvent for fat-soluble constituents)	16·0
VITAMINS			
Pyridoxine	0·025		
Pyridoxal	0·025	ANTIBIOTICS	
Biotin	0·01	Sodium penicillin G	
Folic acid	0·01	(added just before use)	1·0
Choline	0·50	Dihydrostreptomycin	
Inositol	0·05	sulphate	100·0
p-Aminobenzoic acid	0·05	n-Butyl parahydroxy-	
Vitamin A	0·10	benzoate	0·2
Ascorbic acid (Vit. C)	50·00		
Calciferol (Vit. D)	0·10	INORGANIC SALTS	
α-Tocopherol phosphate		NaCl	6,800·0
(Vit. E)	0·01	KCl	400·0
Menadione (Vit. K)	0·01	CaCl$_2$	200·0
		MgSO$_4$.7H$_2$O	200·0
COENZYMES		NaH$_2$PO$_4$.H$_2$O	140·0
DPN (95% pure)	7·0	NaHCO$_3$	2,200·0
TPN (80% pure)	1·0	Fe, as Fe(NO$_3$)$_3$	0·1
CoA (75% pure)	2·5		
TPP (88% pure)	1·0		
FAD (60% pure)	1·0		
UTP (90% pure)	1·0		
Glutathione			
(100% pure)	10·0		

* Aqueous Tween 80 also serves as the final diluent of an alcoholic stock solution of fat-soluble constituents.

TABLE VIII

PROTEIN-FREE CHEMICALLY DEFINED
MEDIUM NCTC 109

Concentration

	Milligrams per 1000 ml.	Approx. Equiv. in millimoles
L-Alanine	31·48	0·35
L-Alpha amino butyric acid	5·51	0·05
L-Arginine	25·76	0·15
L-Asparagine	8·09	0·06
L-Aspartic acid	9·91	0·07
L-Cystine	10·49	0·04
L-Cysteine	26·00	0·21
D-Glucosamine	3·20	0·02
L-Glutamic acid	8·26	0·05
L-Glutamine	135·73	0·93
Glycine	13·51	0·18
L-Histidine	19·73	0·13
Hydroxy-L-proline	4·09	0·03
L-Isoleucine	18·04	0·14
L-Leucine	20·44	0·16
L-Lysine	30·75	0·21
L-Methionine	4·44	0·03
L-Ornithine	7·38	0·06
L-Phenylalanine	16·53	0·10
L-Proline	6·13	0·05
L-Serine	10·75	0·10
L-Taurine	4·18	0·03
L-Threonine	18·93	0·16
L-Tryptophan	17·50	0·09
L-Tyrosine	16·44	0·09
L-Valine	25·00	0·21
Thiamine hydrochloride (Vitamin B₁)	0·025	
Riboflavin	0·025	
Pyridoxine hydrochloride (Vitamin B₆)	0·0625	
Pyridoxal hydrochloride	0·0625	
Niacin	0·0625	
Niacinamide (Nicotinamide)	0·0625	
Pantothenate, calcium salt dextrorotatory	0·025	
Biotin	0·025	
Folic acid	0·025	
Choline chloride	1·25	
i-Inositol	0·125	
p-Aminobenzoic acid	0·125	
Vitamin B₁₂	1·00	
Vitamin A (Crystalline alcohol)	0·25	
Calciferol (Vitamin D)	0·25	
Menadione (Vitamin K)	0·025	
Alpha tocopherol phosphate, disodium salt (Vitamin E)	0·025	
Glutathione—Monosodium salt	10·10	
Ascorbic acid	49·90	
Cysteine hydrochloride	259·90	

TABLE VIII (*contd.*)

PROTEIN-FREE CHEMICALLY DEFINED
MEDIUM NCTC 109

Concentration

	Milligrams per 1000 ml.	*Approx. equiv. in millimoles*
Diphosphopyridine nucleotide (Cozymase, coenzyme 1)	7·0	
Triphosphopyridine nucleotide—Sodium salt	1·0	
Coenzyme A	2·5	
Cocarboxylase	1·0	
Flavin adenine dinucleotide	1·0	
Uridine triphosphate—Sodium salt	1·0	
Deoxyadenosine	10·0	
Deoxycytidine—HCl	10·0	
Deoxyguanosine	10·0	
Thymidine	10·0	
5-methyl-cytosine	0·1	
Tween 80	1·25	
Glucuronolactone	1·8	
Sodium glucuronate	1·8	
Sodium acetate	50·0	
Phenol red	20·0	
Sodium chloride	6800·0	
Potassium chloride	400·0	
Calcium chloride	200·0	
Magnesium sulphate	200·0	
Sodium monobasic phosphate	140·0	
Sodium bicarbonate	2200·0	
Glucose	1000·0	

and there can be little doubt that they contain many materials that the cells do not require.

Many attempts have been made to simplify them and to identify the essential components. The most accurately defined medium of this sort is undoubtedly the one devised by Eagle (1955). However, except in one isolated case, it is unable to support growth in the total absence of added biological fluid and before considering it Waymouth's (1958) medium MB 752/1 (Table IX) may be examined. It is, in a way, a compromise. It is much simpler than most of the other synthetic media but it contains rather more components than Eagle's medium since this contains only those which are essential for minimal growth rather than those for optimal growth. Previously Dr. Waymouth devised some simple media which would support cell-growth with the addition of pure albumin and peptone but without the inclusion of serum. Medium MB 752/1, in the absence of any addition, has supported the rapid growth of a subline of the strain L mouse subcutaneous fibroblast and some other cells through many passages.

TABLE IX

WAYMOUTH'S MEDIUM MB 752/1

	Milligrams per 1000 ml.	Equivalent in millimoles
NaCl	6000	103
KCl	150	2·0
$CaCl_2.2H_2O$	120	0·82
$MgCl_2.6H_2O$	240	1·18
$MgSO_4.7H_2O$	200	0·81
Na_2HPO_4	300	2·11
KH_2PO_4	80	0·59
$NaHCO_3$	2240	26·7
Glucose	5000	27·8
Ascorbic acid	17·5	0·1
Choline. HCl	250	1·8
Cysteine. HCl	90	0·57
Glutathione	15	0·05
Hypoxanthine	25	0·18
Glutamine	350	2·38

The above ingredients, made up at double the stated concentrations, in glass distilled water, constitute solution BNI. Prepared by dissolving all components except the three buffer salts *first*, in about 80 per cent. of the water. Then add the buffer salts in a small volume of water. This prevents precipitation of Ca or Mg phosphates.

Thiamine HCl	10	0·03
Ca Pantothenate	1·0	0·003
Riboflavin	1·0	0·003
Pyridoxin. HCl	1·0	0·003
Folic acid	0·4	0·0008
Biotin	0·02	0·00008
m-Inositol. $2H_2O$	1·0	0·005
Nicotinamide	1·0	0·008
Vitamin B_{12}	0·2	0·00015

A stock solution of the B vitamins is conveniently made at 40 times the above concentrations.

TABLE IX (*contd.*)

WAYMOUTH'S MEDIUM MB 752/1

	Milligrams per 1000 ml.	Equivalent in millimoles
L-Cystine	15	0·06
Glycine	50	0·66
L-Phenylalanine	50	0·30
L-Glutamic acid	150	1·02
L-Aspartic acid	60	0·46
L-Tyrosine	40	0·22
L-Lysine. HCl	240	1·42
L-Proline	50	0·44
L-Methionine	50	0·34
L-Threonine	75	0·64
L-Valine	65	0·55
L-Isoleucine	25	0·19
L-Leucine	50	0·38
L-Tryptophan	40	0·20
L-Arginine. HCl	75	0·36
L-Histidine. HCl	150	0·80
NaOH	to pH 7·4	2·5

The amino acids are conveniently made up in a stock at ten times the above concentrations.

Medium 752/1 is made by adding to 37·5 ml water, 50·0 ml of BNI + 2·5 ml of the stock B vitamin solution + 10·0 ml of the stock amino acid solution (total 100 ml).

Eagle's medium (Table X) is the simplest of the defined media in general use. It has been established that all its components are essential for cell growth and that most of the other components of more complicated media are not. Being relatively simple it provides a useful example of the method of preparing a 'synthetic' medium and this will be described in detail.

Preparation of Eagle's medium

As has been indicated earlier, all complicated media are prepared as a series of stock solutions, these being combined

TABLE X

EAGLE'S MEDIUM, 1959

	Concentration	
	Milligrams per 1000 ml.	Approx. equiv. in millimoles
L-Arginine	105	0·6
L-Cystine	24	0·2
L-Histidine	31	0·2
L-Isoleucine	52	0·4
L-Leucine	52	0·4
L-Lysine	58	0·4
L-Methionine	15	0·1
L-Phenylalanine	32	0·2
L-Threonine	48	0·4
L-Tryptophan	10	0·05
L-Tyrosine	36	0·2
L-Valine	46	0·4
L-Glutamine	292	2·0
Choline	1	
Nicotinic acid	1	
Pantothenic acid	1	
Pyridoxal	1	
Riboflavine	0·1	
Thiamine	1	
i-Inositol	2	
Folic acid	1	
Glucose	2000	
NaCl	8000	
KCl	400	
CaCl$_2$	140	
MgSO$_4$.7H$_2$O	100	
MgCl$_2$.6H$_2$O	100	
Na$_2$HPO$_4$.2H$_2$O	60	
KH$_2$PO$_4$	60	
NaHCO$_3$	350	
Phenol red	20	
Penicillin	0·5	

(This version is based on Hanks' BSS instead of on Earle's BSS.)

immediately before the medium is required for use. The reasons for grouping materials together will be described in parenthesis in each case.

STOCK SOLUTION 1.—Hanks' balanced salt solution, with glucose and bicarbonate omitted. (By leaving out these two substances it is possible to sterilise the salt solution by autoclaving. Also, glucose can combine with some amino-acids and alkaline conditions can induce degradation of various substances so that it is undesirable to have either present in making up some of the other stock solutions.)

STOCK SOLUTION 2 (× 100).—Dissolve the following L-amino-acids in 100 ml. of stock solution 1 by heating to about 80° C: 1·05 g. arginine; 0·24 g. histidine; 0·58 g. lysine; 0·52 g. leucine; 0·52 g. iso-leucine; 0·15 g. methionine; 0·32 g. phenylalanine; 0·48 g. threonine; 0·10 g. tryptophan; 0·46 g. valine. (This is a general amino-acid stock solution, containing the more soluble and more stable amino-acids.)

STOCK SOLUTION 3 (× 100).—Dissolve the following L-amino-acids in 0·1 N HC1: 0·36 g. tyrosine; 0·24 g. cystine. (These two amino-acids are less soluble than the others and are most conveniently made up separately in dilute acid.)

STOCK SOLUTION 4 (× 1,000).—Dissolve the following B vitamins in 100 ml. of stock solution 1: 0·1 g. choline; 0·1 g. nicotinic acid; 0·1 g. pantothenic acid; 0·1 g. pyridoxal; 0·01 g. riboflavin; 0·1 g. thiamine (aneurin); 0·2 g. inositol. (This is a general stock solution of the more soluble B vitamins. Since they are required in very small amounts, it is more convenient to prepare a strong stock than to weigh out the very small amounts required for a more dilute stock solution.)

STOCK SOLUTION 5 (× 100).—Dissolve 0·01 g. folic acid in 100 ml. of stock solution 1 by the addition of a few drops of 0·5 N Na OH (until the pH is about neutral as judged by the colour of the phenol red). (This vitamin is much less soluble than the rest and therefore cannot be made up at 1,000 times working strength with the other B vitamins.)

STOCK SOLUTION 6 (×100).—Dissolve 20 g. glucose in stock solution 1. (Glucose is best kept out till the end since it can form complexes with some of the amino-acids if heated together with them. Also if it is kept as a separate stock solution it is easy to adjust the glucose concentration in the medium as desired.)

STOCK SOLUTION 7.—Dissolve 1·4 g. sodium bicarbonate in 100 ml. distilled water. (The majority of labile compounds are more stable in slightly acid conditions than in slightly alkaline conditions. Thus it is best to keep alkali out of the medium until the end.)

STOCK SOLUTION 8 (× 100).—Dissolve the following antibiotics in 100 ml. distilled water: 200,000 units sodium penicillin G ; 0·5 g. streptomycin sulphate. (These, being labile, are best made up separately and stored in small aliquots frozen solid.)

STOCK SOLUTION 9 (× 100).—Dissolve 2·92 g. glutamine in 100 ml. stock solution 1. (Glutamine is also labile and is best made up in the same way and stored in small aliquots frozen solid.)

Stock solutions 1 - 7 are quite stable and they can safely be stored at ordinary refrigerator temperatures. It is advisable to sterilise them by filtration through sintered glass before doing so. As has already been mentioned, the remaining solutions are best stored in the frozen condition after sterilisation. (It is as well to note that labile chemicals, such as glutamine, should be stored in cool, dry conditions. The easiest way to do this is to keep them in sealed jars, containing silica gel, in the refrigerator or deep-freeze cabinet.)

Each week a 'working stock solution' is made up from the above stock solutions by combining them in the following quantities :

Stock solution 2 - 10 ml.; stock solution 3 - 10 ml.; stock solution 4 - 1 ml.; stock solution 5 - 10 ml.; stock solution 6 - 10 ml.; stock solution 8 - 10 ml.; stock solution 9 - 10 ml.

This provides 61 ml. of 'working stock solution', which is enough to make up 1 litre of medium. It can be stored for a week or so in the refrigerator without loss of potency.

To make up 100 ml. of growth medium containing, say, 10 per cent. of horse serum, the following are mixed immediately before use: 84 ml. stock solution 1 ; 6·1 ml. 'working stock solution'; 10 ml. horse serum. Stock solution 7 (sodium bicarbonate) is then added to adjust the pH to between 7·2 and 7·4. When fresh serum is being used inositol can safely be omitted. However, the medium as described will support adequate growth for some time even when supplemented with exhaustively dialysed serum and it is therefore useful for many experimental procedures.

TABLE **XI**

CONSTITUENTS OF CULTURE MEDIUM
FOR L-5178 LYMPHOBLASTS

		Medium concentration
		(gm./l.)
A.	NaCl	8·0
	KCl	0·4
	$MgCl_2.6H_2O$	0·1
	Na_2HPO_4	0·06
	$NaH_2PO_4H_2O$	0·067
B.	Glucose	1·0
C.	$NaHCO_3$	1·0
D.	5% acid hydrolyzed casein + tryptophan, 0·5 mg/ml.	5 ml/l.
		(mg/l.)
E.	Glycine	20
	Cystine	7·5
	Histidine	20
F.	Glutamine	200
G.	Vitamins:	
	Thiamin.HCl	1·0
	Nicotinamide	0·5
	Ca-Pantothenate	0·5
	Pyridoxal.HCl	0·5
	D-Ribose	0·5
	Riboflavin	0·5
	Choline chloride	1·5
	i-Inositol	1·5
H.	Biotin	0·01
I.	Ascorbic acid	1·6
	Glutathione (reduced)	1·5
J.	Serum	2–10%
K.	Peptone	0·06%
L.	Folic acid	10 mg/l.
M.	Penicillin	100 units/ml.
	Streptomycin	0·050 mg/ml.
O.	Phenol red	10 mg/l.
P.	$CaCl_2.H_2O$	0·182 gm/l.

The principles employed in making up Eagle's medium are identical with those used for the more complicated media.

OTHER SYNTHETIC MEDIA FOR MAMMALIAN TISSUES

Many media in addition to those already mentioned have been described in the literature. Most of them are not generally used but two others are of special interest and will therefore be discussed.

TABLE XII

TROWELL'S MEDIUM T8 (1959)

	Milligrams per 1000 ml.	Approx. equiv. in millimoles
NaCl	6100	104
KCl	450	6
CaCl	220	2
MgSO$_4$.7H$_2$O	250	1
NaH$_2$PO$_4$.2H$_2$O	450	3
NaHCO$_3$	2820	33·5
Glucose	4000	22
L-Arginine HCl	21	0·1
L-Cysteine HCl	47	0·3
L-Histidine HCl	10	0·05
L-Isoleucine	26	0·2
L-Leucine	26	0·2
L-Lysine HCl	36	0·2
*L-Methionine	7·5	0·05
*L-Phenylalanine	16·5	0·1
*L-Threonine	24	0·2
L-Tryptophan	4	0·02
L-Tyrosine	18	0·1
L-Valine	23	0·2
Thiamine HCl	17	0·05
p-Aminobenzoic acid	35	0·25
Insulin	50	0·001
Chloramphenicol	30	0·1
Phenol red	10	0·03

* Trowell used DL amino acids at double these concentrations in his original medium.

The first of these is shown in Table XI and was evolved by Fischer (1958) for the cultivation of the L-5178 Y ascites tumour of mice. It deserves mention because, although it is far from rigorously defined, it is the only medium currently available which seems to support the continuous propagation of this strain. The L-5178 Y cell is particularly interesting since it is of lymphoblastic type and grows spontaneously in suspension. In the author's experience this medium has proved a very useful general nutrient solution for the cultivation of exacting cell strains.

The other medium of special interest is that devised for adult mammalian organ cultures by Trowell (1955) and designated medium T8 (Table XII). This protein-free medium is extremely simple in composition and has been used to maintain fragments of many adult tissues for from some days to a few weeks in a healthy condition. It must be borne in mind that the function of this medium is quite different from that of media for rapidly-growing cell strains because the organ fragments have a relatively low mitotic rate (sometimes no mitoses at all) and they are maintained *in vitro* for a relatively short period of time.

MEDIA FOR CULTURE OF TISSUES FROM COLD-BLOODED VERTEBRATES

By far the greatest volume of work in tissue culture has been done with tissues from warm-blooded animals. However, tissues from a great many other sources have been successfully grown and there seems no reason to believe that any animal or plant tissue will prove completely refractory to attempts to grow it *in vitro*.

Naturally, the more divergent the species the more divergent are the nutritional requirements likely to be and when we examine entirely different phyla we find considerable differences in the basic needs for growth of tissue *in vitro*. However, having drawn attention to this obvious fact, it must be remarked that the most extraordinary thing about known nutritional requirements of different cells is their general similarity. Even between plants and animals the differences in requirements for inorganic ions are quantitative rather than qualitative and the greatest divergencies are in the requirements for vitamins and amino-acids. Even these reflect greater degrees of metabolic autonomy rather than fundamentally different needs. Some of the more complex chemical molecules such as certain of the hormones which are characteristic for different organisms do not seem to be necessary for the survival of unorganised (and even, in some cases, organised) cell growth.

The cells of many cold-blooded animals, particularly of embryonic and larval stages, will survive for some time at 18° C. in a suitable salt solution, due to the fact that they often contain stores of food materials. Salt solutions for cold-blooded animals are similar to those for mammalian and avian tissues, differences being due mainly to different osmotic pressure requirements.

Some balanced salt solutions for cold-blooded animals are shown in Table XIII.

TABLE XIII

BALANCED SALT SOLUTIONS FOR COLD-BLOODED VERTEBRATES

Substance	Holtfreter (Amphibia and fish)	Frog Ringer (Amphibia)	Cortland (Brown trout)	Holmes & Stott (Cutthroat trout)	Keynes & Martins-Ferreira (Electric eel)
NaCl	3·50	6·5	7·25	7·41	9·88
KCl	0·05	0·14	0·38	0·37	0·37
CaCl$_2$.2H$_2$O	0·10	0·16	0·23		0·44
MgCl$_2$.6H$_2$O					0·30
MgSO$_4$.7H$_2$O		0·39	0·23	0·31	
NaH$_2$PO$_4$.H$_2$O			0·41	0·40	0·04
Na$_2$HPO$_4$.2H$_2$O				0·20	0·21
KH$_2$PO$_4$				0·17	
NaHCO$_3$	0·20	0·20	1·00	0·31	
Glucose			1·00		

In order to support prolonged survival of cells from these animals natural media, analogous to those used for warm-blooded animals, have been employed. Both fish and amphibian tissue have been grown in media consisting of the appropriate salt solution supplemented with serum or plasma and embryo extract. In both cases avian serum and embryo extract have been used successfully but some workers have considered homologous media preferable. In this respect it is worth remembering that the first effective tissue cultures were made from tissues from a cold-blooded animal and the medium consisted of clotted frog lymph.

The same synthetic media as have been used for mammalian tissues have now proved successful for growth of amphibian and fish tissues when allowance has been made for differences in salt concentrations.

MEDIA FOR INVERTEBRATE TISSUES

Similar considerations apply to the cultivation of invertebrate tissues and cells. Again, the basis of the medium is always a salt solution providing the inorganic ions in a mixture which produces a suitable osmotic pressure and pH. Some examples of salt solutions for invertebrates are shown in Table XIV. Clearly they all resemble salt solutions for vertebrate tissues in their general com-

TABLE XIV

BALANCED SALT SOLUTIONS FOR SOME INVERTEBRATES

(Grams per litre)

Substance	Modified Locke (Insects)	Carlson (Grass-hoppers)	Wyatt (Lepid-optera)	Li et al. (Hydra)
NaCl	9·00	7·00		0·58
KCl	0·42	0·20	2·98	0·75
CaCl$_2$	0·25	0·02	0·81	1·11
MgCl$_2$6H$_2$O		0·10	3·04	
MgSO$_4$7H$_2$O			3·70	1·00
NaH$_2$PO$_4$		0·20	1·1	
NaHCO$_3$	0·20	0·05		1·68
Glucose	2·50	0·80	0·70*	10·00
Phenol Red				0·10
Streptomycin				0·125

* Fructose and sucrose also added at 0·4 g/litre.

position although the ratios of different salts vary. Conditions for each species have to be established but, having determined these, certain other rules follow. In the first place the defined supplements required are very much the same as those for vertebrate tissues. Medium 199 has actually been used directly for growth of some insect tissues and the medium by Martignoni and Scallion is a straightforward adaptation of Eagle's medium, only the basal salt solution being changed. The pH of media for insect tissues requires to be a little more acid than that for vertebrate tissues, usually in the range 6·3-6·9. The osmotic pressure may vary from slightly below that used for vertebrate tissues for insects which feed on animal material to more than twice as great for insects which feed on vegetable matter. In insect blood the concentrations of amino-acids are sometimes very high and hence contribute significantly to the osmotic pressure. This is taken into account in, for instance, Wyatt's medium.

It was mainly Wyatt's pioneering work which led to the development of satisfactory synthetic supplements for use with insect materials. Wyatt's medium, which is shown in Table XV, was

TABLE XV

WYATT'S MEDIUM FOR INSECT TISSUES

	Milligrams per 1000 ml.	*mM.*
1. INORGANIC SALTS		
NaH_2PO_4	1,100	8
$MgCl_2.6H_2O$	3,040	15
$MgSO_4.7H_2O$	3,700	15
KCl	2,980	40
$CaCl_2$	810	7·2
2. SUGARS		
Glucose	700	3·9
Fructose	400	2·2
Sucrose	400	1·1
3. ORGANIC ACIDS		
Malic	670	5
α-Ketoglutaric	370	2·5
Succinic	60	0·5
Fumaric	55	0·5
4. AMINO-ACIDS		
L-Arginine HCl	700	3·3
DL-Lysine HCl	1,250	6·9
L-Histidine	2,500	15·7
L-Aspartic acid	350	2·63
L-Asparagine	350	2·65
L-Glutamic acid	600	4·08
L-Glutamine	600	4·11
Glycine	650	8·66
DL-Serine	1,100	10·5
DL-Alanine	450	5·05
β-Alanine	200	2·25
L-Proline	350	3·2
L-Tyrosine	50	0·27
DL-Threonine	350	2·94
DL-Methionine	100	0·67
L-Phenylalanine	150	0·9
DL-Valine	200	0·7
DL-Isoleucine	100	0·77
DL-Leucine	150	1·44
L-Tryptophan	100	0·61
L-Cystine	25	0·1
Cysteine HCl	80	0·5

developed on the basis of an analysis of the haemolymph of the silkworm and with it she obtained good growth of silkworm cells.

TABLE XVI

GRACE'S MEDIUM FOR INSECT TISSUES

	Milligrams per 1000 ml.	mM.
1. INORGANIC SALTS		
NaH_2PO_4	1,100	8
$MgCl_2 . 6H_2O$	3,040	15
$MgSO_4 . 7H_2O$	3,700	15
KCl	2,980	40
$CaCl_2$	810	7·2
2. SUGARS		
Glucose	700	3·9
Fructose	400	2·2
Sucrose	400	1·1
3. VITAMINS		
Thiamine	0·01	
Riboflavine	0·01	
Ca pantothenate	0·01	
Pyridoxine	0·01	
Nicotinic acid	0·01	
Biotin	0·01	
Folic acid	0·01	
Choline	0·01	
m-inositol	2·00	
4. AMINO-ACIDS		
L-Arginine HCl	700	3·3
DL-Lysine HCl	1,250	6·9
L-Histidine	2,500	15·7
L-Aspartic acid	350	2·63
L-Asparagine	350	2·65
L-Glutamic acid	600	4·08
L-Glutamine	600	4·11
Glycine	650	8·66
DL-Serine	1,100	10·5
DL-Alanine	450	5·05
β-Alanine	200	2·25
L-Proline	350	3·2
L-Tyrosine	50	0·27
DL-Threonine	350	2·94
DL-Methionine	100	0·67
L-Phenylalanine	150	0·9
DL-Valine	200	0·7
DL-Isoleucine	100	0·77
DL-Leucine	150	1·44
L-Tryptophan	100	0·61
L-Cystine	25	0·1
Cysteine HCl	80	0·5
5. MISCELLANEOUS		
Malic acid	670	5
α-Ketoglutaric acid	370	2·5
Succinic acid	60	0·5
Fumaric acid	55	0·5
Cholesterol	30	

This medium has now been improved by Grace (1958) by the addition of some vitamins of the B group. When Grace's medium, illustrated in Tables XVI, is supplemented with about 3 per cent. of heat-treated haemolymph (concentrations up to 50 per cent. have also been used) excellent growth of silkworm cells is obtained, and Grace has succeeded in establishing four permanent strains of insect cells.

As with vertebrate tissues useful media have been developed using protein hydrolysates (such as lactalbumin hydrolysate) in place of amino-acid mixtures and yeast hydrolysate in place of B vitamins (Chapter XIV).

Very few attempts have been made to culture invertebrate tissues other than arthropod tissues. However, some success has been obtained with Hydra cells and in at least one case Eagle's medium was used with the modified Earle's salt solution developed by Li et al. In other studies the supplements were again similar to those used for warm-blooded vertebrates. Hence, it would seem reasonable to predict that tissues from almost all animals could be grown in similar mixtures modified only with regard to pH and the ratios of different ions.

MEDIA FOR PLANT TISSUES

The nutrition of plant cells was examined in detail and described accurately some years ago, so that completely synthetic media for the growth of plant tissues have been available for a long time. The reason for this is mainly that the problem of plant cell nutrition is considerably simpler than the problem of animal cell nutrition. Plants have a very much more versatile metabolism than animals and can use simpler molecules for almost all their synthetic processes. Thus, in addition to an inorganic salt mixture (corresponding to the xylem sap) the only materials required for good growth are sucrose, a mixture of vitamins and some glycine (corresponding to the essential components of the phloem sap). White's nutrient solution for plants is of this very simple form. It is illustrated in Table XVII.

A more complicated solution has been devised by Gautheret and his co-workers. This contains many of the trace elements and cysteine instead of glycine. White's medium is adequate for roots and many plant tumour tissues as well as a number of other

TABLE XVII

WHITE'S MEDIUM FOR PLANT TISSUES

	mg./litre
$Ca(NO_3)_2$	200
$MgSO_4$	360
Na_2SO_4	200
KNO_3	80
KCl	65
NaH_2PO_4	16·5
KI	0·75
$Fe_2(SO_4)_3$	2·5
$MnSO_4$	4·5
$ZnSO_4$	1·5
H_3BO_3	1·5
Glycine	3·0
Thiamine	0·1
Niacin	0·5
Pyridoxine	0·1
Sucrose	20,000

TABLE XVIII

GAUTHERET'S SOLUTION

	mg./litre
$Ca(NO_3)_2$	100
KNO_3	25
$MgSO_4$	25
KH_2PO_4	25
$Fe_2(SO_4)_3$	50
$MnSO_4$	2
KI	0·5
$ZnSO_4$	0·1
H_3BO_3	0·15
$Ti_2(SO_4)_3$	0·2
$NiSO_4$	0·05
$CoCl_2$	0·05
$CuSO_4$	0·05
Glucose	30,000
Agar	6,000
Cysteine—HCl	10
Thiamine	1
Ca pantothenate	0·1
Biotin	0·1
Inositol	100
Naphthalene acetic acid	0·3

materials. On the other hand, Gautheret's solution is widely used (with modifications) for normal tissues. As a rule no addition to these media is required, but in the case of a few plant tissues a natural supplement to the synthetic mixtures has been found useful. Supplements used have been yeast extracts and coconut milk.

BIBLIOGRAPHY

BAKER, L. E. (1936). Artificial media for the cultivation of fibroblasts, epithelial cells and monocytes. *Science* **83**, 605.

BAKER, L. E. & EBELING, A. H. (1939). Artificial maintenance media for cell and organ cultivation. I. The cultivation of fibroblasts in artificial and serumless media. *J. exp. Med.* **69**, 365.

BARON, S. & LOW, R. J. (1958). New maintenance medium for cell culture. *Science* **128**, 89.

BERGMANN, M. & NIEMANN, C. (1936). On blood fibrin. A contribution to the problem of protein structure. *J. biol. Chem.* **115**, 77.

BIGGERS, J. D., RINALDINI, L. M. & WEBB, M. (1957). The study of growth factors in tissue culture. *Symp. soc. exp. Biol.* **11**, 264.

BIGGERS, J. D., WEBB, M., PARKER, R. C. & HEALY, G. M. (1957). Cultivation of embryonic chick bones on chemically defined media. *Nature (Lond.)* **180**, 825.

BOLL, W. G. & STREET, H. E. (1951). Studies on the growth of excised roots. I. The stimulatory effect of molybdenum and copper on the growth of excised tomato roots. *New Phytol.* **50**, 52.

CAPLIN, S. M. & STEWARD, F. C. (1948). Effect of coconut milk on the growth of explants from carrot root. *Science* **108**, 655.

CAPLIN, S. M. & STEWARD, F. C. (1949). A technique for the controlled growth of excised plant tissue in liquid media under aseptic conditions. *Nature (Lond.)* **163**, 920.

CHANG. R. S. & GEYER. R. P. (1957). A serum albumin medium for the cultivation of human epithelial-like cells. *J. Immunol.* **79** 455.

DAY, M. F. & GRACE, T. D. C. (1959). Review of recent work on insect tissue culture. *Ann. Rev. Entom.* **4**, 17.

DORMER, K. J. & STREET, H. E. (1949). The carbohydrate nutrition of tomato roots. *Ann. Bot.* **13**, 199.

EAGLE, H. (1955). The specific amino acid requirements of mammalian cells (strain L) in tissue culture. *J. biol. Chem.* **214**, 839.

EAGLE, H. (1955). The specific amino-acid requirements of a human carcinoma cell (strain HeLa) in tissue culture. *J. exp. Med.* **102**, 37.

EAGLE. H. (1955). The minimum vitamin requirements of the L and HeLa cells in tissue culture, the production of specific vitamin deficiencies and their cure. *J. exp. Med.* **102**, 595.

EAGLE, H. (1959). Amino acid metabolism in mammalian cell cultures. *Science* **130**, 432.

EAGLE, H. (1960). The sustained growth of human and animal cells in a protein-free environment. *Proc. nat. Acad. Sci. (Wash.)* **46**, 427.

EAGLE, H., OYAMA, V. I., LEVY, M. & FREEMAN, A. (1956). Myo-inositol as an essential growth factor for normal and malignant human cells in tissue culture. *Science* **123**, 845.

EAGLE, H., OYAMA, V. I. & LEVY, M. (1957). Amino-acid requirements of normal and malignant human cells in tissue culture. *Arch. Biochem.* **67**, 432.

EARLE, W. R. (1934). A technique for the adjustment of oxygen and carbon dioxide tensions, and hydrogen ion concentration, in tissue cultures planted in Carrel flasks. *Arch. exp. Z.* **16** 116.

EVANS, VIRGINIA J., BRYANT, J. C. & FIORAMONTI, MARY C., McQUILKIN, W. T., SANFORD, KATHERINE K. & EARLE, W. R. (1956). Studies of nutrient media for tissue cells *in vitro*. I. A protein-free chemically defined medium for cultivation of Strain L cells. *Cancer Res.* **16,** 77.

EVANS, VIRGINIA J., BRYANT, J. C., McQUILKIN, W. T., FIORAMONTI, MARY C., SANFORD, KATHERINE K., WESTFALL, B. B. & EARLE, W. R. (1956). Studies of nutrient media for tissue cells *in vitro*. II. An improved protein-free chemically defined medium for long-term cultivation of strain L-929 cells. *Cancer Res.* **16,** 87.

EVANS, VIRGINIA J., FIORAMONTI, M. D. & EARLE, W. R. (1959). Studies of nutrient media for tissue cells *in vitro*. V. The effect of the coenzymes of medium NCTC 109 on the proliferation of NCTC strain 2071 and NCTC strain 2937. *Amer. J. Hyg.* **70,** 28.

EVANS, VIRGINIA J., FIORAMONTI, M. C. & EARLE, W. R. (1960). Studies of nutrient media for tissue cells *in vitro*. VI. The effect of nucleic acid derivatives mixture of medium NCTC 109 on NCTC strain 2071 and NCTC strain 2981. *Amer. J. Hyg.* **71,** 168.

EVANS, VIRGINIA J., KERR, H. A., McQUILKIN, W. T., EARLE, W. R. & HULL, R. N. (1959). Growth *in vitro* of a long-term strain of monkey kidney cells in medium NCTC 109 free of any added protein. *Amer. J. Hyg.* **70,** 297.

FISCHER, A. (1941). Die Bedeutung der Aminosäuren für die Gewebezellen in vitro. *Acta physiol. scand.* **2,** 143.

FISCHER, A., ASTRUP, T., EHRENSVÄRD, G. & OEHLENSCHLÄGER, V. (1948). Growth of animal tissue cells in artificial media. *Proc. Soc. exp. Biol.* *(N.Y.)* **67,** 40.

FISCHER, G. A. (1958). Studies of the culture of leukemic cells *in vitro*. *Ann. N.Y. Acad. Sci.* **78,** 673.

FREW, J. G. H. (1928). Technique for the cultivation of insect tissue. *Brit. J. exp. Biol.* **6,** 1.

GAVRILOV, W. & COWEZ, S. (1941). Essai de culture in vitro de tissus de moustiques et d'intestins de lapins adults infectés. *Ann. parasit.* *(Paris)* **18,** 180.

GAUTHERET, R. J. (1934). Culture du tissu cambial. *C.R. Acad. Sci., Paris* **198,** 2195.

GAUTHERET, R. J. (1935). Recherches sur la culture des tissus végétaux: *Essais de culture de quelques tissus méristématiques,* 279 pp. Université de Paris: Thesis.

GAUTHERET, R. J. (1937). Nouvelles recherches sur la culture du tissu cambial. *C.R. Acad. Sci. (Paris)* **205,** 572.

GAUTHERET, R. J. (1939). Sur la possibilité de réaliser la culture indéfinie des tissus de tubercules de carotte. *C.R. Acad. Sci. (Paris)* **208,** 118.

GAUTHERET, R. J. (1942). *Manuel Technique de Culture des Tissus Végétaux,* p. 172. Paris: Masson.

GAUTHERET, R. J. (1947). Sur les besoins en hetero-auxine des cultures de tissus de quelques végétaux. *C.R. soc. Biol. (Paris)* **141,** 627.

GAUTHERET, R. J. (1947). Action de l'acide indole-acetique sur le developpement des tissus normaux et des tissus de crown-gall de topinambour cultivés *in vitro*. *C.R. Acad. Sci. (Paris)* **224,** 1728.

GAUTHERET, R. J. (1955). The nutrition of plant tissue cultures. *Annu. Rev. Pl. Physiol.* **6,** 433.

GRACE, T. D. C. (1958). The prolonged growth and survival of ovarian tissue of the promethea moth (callosomia promethea) *in vitro*. *J. gen. Physiol.* **41,** 1027.

GRACE, T. D. C. (1958). Effects of various substances on growth of silkworm tissues *in vitro*. *Aust. J. biol. Sci.* **2,** 407.

GWATKIN, R. B. L. & SIMINOVITCH, L. (1960). Multiplication of single mammalian cells in a nonbicarbonate medium. *Proc. Soc. exper. Biol.* *(N.Y.)* **103,** 718.

HAM, R. G. (1963). An improved nutrient solution for diploid Chinese hamster and human cell lines. *Exp. Cell Res.* **29,** 515.

HANKS, J. H. & WALLACE, R. E. (1949). Relation of oxygen and temperature in the preservation of tissues by refrigeration. *Proc. Soc. exp. Biol. (N.Y.)* **71,** 196.

HARRIS, M. (1952). The use of dialyzed media for studies in cell nutrition. *J. cell. comp. Physiol.* **40,** 279.

HEALY, G., FISHER, DOROTHY & PARKER, R. C. (1954). Nutrition of animal cells in tissue culture. IX. Synthetic medium No. 703. *Canad. J. Biochem.* **32,** 327.

HEALY, G., FISHER, DOROTHY & PARKER, R. C. (1955). Nutrition of animal cells. X. Synthetic medium No. 858. *Proc. Soc. exp. Biol. (N.Y.)* **89,** 71.

HELLER, R. (1954). Les besoins mineraux des tissus en culture. *Ann. Biol.* **30,** 361.

HENDERSON, J. H. M. (1954). The changing nutritional pattern from normal to habituated sunflower callus tissue *in vitro. Ann. Biol.* **30,** 329.

HETHERINGTON, D. C. (1946). Effect of some of the B complex vitamins upon chick tissue cultures. *Proc. Soc. exp. Biol. (N.Y.)* **62,** 312.

HILDEBRANDT, A. C. & RIKER, A. J. (1953). Influence of concentrations of sugars and polysaccharides on callus tissue growth *in vitro. Amer. J. Bot.* **40,** 66.

HOLMES, W. N. & STOTT, G. E. (1960). Studies of the respiration rates of excretory tissues in cutthroat trout (*Salmo clarki clarki*), I and II. *Phys. Zool.* **33,** 9.

HOLTFRETER, J. (1931). Über die Aufzucht isolierter Teile des Amphibienkeimes. *Arch. EntwGesch.* **124,** 404.

KEYNES, R. D. & MARTINS-FERREIRA, H. (1953). Membrane potentials in the electroplates of the electric eel. *J. Physiol.* **119,** 315.

KREBS, H. A. (1950). Body size and tissue respiration. *Biochim. biophys. Acta* **4,** 249.

LEWIS, MARGARET R. & LEWIS, W. H. (1911). The growth of embryonic chicken tissues in artificial media, agar and bouillon. *Johns Hopk. Hosp. Bull.* **22,** 126.

LEWIS, MARGARET R. & LEWIS, W. H. (1911). The cultivation of tissues from chick embryos in solutions of NaCl, CaCl$_2$, KCl and NaHCO$_3$. *Anat. Rec.* **5,** 277.

LOCKHART, R. Z. & EAGLE, H. (1959). Requirements for growth of single human cells: *Non essential* amino acids, notably serine, are necessary and sufficient nutritional supplements. *Science* **129,** 252.

McQUILKEN, W. T., EVANS, VIRGINIA J. & EARLE, W. R. (1957). The adaptation of additional lines of NCTC Clone 929 (Strain L) cells to chemically defined protein-free medium NCTC 109. *J. nat. Cancer Inst.* **19,** 885.

MOREL, G. & WETMORE, R. H. (1951). Fern callus tissue cultures. *Amer. J. Bot.* **38,** 141.

MORGAN, J. F. (1958). Tissue culture nutrition. *Bact. Rev.* **22,** 20.

MORTON, H. J., PASIEKA, A. E. & MORGAN, J. F. (1956). The nutrition of animal tissues cultivated *in vitro. J. biophys. biochem. Cytol.* **2,** 589.

NAGLE, S. C., JR., TRIBBLE, H. R., JR., ANDERSON, R. E. & GRAY, N. D. (1963). A chemically defined medium for growth of animal cells in suspension. *Proc. Soc. exp. Biol. (N.Y.)* **112,** 340.

NEUMAN, R. E. & McCOY, T. A. (1958). Growth-promoting properties of pyruvate, oxalacetate and α-ketoglutarate for isolated Walker carcinosarcoma 256 cells. *Proc. Soc. exp. Biol. (N.Y.)* **98,** 303.

PARKER, R. C., HEALY, G. & FISHER, DOROTHY (1954). Nutrition of animal cells in tissue culture. VII. Use of replicate cell culture in the evaluation of synthetic media. *Canad. J. Biochem.* **32,** 306.

PAUL, J. (1959). Environmental influences on the metabolism and composition of cultured cells. *J. exp. Zool.* **142.**

PLANTEFOL, L. & GAUTHERET, R. J. (1941). Sur l'intensité des échanges respiratoires des tissus végétaux en culture: tissu primitif et tissu néoformé. *C.R. Acad. Sci. (Paris)* **213,** 627.

PRESTON, M. M'E. (1948). Amphibian tissue culture for biophysical research. *Nature (Lond.)* **161,** 203.

PRESTON, M. M'E. (1949). The cultivation *in vitro* of various amphibian tissues. *J. roy. micr. Soc.* **69,** 65.

PUMPER, R. W. (1958). Adaptation of tissue culture cells to a serum-free medium. *Science* **128,** 363.

RIKER, A. J. & GUTSCHE, A. E. (1948). The growth of sunflower tissue *in vitro* on synthetic media with various organic and inorganic sources of nitrogen. *Amer. J. Bot.* **35,** 227.

RINGER, S. (1895). Further observations regarding the antagonism between calcium salts and sodium, potassium and ammonium salts. *J. Physiol.* **18,** 425.

ROSE, W. C. (1932). The amino acids in nutrition. *Yale J. Biol. Med.* **4,** 519.

ROSENBERG, S. & KIRK, P. L. (1953). Tissue culture studies. Identification of components and synthetic replacements for the active fraction of chick embryo extract ultrafiltrate. *J. gen. Physiol.* **37,** 239.

SHANTZ, E. M. & STEWARD, F. C. (1952). Coconut-milk factor: The growth-promoting substances in coconut milk. *J. Amer. chem. Soc.* **74,** 6133.

SKOOG, F. (1951). Chemical control of growth and organ formation in plant tissues. *Ann. Biol.* **26,** 545.

STEWARD, F. C., CAPLIN, S. M. & MILLAR, F. K. (1952). Investigations on growth and metabolism of plant cells. I. New techniques for the investigation of metabolism, nutrition and growth of undifferentiated cells. *Ann. Bot. (Lond.)* **16,** 57.

STREET, H. E. & LOWE, J. S. (1950). The carbohydrate nutrition of tomato roots. II. The mechanism of sucrose absorption by excised roots. *Ann. Bot. (Lond.)* **14,** 307.

STREET, H. E. & McGREGOR, S. M. (1952). The carbohydrate nutrition of tomato roots. III. The effects of external sucrose concentration on the growth and anatomy of excised roots. *Ann. Bot. (Lond.)* **16,** 185.

STREET, H. E. (1954). Factors controlling meristematic activity in excised roots. V. Effects of β-indolylacetic acid, β-indolylacetonitrile and α-(1-naphthyl methylsulphide)-propionic acid on the growth and survival of roots of Lycopersicum esculentum, Mill. *Physiol. Plant.* **7,** 212.

STREET, H. E., McGREGOR, S. M. & SUSSEX, I. M. (1954). Effects of 3-indolylacetic acid and 3-indolylacetonitrile on the growth of excised tomato roots. *J. exp. Bot.* **5,** 204.

SWIM, H. E. & PARKER, R. F. (1955). Nonbicarbonate buffers in cell culture media. *Science* **122,** 466.

SWIM, H. E. & PARKER, R. F. (1958). The amino acid requirements of a permanent strain of altered uterine fibroblasts (U12-705). *Canad. J. Biochem.* **36,** 861.

TRAGER, W. (1935). Cultivation of the virus of Grasserie in silkworm tissue cultures. *J. exp. Med.* **61,** 501.

TROWELL, O. A. (1955). The culture of lymph nodes in synthetic media. *Exp. Cell Res.* **9,** 258.

TYRODE, M. V. (1910). The mode of action of some purgative salts. *Arch. int. Pharmacodyn.* **20,** 205.

UHLENHUTH, E. (1914). The cultivation of the skin epithelium of adult frog Rana pipiens. *J. exp. Med.* **20,** 614.

VOGELAAR, J. P. M. & ERLICHMAN, ELEANOR (1933). A feeding solution for cultures of human fibroblasts. *Amer. J. Cancer* **18,** 28.

WAYMOUTH, CHARITY (1956). A serum-free nutrient solution sustaining rapid and continuous proliferation of strain L (Earle) mouse cells. *J. nat. Cancer Inst.* **17,** 315.

WAYMOUTH, CHARITY (1959). Rapid proliferation of sublines of NCTC Clone 929 (Strain L) mouse cells in a simple chemically defined medium (MB 752/1). *J. nat. Cancer Inst.* **22,** 1003.

WHITE, P. R. (1934). Potentially unlimited growth of excised tomato root tips in a liquid medium. *Pl. Physiol.* **8,** 489.

WHITE, P. R. (1937). Amino acids in the nutrition of excised tomato roots. *Pl. Physiol.* **12,** 793.

WHITE, P. R. (1937). Vitamin B_1 in the nutrition of excised tomato roots. *Pl. Physiol.* **12,** 803.

WHITE, P. R. (1939). Potentially unlimited growth of excised plant callus in an artificial nutrient. *Amer. J. Bot.* **26,** 59.

WHITE, P. R. (1945). Respiratory behavior of bacteria-free crown-gall tissues. *Cancer Res.* **5,** 302.

WHITE, P. R. (1946). Cultivation of animal tissues *in vitro* in nutrients of precisely known constitution. *Growth* **10,** 231.

WHITE, P. R. (1949). Prolonged survival of excised animal tissue *in vitro* in nutrients of known constitution. *J. cell comp. Physiol.* **34,** 221.

WOLFF, E. M. (1953). Sur la croissance et la différenciation en milieu synthétique de la syrinx de l'embryon de poulet. *C.R. Soc. Biol. (Paris)* **147,** 864.

WOLFF, E. M. (1955). Les besoins spécifiques en acides aminés de la syrinx de l'embryon de poulet cultivée *in vitro* sur un milieu entièrement synthétique. *C.R. Acad. Sci. (Paris)* **240,** 1016.

WOLF, K. (1963). Physiological salines for fresh-water teleosts. *The Progressive Fish-Culturist,* July 1963, p. 135.

WOLF, K. & QUIMBY, M. C. (1964). Amphibian cell culture: permanent cell line from the bullfrog (Rana catesbeiana). *Science* **144,** 1578.

WORDEN, J. L. (1961). Proliferation of mammalian cells in ion-controlled environment. *J. nat. Cancer Inst.* **26,** 801.

WYATT, H. F. (1961). Cation requirements of HeLa cells in tissue culture. *Exp. Cell Res.* **23,** 97.

WYATT, S. S. (1956). Culture in vitro of tissue from the silkworm, Bombyx Mori L. *J. gen. Physiol.* **39,** 841.

PART II
PREPARATION OF MATERIALS

~~~~~~~~~~~~~~~~~~~~~~~~~~~~~~~~~~~~~~~

CHAPTER VII

PREPARATION OF APPARATUS

CONTAMINATION of media with bacteria is the greatest hazard in most tissue culture procedures, but almost as important is contamination with noxious chemical substances. For this reason particular care must be taken in the selection and preparation of materials. This includes not only chemicals used for media but also apparatus, such as stoppers and glassware, with which media may come in contact.

Glassware

Although cells have been grown on many substrates, including cellophane, perspex, polystyrene and other plastics, the material most commonly used is glass, since this is so readily available. Glasses vary very considerably in their composition and some contain materials which are highly toxic to cells, such as lead and arsenic. Since these substances are slowly brought into solution by the slightly alkaline media used in tissue culture, toxicity to cells can sometimes be traced to this source. It is often stated that only borosilicate glasses should be used for tissue culture since their formulae are more standard and they are less soluble in alkali. However, both soda glasses and borosilicate glasses have been found to be toxic on occasions while glasses of both types have also been found to be highly satisfactory. Thus, it is best to find a brand of glass which has no toxic properties and to use it empirically. Two glasses which appear quite satisfactory are the borosilicate glass made by Pyrex and the soda glass used for most medical prescription bottles in this country. It is worth mentioning here that new glassware is often found to be rather unsatisfactory for culturing cells. After it has been used at least once, it seems to give more satisfactory results, even when rigorous cleaning methods are used. The reason for this is obscure but it may well have to do with the surface charge on the glass, which has been shown by Rappaport to be important in permitting cells to stick.

Rappaport and her colleagues observed that the extent to which glass permitted cells to adhere was related to the charge density on its surface. The nett negative charge could be determined easily by measuring the amount of stain retained when the surface was covered with 0·005 per cent. crystal violet for one minute and then rinsed in water. The retained crystal violet was dissolved up in ethanol for colorimetric determination. They found that soda glasses had a higher charge density than borosilicate glasses and that the charge density could be increased and stabilised by a process which involved treatment with 0·1 M EDTA in dilute (0·025 N) NaOH at 122° C. for 30 minutes, followed by treatment with sodium carbonate. The treatment is somewhat complicated and the surface obtained unstable so that it does not commend itself for routine cell culture. However, Rappaport was able to show that the requirement of HeLa and monkey kidney cells for serum could be abolished if they were inoculated into glassware prepared in this way.

Plastic vessels

Polystyrene vessels are now widely used for cell culture. Most commercially available polystyrene dishes are unsuitable because cells will not adhere to them. It is essential that the surface of the plastic should carry a negative charge which will bind sodium ions. (According to Rappaport the suitability of a surface is directly related to the density of sodium ions.) Of the commercially available dishes those manufactured by Falcon plastics are probably best. 'Nunclon' dishes, made in Denmark are almost as satisfactory and for many purposes are equally good. Ordinary grade polystyrene dishes can be made suitable by sulphonating the surface layer of polystyrene. This can be achieved by treating the dishes with concentrated sulphuric acid for one hour and then, after washing in water, with 10 per cent. sodium carbonate for ten minutes (personal communication from Dr. H. Rubin). After washing until neutral these are as satisfactory as the other dishes and, if handled with care, are usually sterile after processing.

These dishes are not usually re-used but, if desired, they can be cleaned with detergent and sterilised with 70 per cent. ethanol. The dishes are wrapped while still wet with alcohol and dried in an incubator.

Stoppers for culture vessels

Rubber stoppers contain substances which are toxic to tissue culture cells. This seems to be due to chemicals used in processing since stoppers made from virgin rubber and pure gum rubber are less toxic than ordinary black or red stoppers. In order to remove surface impurities rubber stoppers (and all other rubber articles coming in contact with cells) should first be boiled in dilute alkali (5 per cent. sodium carbonate) and exhaustively rinsed with water. Thereafter they can be cleaned in the same way as glassware. However, it has been shown that even exhaustive cleaning does little to diminish the toxic properties of rubber and therefore care must always be taken to ensure that medium does not come in contact with rubber stoppers. This can be done either by using vessels designed to prevent it (most vessels used in tissue culture) or by using stoppers made of some material other than rubber. Silicone rubber stoppers have been introduced to provide a solution to this problem but they are rather expensive and it is rarely necessary to resort to them since there is practically no chance of prolonged contact of medium with stoppers in most vessels used in tissue culture.

The remarks about rubber stoppers also apply to rubber liners in screw-cap bottles and it should be noted that silicone liners are available relatively cheaply.

The toxicity of rubber stoppers is particularly marked when protein-free synthetic media are used and is much less of a problem when there is a high concentration of protein in the medium.

Rubber tubing

The same considerations apply to rubber tubing. In most cases where tubing is used the medium is exposed to it only very briefly (*e.g.* in dispensing apparatus) so that rarely is any trouble experienced from this source. However, silicone rubber tubing is now available at relatively low cost and is best used where there is any risk of toxicity. Silicone rubber has the additional advantage that it can be sterilised by dry heat so that it is dry when required for use.

Instruments, etc.

Needless to say, surgical instruments must be kept scrupulously clean and they should be wiped and dried immediately after use.

Special cleaning is unnecessary for instruments which have been in routine use, but new instruments, and particularly new detachable knife blades, usually have a protective coating, either of grease or of an anti-rust compound. They should, therefore, be wiped with a swab soaked in carbon tetrachloride and then a wet cloth before being dried and sterilised. If this is not done a very poor growth will be obtained in tissues handled with them.

CLEANING PROCEDURES
GLASSWARE

All glassware should be placed in water immediately after use. In this way, proteinaceous deposits are prevented from drying out and this greatly facilitates cleaning. The collected glassware is prepared by removing cotton-wool plugs, etc., and by rinsing with water. It is then subjected to whatever cleaning method is employed. A great many procedures have been recommended and these can be divided into four general groups:

     (1) Cleaning with alkalies.
     (2) Cleaning with detergents.
     (3) Cleaning with oxidising acids.
     (4) Cleaning by ultrasonics.

Alkalies

Many different alkalies have been used. The most popular are soft soap, sodium triphosphate, sodium carbonate and sodium metasilicate. There is little to choose between them but sodium metasilicate is probably the most commonly used. It is considered to be particularly suitable since it introduces no foreign ions to the glassware and, if a monolayer of metasilicate remains, it is deposited as glass on neutralisation.

The usual practice is to prepare the alkali solution in a concentration about 100 times stronger than ultimately required. The glassware is boiled in water to which this stock solution has been added. The glassware is subsequently treated with dilute acid and then rinsed with water, dried and sterilised.

A detailed description follows of the use of sodium metasilicate as a cleaning solution (Harding & Trebler, 1947). The solutions required are as follows:

1. Sodium metasilicate solution (× 100).

                 Sodium metasilicate   360 g.
                 Calgon or calgolac   40 g.

Dissolve in a gallon of water and filter. For use add this as 1 part in 100 to tap water.

2. Normal hydrochloric acid.

3. A supply of deionised water.

It is desirable to have several containers so that glassware can be transferred from one to another. An electrically heated domestic wash boiler for boiling up glassware, and large fish tanks or polythene baby baths for soaking glassware are very suitable. The procedure is as follows:

(1) The glassware is scrubbed in water to remove debris.

(2) It is transferred to a boiler containing metasilicate solution. This is brought to boiling point, maintained there for 20 minutes and allowed to cool.

(3) The glassware is removed from the boiler and rinsed thoroughly two or three times with ordinary tap water.

(4) It is then placed in a bath containing dilute hydrochloric acid (N/100). After soaking in this for some hours it is given a final rinse with tap water followed by one with deionised water and is allowed to drain. Subsequently, it is dried in an oven and prepared for sterilisation.

All glassware is treated in exactly the same way with the exception of the following items:

PIPETTES.—Pipettes are collected in jars containing water and before cleaning cotton-wool plugs are removed. They are rinsed thoroughly in a pipette-washer of the siphon type and transferred to a large jar containing metasilicate solution. After soaking in this for 24 hours they are rinsed quickly and transferred to another jar of N/100 hydrochloric acid. Finally, after another quick rinse in tap water, they are placed in 95 per cent. alcohol, drained, dried and sterilised.

COVER SLIPS.—Cover slips have to be handled separately because of their small size and fragility, but the same general principles of cleaning are applied. They are dropped one by one into a beaker of boiling metasilicate solution then removed, rinsed, treated with 95 per cent. alcohol and dried. Finally, they are polished between two boards covered with cloth, transferred to Petri dishes and sterilised by dry heat.

Detergents

Detergents are quite widely used in the cleaning of glassware. They have the advantage that no boiling is required. On the other hand, they are difficult to remove and very thorough rinsing indeed is required. Also, many detergents are toxic to cells so that care has to be taken in choosing one. A detergent which has been evolved specially for cleaning tissue culture glassware is that known as Microsolve and manufactured by Microbiological Associates of Bethesda, U.S.A. This detergent is practically non-toxic. Other suitable detergents include 7X, Haemosol and Stergene. The cleaning procedure is exactly the same as with alkalies except that boiling is unnecessary and the hydrochloric acid rinse can be omitted.

A detergent we have found entirely suitable for tissue culture glassware is R.B.S. 25. It is highly efficient and relatively easily rinsed off. A suitable procedure for all kinds of glassware is as follows.

All glassware is first rinsed and all labels and pencil marks removed. (The easiest way to remove wax-pencil and Magic Marker marks is to soak the glassware in warm detergent for some hours and then to wipe off the marks with a cloth carrying some abrasive cleaning powder.) It is then transferred to a tank containing R.B.S. 25 (a 1 in 200 solution is satisfactory). After soaking overnight the glassware is removed and rinsed thoroughly with tap water followed by a single rinse with deionised or distilled water. If the glassware has been rinsed in this way before putting it into detergent this can be used over and over again for some weeks before it becomes necessary to renew it.

Pipettes can be cleaned similarly. After soaking in detergent they are thoroughly rinsed with water in a pipette washer, drained and dried in a drying oven.

Coverslips can be handled very satisfactorily in a similar way. The main precaution is to prevent coverslips from piling up in such a way that the detergent does not reach the surface to be cleaned.

Oxidising acids

Many workers insist on the use of strongly oxidising acids for cleaning glassware, but it is rarely necessary to use them for biological materials. The acids most commonly used are hot sulphuric acid, chromic acid, and nitric acid. They have the disadvantage that a certain amount of danger is involved in their use. The technical staff have to be well-trained and reliable. On the other hand, they certainly remove all organic material and probably etch the glass less than alkalies. However, they are difficult to remove and in the case of chromic acid it has been shown that a monolayer tends to remain on the glass even after very prolonged

FIG. 15

Apparatus for coating the inside of vessels with a layer of chromic acid. On pressing the hand bellows a jet of chromic acid is forced into a vessel held over the filter funnel.

rinsing. Nevertheless, chromic acid is frequently used. It is best prepared as follows: 40 g. of potassium dichromate are placed in a 5-litre Pyrex beaker and a little water added to dissolve it. Concentrated sulphuric acid is then added to make up one litre. The solution should be yellow-brown in colour. The development of a green colour indicates that the chromic acid has become reduced and it is then useless and should be discarded. Chromic acid is highly corrosive and must be used with great care. It is very often adequate to cover the inside of the glassware with a thin layer of the acid and for this purpose the simple apparatus illustrated can be used. On pumping with the hand bellows a jet of chromic acid is forced up inside the funnel into the vessel to be cleaned.

The acid drains back into the flask when the hand bellows is released. It is usually adequate to leave glassware in contact with chromic acid at room temperature. Only very occasionally is it necessary or desirable to use chromic acid at a higher temperature and this must be done with the greatest care.

Nitric acid is frequently used for cleaning small objects, particularly cover glasses. The same remarks apply to nitric acid as to chromic acid. The cover glasses are usually dropped into nitric acid and then removed and rinsed very thoroughly indeed. Note that nitrate can occur physiologically and is probably a very much less toxic ion than chromate so that it is much less objectionable.

At the National Cancer Institute in the United States, large steam kettles filled with concentrated sulphuric acid are used for cleaning all the glassware. Very few other laboratories use this technique, however.

PARAFFINED OBJECTS.—Depression slides and other objects which have received coatings of paraffin must be handled separately since the melted paraffin will form a layer on the surface of the washing solution which will subsequently be deposited on all other glassware. Most of the paraffin is scraped off with a knife or razor blade and the slides are placed in a basin or beaker with a large pad of gauze in the bottom to prevent damage. They are then covered with water or metasilicate solution which is brought to the boil. The paraffin is floated off by flooding the vessel with water while the surface layer is poured off. The slides, thus partially cleaned, can then be carried through the normal procedure for glassware.

SILICONED OBJECTS.—Glassware which has been treated with silicone is best handled separately since the silicone may be disseminated to all the other material being cleaned simultaneously. Silicone can be removed by heating in 0·5 N NaOH or by treating the glassware with alcoholic KOH. In either case it is best to float off the scum in the same way as was described above for the cleaning of paraffined objects.

SINTERED GLASS FILTERS.—These are best treated with oxidising acids. They are cleaned with concentrated sulphuric acid to which a few crystals of sodium nitrate and sodium chlorate have been added. The mixture is allowed to percolate through and subsequently the filters are rinsed very thoroughly with a very large volume of distilled or deionised water before drying and sterilising.

Ultrasonics

Special apparatus has been developed for cleaning glassware utilising very high frequency sonic oscillations. These are very effective but have no advantage over other methods for most purposes. Their particular value is for fine scientific instruments having inaccessible holes and cavities.

Automatic washing machines

For large scale routine cleaning of glassware an automatic glassware washing machine is often a good investment. This kind of apparatus is particularly useful for handling large numbers of test-tubes and Petri dishes. It is less satisfactory where a wide assortment of vessels, including different types of bottles have to be handled.

BIBLIOGRAPHY

HARDING, H. G. & TREBLER, H. A. (1947). Detergents for dairy plants and methods of their evaluation. *Food Tech. Lond.* **1,** 478.

PARKER, R., MORGAN, J. & MORTON, HELEN (1951). Toxicity of rubber stoppers for tissue cultures. *Proc. Soc. exp. Biol. N.Y.* **76,** 444.

PETERSON, E. R., DEITCH, A. D. & MURRAY, M. R. (1959). Type of glass as a factor in maintenance of coverslip cultures. *Lab. Invest.* **8,** 1507.

RAPPAPORT, C. (1960). Studies on properties of surfaces required for growth of mammalian cells in synthetic medium. II. The monkey kidney cell. *Exp. Cell Res.* **20,** 479.

RAPPAPORT, C. & BISHOP, C. B. (1960). Improved method for treating glass to produce surfaces suitable for the growth of certain mammalian cells in synthetic medium. *Exp. Cell Res.* **20,** 580.

RAPPAPORT, C., POOLE, J. P. & RAPPAPORT, H. P. (1960). Studies on properties of surfaces required for growth of mammalian cells in synthetic medium. I. The HeLa cell. *Exp. Cell Res.* **20,** 465.

RIGHTSEL, W. A., SCHULTZ, P., MUETHING, D. & McLEAN, I. W., JR. (1956). Use of vinyl plastic containers in tissue cultures for virus assays. *J. Immunol.* **76,** 464.

CHAPTER VIII

PREVENTION OF CONTAMINATION

MEDIA for the cultivation of cells and tissues are highly nutritious not only for animal cells but also for bacteria and fungi. The majority of these micro-organisms have a much more rapid growth-rate than cells and frequently produce toxins which are lethal to them. Hence, the most important part of tissue culture technique comprises the avoidance of contamination and the growth of tissues in aseptic conditions.

Contamination of materials can be prevented in two ways:

(1) Sterilisation.—This term implies the removal of micro-organisms already present.

(2) Aseptic technique.—This term implies the prevention of contamination of materials already sterile.

In tissue culture work the sources of contamination are as follows:

(1) The apparatus.
(2) The culture medium.
(3) The tissue itself.
(4) The atmosphere in which the operation is performed.
(5) The operator.

Before commencing work apparatus is rendered bacteria-free by sterilisation. Likewise, the medium is usually sterilised before use but some components are prepared aseptically. The tissue is usually obtained in a sterile condition by the application of aseptic principles but occasionally it is necessary to sterilise it. Contamination from other sources is prevented almost entirely by the application of the aseptic technique.

I. STERILISATION PROCEDURES

While certain rules-of-thumb are used in sterilising, and will be outlined, it should be appreciated that there are few absolute rules. Exposure to given sterilising conditions will kill a definite proportion of contaminating organisms, say 99 per cent. In this case if 20 organisms were originally present the chances are that the material would be sterile. However, if there were 10,000 organisms originally clearly it would not be. Hence the cleaner the material initially the more successful is sterilisation likely to be. Some organisms are much more resistant than others and therefore conditions likely to kill the hardiest have to be used.

Sterilisation can be achieved by:

(1) Physical destruction of micro-organisms, *i.e.* by dry heat, moist heat and radiation.

(2) Chemical destruction of micro-organisms, *i.e.* by antiseptics and antibiotics.

(3) Physical removal of micro-organisms, *i.e.* by filtration, centrifugation and washing.

Most *apparatus* is sterilised by dry heat or by moist heat. In general, apparatus which is not damaged by high temperatures is sterilised by dry heat since this is the most convenient method. Where excessive heat can damage the material, moist heat is used. It is more efficient than dry heat because of the high latent heat of steam which rapidly transfers its energy to the materials being sterilised. Autoclaving (sterilising by steam under pressure) is frequently used for solutions, rubber ware, cloth and so on. Simple boiling is used for instruments and is sufficiently reliable for the vast majority of procedures. Sometimes it is impossible to use heat sterilisation, for example, in the case of certain plastics which soften at temperatures about 100° C. In these cases antiseptics are used but they should be of a relatively innocuous type and readily volatile. Seventy per cent. ethyl alcohol is the one most commonly used. Ultra-violet radiation can also be employed for some pieces of apparatus, *e.g.* plastic trays.

Solutions are nearly all amenable to filtration but some, such as plasma and embryo extract, cannot be satisfactorily filtered and these have to be prepared aseptically. A few simple solutions which are not damaged by heat can be autoclaved. Since proteins are coagulated at high temperatures, this procedure cannot be applied to serum, embryo extract, plasma, or other media of biological type. However, salt solutions can be autoclaved provided certain precautions are taken. These have been described in the section on synthetic media.

Solutions can also be sterilised by ultra-violet radiation. This requires special apparatus and has not been widely applied in tissue culture. Antibiotics are frequently added to growth media but they should not be added with the object of killing organisms present, rather should they be added as an auxiliary safety measure in case of accidental contamination.

For *laboratory benches and tables,* some sort of antiseptic is used. Again, alcohol is commonest and benches can be swabbed down with it to reduce the number of bacteria present. The most valuable measure in sterilising surfaces of this sort is the laying of dust which may otherwise be disturbed during working and settle on the apparatus. For this reason, many people prefer to wipe benches before use with a thin oil which forms a slightly adhesive layer and prevents dust being disturbed. It is a good practice to have laboratory floors treated with oil every few days for this reason. Bench tops can also be sterilised by ultra-violet radiation but in this case it should always be remembered that only those surfaces on which the radiation falls directly will be sterilised. All areas within shadows remain unaffected.

The sterilisation of *air* can be achieved in a number of ways. As a general rule, it is not necessary to sterilise air since contamination from this source can be prevented by ordinary aseptic technique. However, as discussed in the next chapter, if the project in hand necessitates a source of sterile air, this can be achieved most satisfactorily by a filtration system, conveniently combined with an air-conditioning unit. Air can also be sterilised with ultra-violet radiation by arranging an ultra-violet lamp so that all the air in the room is sterilised for a period before it is used.

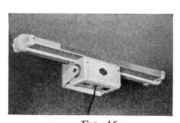

FIG. 16

Ultra-violet lamp of a type convenient for air sterilisation. (Hanovia.)

If this is done then precautions must be taken to ensure that the lamp is not switched on when the room is being used since eye injuries may result. Air can also be sterilised by precipitating dust and micro-organisms by means of an aerosol. In order to produce an aerosol, it used to be the practice in many laboratories to fill the aseptic room with a cloud of steam which was allowed to settle before commencing work. This creates conditions of humidity within the room and this is undesirable since it favours the growth of fungi and the survival of mites. Another type of aerosol that has been used is ethylene glycol which is vapourised by placing a beaker containing it on a hot-plate or in a hot bath.

Sterilisation by dry heat

Most apparatus and almost all glassware can be sterilised by this method. An oven is used and it is desirable, if possible, to use one with a forced air circulation. However, any oven will suffice and a domestic kitchen oven is quite suitable. It is important to raise all the contents of the oven to a sterilising temperature for a suitable period of time and the material to be sterilised should be arranged in such a way that air can circulate freely.

The disadvantage of this type of sterilisation is that, dry air being a poor conductor of heat, relatively cool pockets may remain within the contents of the oven. Consequently, a rather high temperature for a rather long time is recommended and 90 minutes at 160° C. is usually employed. It is sometimes useful to mark the glassware with a temperature-sensitive paint to show that this temperature has, in fact, been reached. Several kinds of such paints are available (*e.g.* Thermocolor by Griffin & George).

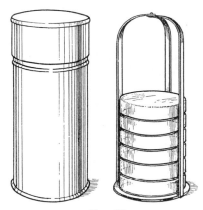

Fig. 17

A useful type of can for sterilisation of Petri dishes.

Fig. 18

Glass pipette holders of this type are particularly useful for Pasteur pipettes and can be made to order.

Materials put into the oven are conveniently sterilised in tin containers, *e.g.* biscuit tins. However, before using tins for sterilising glassware they should be placed open in the oven and heated to sterilisation temperature for a period of two or three hours. This drives off various volatile materials which would otherwise be transferred to the glassware. It should be noted that some tins are lacquered inside and these are not suitable since the lacquer is burned or volatilised and the products are deposited on the glassware.

Glass articles can be wrapped in aluminium foil or in paper for sterilisation. Pure kraft paper should be used and not the artificial variety. If it is overheated kraft paper becomes brittle and tends to release volatile tars which are transferred to the glass. Some care is therefore necessary to avoid this. A special paper (Patapar) is available in the United States and is superior to kraft paper for heat sterilisation.

Sterilisation by moist heat

Sterilisation by moist heat is usually carried out in the autoclave. A domestic pressure cooker is sometimes more convenient for sterilising small amounts. It operates on exactly the same principle as the autoclave. The old vertical autoclave is not so satisfactory as the modern horizontal type which should be used, if possible. Sterilisation can be carried out in an autoclave at 5, 10 or 15 lb. pressure and the recommended procedure is to autoclave at 15 lb. pressure for 20 minutes. Solutions should be sterilised for a rather shorter time, about 15 minutes as a rule. In older types of autoclaves it is necessary to control sterilisation by time and pressure, but it is better to control it by temperature and in most modern autoclaves this can be done by reading the thermometer situated in the steam outlet line. A temperature of 115° C. should be maintained for about 15 minutes. Almost all known organisms are destroyed within about one minute in such conditions but it is necessary to maintain them for 15 to 20 minutes because air pockets may exist within the sterilisation packages or steam may be unable to reach various parts for other reasons. In case inadequate steam penetration occurs, it is advisable to use sterilisation controls of some sort. These are readily available from any surgical supplier. They are placed in the package and change of colour indicates adequate sterilisation. In many modern autoclaves the chamber can be evacuated after sterilisation to facilitate drying of materials. If solutions are being sterilised this stage must, of course, be omitted as otherwise the solutions will boil off.

In operating the autoclave, it is essential to ensure that all air is displaced by steam before the pressure is allowed to rise. In modern autoclaves this occurs naturally because of the design. In older autoclaves it is essential, after closing the lid, to allow steam to escape for a considerable time. If it is allowed to escape under water it is possible to tell when most of the air has been removed, since the steam produced is immediately dissolved and this gives rise to a loud, rattling noise. When this point has been reached the autoclave is closed and the pressure allowed to rise to 15 lb. After 20 minutes the gas or electricity is shut off and the pressure and temperature allowed to fall over another 20 minutes to half an hour. By thus gently lowering the pressure, solutions are prevented from boiling. In using the autoclave, the same considerations have to be kept in mind as in sterilising by dry heat. In particular, the packages should be so arranged that steam will gain access to all parts.

Materials may be prepared for sterilisation in the autoclave by wrapping either in gauze or in paper. For this purpose, again kraft paper can be used, but much better is Patapar, which has already been mentioned in connection with sterilisation by dry heat. This material is tough and does not release any noxious materials. In the case of large glass vessels, if the entire vessel is not enclosed in this way, all orifices should be closed by means of cotton-wool plugs or by paper or aluminium foil coverings.

Solutions should be sterilised in bottles or flasks, stoppered with plugs of cotton-wool wrapped in gauze. Alternatively, they can be fitted with rubber stoppers or screw-caps but these should be left loose during autoclaving and tightened afterwards. Cotton-wool plugs are preferable since, as the solution cools, air is sucked into the vessels and this is filtered by the cotton. With the other method there is always a risk, although quite a small one, of sucking organisms into the medium. Even with a very efficient autoclave it takes some time to heat large volumes of liquid and it is best not to dispense volumes larger than 500 ml. to each container unless the conditions for sterilisation of larger volumes have been determined empirically.

Moist heat in the form of boiling water can also be used for sterilisation. Very few organisms will survive boiling water for more than a few seconds and therefore this technique is very convenient for rapid sterilisation of syringes and instruments. They should be protected from bumping by wrapping them in gauze.

Radiations

Radiations can also be used for sterilisation. Ultra-violet light has been used, for instance, in the sterilisation of plastic trays used for metabolic inhibition tests. It has to be used with care, however, since shadowed areas are unaffected. Gamma rays are now being used more extensively in the sterilisation of prepacked materials. Doses of the order of 2·5 M rad. are required and a cobalt 60 source is usually employed. However, it should be remembered that these radiations are capable of producing chemical changes in the substances irradiated. At the present moment they have rather limited uses and the only general application of radiations is in the ultra-violet sterilisation of cubicles and rooms, particularly where pathogens such as viruses are handled.

Antiseptics

As has already been mentioned above, certain antiseptics are quite commonly used for swabbing down laboratory benches and shelves and for this purpose 70 per cent. alcohol is the safest since not only is it volatile but it is relatively non-toxic, at least in low concentrations. Ether can also be used as an antiseptic in this way, but it is not recommended since it is rather volatile and inflammable. The only other chemical substance commonly used for sterilisation is chloroform which is frequently added to solutions to preserve them, e.g. stock solutions of balanced salt solution. The chloroform is driven off during autoclaving.

Plastic dishes can also be sterilised with alcohol. The dishes are washed with 95 per cent. alcohol, then placed in paper bags while wet and left in an incubator to dry, when they are ready for use.

Plastics and other heat-labile materials can be sterilised in ethylene oxide vapour; 52 g. per litre is used in an atmosphere of 20 per cent. humidity or higher at a temperature of 30-35° C. In these conditions most objects are effectively sterilised in four to six hours.

Antibiotics

Very many antibiotics have been used in tissue culture work and most of the available data is summarised in Tables XIX and XX. It is bad practice to become completely dependent on antibiotics for three reasons. In the first place there is a danger of concealing sloppy techniques. Secondly, when contaminations arise the organisms are already resistant. Thirdly, cryptic contaminations and development of L forms may be fostered. At the same time, nothing is to be gained by trying to conduct routine tissue culture without them. It should be observed, however, that many antibiotics are quite toxic to cells and in some cases the levels of toxicity approach the effective levels.

By far the most useful general antibiotic is penicillin. It is usually added as sodium penicillin G to media to give a final concentration of 20 to 50 units per ml. At these concentrations it is completely harmless to all cell types and is inhibitory to the vast majority of bacteria. As a routine the author recommends that only penicillin should be used in media but if contamination by penicillin-resistant organisms is to be expected then streptomycin may also be used and should be added to give a final concentration of 50 µg. per ml. Fungal infections may be inhibited by the use of Mycostatin (nystatin). This fungistatic agent should be added to give a final concentration of 20 µg. per ml. It should be noted that mycostatin is unstable and has usually deteriorated almost completely after 2-3 days in tissue culture medium at 37° C. Amphotericin B (Fungizone) is also effective against many fungi at a concentration of 2·5 µg./ml. In the author's opinion it is better to retain these latter antibiotics for use in an emergency if a contamination should arise in a valuable strain, since sometimes such contaminations can be eliminated by the use of high concentrations of antibiotics.

For the elimination of contamination by mycoplasma (PPLO) kanamycin (Kannasyn) is effective at concentrations of 100-200 µg./ml. Overnight treatment with higher concentrations (600 µg./ml.) will sometimes eradicate infection.

In addition to their routine use in media, antibiotics can be used at much higher concentrations to sterilise contaminated tissues prior to explantation (see page 132).

Filtration

Many different kinds of filters are available. They can be divided into four main groups:

       (1) Asbestos pads.

       (2) Kieselguhr and porcelain filters.

       (3) Sintered glass filters (fritted glass filters).

       (4) Millipore filters.

9

TABLE XIX

EFFECT OF ANTIBIOTICS ON TISSUE CULTURES

Antibiotic	Tissue	Concentration initiating depression µg/ml.	Concentration for complete inhibition µg/ml.	Ref.
Aureomycin	chick heart	1	1,000	6
	chick heart	0·1	—	1
	chick heart, aorta			
	frontal bone	500	>4,000	5
	human skin	200	—	2
	mouse heart	80		9
	chick heart	500	—	7
	human skin	20	110	8
	L strain	500	4,000	Own obs.
Aureomycin with Na glycinate	human skin	60	900	8
Actidione	mouse heart	8 - 10	16 - 20	9
Bacitracin	human skin	900	10,000	8
	chick skin	800	5,000	10
Chloramphenicol	chick heart	10	1,000	6
	chick heart	100	1,000	5
	chick heart	480	>1,200	9
	chick spleen	165	1665	10
	chick skin	135	555	10
	human skin	100	900	8
Dihydrostreptomycin sulphate	chick heart	1,000	—	7
Endomycin	human skin	60	600	8
Erythromycin	chick skin	85	345	10
	chick spleen	30	520	10
Neomycin	human skin	>1,000	10,000	2
	human skin	800	1,600	8
Patulin	chick heart	(1/10,000)	(1/5,000)	7
	mouse leucocytes	—	(1/5,000)	7
Penicillin	human skin	1,000	10,000	8

TABLE XIX (*contd.*)

EFFECT OF ANTIBIOTICS ON TISSUE CULTURES

Antibiotic	Tissue	Concentration initiating depression µg/ml.	Concentration for complete inhibition µg/ml.	Ref.
Penicillin G	human skin	> 600	6,000	2
	L strain	2,500	25,000	Own obs.
Polymyxin	human skin	> 200	1,000	2
Polymyxin E	human skin	>2,000	10,000	2
Polymyxin B	human skin	90	1,200	8
	chick heart	100	2,500	9
Sodium PAS	chick heart	46	—	7
Sodium INAH methansulphonate	chick heart	40	400	7
Streptomycin	chick heart, aorta	250	25,000	4
	frontal bone			
	chick heart	1,000	100,000	3
	human skin	>1,000	10,000	2
	human skin	110	1,800	8
	chick heart	100	10,000	7
	chick heart	60	90,000	9
	L strain	1,000	25,000	Own obs.
Terramycin	human skin	> 20	1,000	2
	chick heart	30	3,000	9
	human skin	90	1,000	8
	chick heart	50	1,000	7
	chick skin	25	100	10
Viomycin	chick heart	150	30,000	9

1. ANTIKAJIAN, G., WRIGHT, LT., PLUMMER, J. I. & WEINTRAUB, S. 1951.
2. CRUIKSHANK, C. N. D. & LOWBURY, E. J. L. (1952).
3. IKEGAKI, K. (1951).
4. KEILOVA, H. (1948).
5. KEILOVA-R. Quoted by Metzger *et al.*
6. LEPINE, P., BARSKI, G. & MAURIN, J. (1950).
7. OISHI, Y. (1954). *Japan. J. exptl. Med.* **24**, 169.
8. HU, F., LIVINGOOD, C. S., JOHNSON, P. & POMERAT, C. M. J. (1953).
9. METZGER, J. F., FUSILLO, M. H., CORNMAN, I. & KUHNS, D. M. (1954).
10. POMERAT, C. M. & LEAKE, C. D. (1954).

TABLE XX

TOXICITY OF ANTIBIOTICS FOR SUSPENSION CULTURES OF L CELLS (NCTC929) AND EHRLICH ASCITES CELLS (SQUIBB No. 2)

Results for L cells quoted in full. Results for Ehrlich cells quoted in parentheses where different. (From Perlman & Brindle.)

Antibiotic	Spectrum	Cytotoxic concn.*	Recommended concn.†
Potassium benzyl-penicillin	Gram-positive bacteria	10,000	100
Streptomycin sulphate	Gram-negative bacteria	>20,000 (15,000)	100
Dihydrostreptomycin sulphate	Gram-negative bacteria	>30,000	100
Neomycin sulphate	Gram-positive and gram-negative	3,000	50
Kanamycin sulphate	Gram-positive and gram-negative	10,000	100
Paromomycin sulphate	Gram-positive and gram-negative bacteria	5,000	100
Viomycin sulphate	Gram-positive and gram-negative bacteria	3,000	50
Polymyxin B sulphate	Gram-negative bacteria	>3,000	50
Chloramphenicol	Gram-positive and gram-negative bacteria	30 (40)	5
Tetracycline hydro-chloride	Gram-positive and gram-negative bacteria and PPLO	35 (60)	10
7-Chlortetracycline	Gram-positive and gram-negative bacteria and PPLO	80 (60)	10
6-Demethyl-7-chlor-tetracycline hydrochloride	Gram-positive and gram-negative bacteria and PPLO	15 (20)	5
5-Hydroxytetracycline hydrochloride	Gram-positive and gram-negative bacteria and PPLO	25	5
Nystatin	Fungi and yeasts	600	50
Amphotericin B deoxycholate	Fungi and yeasts, and PPLO	30	2·5

* Concentration causing 50 per cent reduction in cell multiplication in suspension cultures growing in serum-containing media. Expressed as μg/ml. except for potassium benzylpenicillin and nystatin, which are given in units per ml.
† Concentrations recommended for use in serum-containing media.

Asbestos pads of the Seitz type have the great merit that they effectively remove all micro-organisms but permit a fairly high rate of filtration. The disadvantage is that in some cases at least they release toxic substances which are subsequently inhibitory to growing cells. Most filters, especially washed filters, seem to be satisfactory, but some kinds are not suitable for filtering media for tissue culture, unless very large quantities are to be treated, in which case it becomes worthwhile to subject the filter to very thorough washing. Many types of apparatus are available.

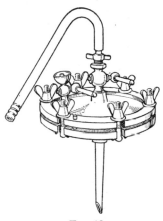

Kieselguhr and porcelain filters are now much less used than formerly. In this group the Selas filter is particularly useful. It can be treated in exactly the same way as the Berkefeld filter but is much more uniform and has a higher

FIG. 19

Apparatus for filtration with asbestos pads by pressure or vacuum. (Made by A. Gallenkamp & Co., Ltd.)

rate of filtration. In both cases a grade should be used which is guaranteed to remove all micro-organisms (Selas 03, Berkefeld W.). New filters should be prepared by scrubbing lightly with a soft brush and then flushing thoroughly in both directions with several litres of ordinary tap water followed by flushing with 200 - 300 ml. of deionised water. They can be sterilised by autoclaving. After use they should be thoroughly washed again in both directions with a very large amount of water. If any protein remains this can be removed by a crude trypsin or pancreatin solution.

When filters become really dirty, they can be cleaned by incinerating in a muffle furnace. The temperature should be raised slowly to 650° C. over a period of three or four hours and allowed to drop back to normal overnight. It is essential that the filters should be thoroughly dry before being put in the muffle furnace, otherwise they will be destroyed. All new filters and all filters which have been cleaned by this technique of incineration should be tested. This is done by submerging each filter in water and introducing air under pressure into it. At the pressure used for filtration no air should normally escape. At a higher pressure a uniform bubbling of air should arise from all over the filter. The appearance of large bubbles from any area indicates defects. For some filters, *e.g.* the Selas filter, a bubbling pressure is given by the manufacturers.

FIG. 20
Apparatus for pressure filtration with filter candles.
(Gallenkamp.)

Sintered glass filters are useful for small quantities of material. They have the disadvantage of filtering slowly. Again bacteriological grades should be used. A No. 5 filter supported on a No. 3 filter is most suitable and this should be referred to as a 3/5 filter. The United States equivalent in fritted glass filters is the UF grade.

Millipore filters are being increasingly used for a wide range of purposes. Their rather high cost is offset by their outstanding advantages, namely, they give a very high filtration rate and are completely non-toxic. The filters are disposable. For filtering large amounts of material many special filter holders are made. A suitable one should hold the disc under strong pressure so that there is no leakage round the side of the disc. For many routine laboratory purposes the Stainless Pressure Filter Holder made by the Millipore Corporation is very suitable. For filtering very small amounts of material millipore discs are effective when used with the Swinney adaptor which fits on to a Luer-lok syringe. For sterilisation of solutions for tissue culture purposes the HA (0.45μ) grade of millipore filter should be used.

In filtering biological materials, it is desirable to use pressure rather than suction. When suction is employed, it causes carbon dioxide to be evolved from the solutions and this gives rise to a radical change in pH. Also protein solutions froth very badly when a vacuum is applied. Filtration by pressure avoids both difficulties.

The other physical means of removing bacteria, centrifugation and washing, are relatively inefficient but are not to be despised on occasions. Heavily contaminated fluids, such as bacterial digests, can be clarified by centrifugation before filtering. Thorough washing of materials with distilled water or sterile BSS will remove micro-organisms very effectively unless they are strongly absorbed to or embedded in the material. Contaminated cultures can sometimes be cleared in this way and cultures should always be washed before trying to eliminate contamination by adding antibiotics to the medium.

Storage of sterile materials

It is convenient to sterilise materials in large batches and then to store them until they are required. Two difficulties may arise, contamination during storage and deterioration due to absorption of toxic substances from the atmosphere.

For these reasons *solutions* are best kept in tightly sealed containers rather than containers stoppered with cotton-wool since otherwise they may readily absorb substances such as formalin or ammonia. The most convenient and cheapest containers for this purpose are medical prescription bottles (" medical flats ") which can be obtained in a great variety of sizes, with silicone liners if desired, and already sterilised (although it may not always be desirable to rely on this). Alkaline solutions should never be stored for a long time in glass, however, since the glass is slowly dissolved and heavy metal ions appear in solution.

Clean sterile *glassware* is subject to the same two dangers. It is not uncommon for laboratories to be lightly infested with mites carried by laboratory animals and these can gain access to stored glassware through paper wrappings and cotton-wool plugs. This is sometimes the cause of unexplained heavy mixed contaminations. Also, particularly in chemical laboratories, stored glassware gradually acquires a deposit of chemicals on the surface with the result that cells will no longer grow in them. Thus it is advisable not to store glassware for more than a week or two and it should be carefully protected from possible contamination by airtight wrapping. The best system to employ is sterilisation of glassware and apparatus in envelopes of nylon film (such as " Portex " autoclave film). This film is supplied in the form of a tube from $\frac{1}{4}$ in. to 20 in. wide and in rolls of suitable lengths. The material to be sterilised is placed in a section of this and the ends are folded over and sealed with a special autoclave adhesive tape to form a closed bag. The packages are then sterilised by autoclaving in the usual manner. The nylon film is permeable to steam but not to bacteria so that after removal from the autoclave the contents remain sterile until required. These materials are obtainable from Portland Plastics Ltd., Bassett House, Hythe, Kent. For sealing packages for autoclaving Scotch hospital autoclave tape No. 222 (Minnesota Mining and Mfg. Co. Ltd.) is particularly useful since it is printed with a heat sensitive ink which gives positive evidence that sterilisation has been adequate.

Chronic contamination (especially PPLO and L forms)

If a rapidly-growing bacterium infects a culture its presence is soon noticed and the culture is usually lost. However, sometimes cultures can be infected with organisms which multiply at about the same rate as the cultured cells. Certain protozoa, such as amoebae have been found contaminating freshly isolated tissues. They are easily recognised on microscopic examination but otherwise may persist for some time, growing slowly along with the cell population. Some slow-growing yeasts may also contaminate a culture for quite a long time before they eventually outgrow the cells and make their presence manifest. The most insidious chronic contaminants are, however, those organisms which live intracellularly without killing the host cells, namely viruses and organisms of the pleuropneumonia group, usually designated pleuropneumonia-like organisms (PPLO) or mycoplasma.

Numerous instances of chronic viral contamination have been described and these have included vaccinia, adenoviruses and foamy disease virus. Many of these turn up in primary cultures and it seems certain that they were present as chronic contaminants in the tissue from which the culture was derived. Some may gain entry later and the fact that human and primate cell lines tend to do better when cultured in human serum may be due to the presence of antibodies against human viruses. In general if cells become chronically infected with viruses there is little to be done about it. Occasionally it may be possible, by cloning, to re-establish an uninfected line but usually it is better to reject the infected cells.

The most serious problem of chronic contamination concerns the organisms of the pleuropneumonia group and the L forms of other organisms. These resemble each other so closely in their general behaviour that there is disagreement about the distinctions between them. They tend to be considered together as pleuropneumonia-like organisms (PPLO). These organisms are present in many animal tissues and give rise to diseases in cows, fowls and man, among other animals. It was found some years ago that animal cell lines were frequently contaminated with them and a number of surveys in 1959-61 showed that from 50-60 per cent. of all cell lines from American sources were infected. PPLO grow intracellularly; they may not give rise to any obvious manifestations or they may simply cause minimal abnormalities, such as a tendency for cells to round up and appear granular. They can, as a rule, be detected only by trying to isolate them in special culture media. They are difficult to culture and to identify.

Some organisms of this kind are almost certainly L forms of other micro-organisms. Some antibiotics are particularly prone to induce the transformation to L forms and penicillin is particularly effective. It is, therefore, suspected that many examples of PPLO contamination are actually due to L forms. In several instances these were shown to be derived from diphtheroid organisms, which reappeared in the culture medium when antibiotics were withdrawn.

PPLO clearly raise many problems if they are present in cells used for experimental purposes. For example, in biochemical experiments in which the incorporation of radio-isotopes is measured the results may be entirely meaningless if PPLO are present. In some virus studies too unexpected results have been explained by the presence of PPLO, which actively break down arginine and hence tend to put the cells into a state of arginine depletion in an otherwise adequate medium. Consequently it is very important in all cell culture work first, to determine whether cells used are free of PPLO; second, if PPLO are present to try to eradicate them; third, if such an attempt has been made to check that it has been successful; fourth, to attempt to culture cells in such conditions that PPLO will not arise or will be readily recognised.

The first and third requirements can be met by checking cells for the presence of PPLO by continuous sterility testing as described below. As will also be described below PPLO can often be eradicated, but this must never be taken on trust and the cells must be shown to be sterile. Finally, by culturing cells in the absence of all antibiotics, either continuously or for two or three passages in every five or six the chances of establishment of L forms can be very greatly reduced.

Sterility testing

Routine sterility testing should be used for all media since filters and filtration techniques sometimes fail. It usually suffices to inoculate some medium into glucose and thioglycollate broth and to incubate at both 20° and 37° C. The larger the sample tested the more likely is a minor failure to be detected. A minimum of 1 per cent. of the total production should be monitored and, for exacting work, it is probably best to use 10 per cent. for testing. Since culture medium is itself excellent for growing most micro-organisms a routine sterility test can be carried out by incubating every tenth aliquot during the preparation of large batches of medium. This procedure is the most practical one in very large scale work where it is important to determine when a filter breaks down. All medium filtered after that point and for an arbitrary volume before it is then rejected.

In cell culture work special methods have to be used to test for PPLO periodically. This is done by spreading 0·1 ml. of infected material on special PPLO agar (Difco) plates. The plates are incubated in a CO_2 incubator at 37° C. for about a week and then examined. PPLO colonies are very minute and have to be looked for with a magnifying lens or a dissecting microscope. The colonies are usually less than half a millimetre in diameter and present a typical 'fried-egg' appearance. Sometimes other objects (even cell colonies) can be mistaken for them and therefore the colonies should be removed from the agar, crushed on a slide and examined at high magnification, either by phase contrast or after staining, to determine that they are mycoplasma. In a very thick culture contaminated with PPLO there will probably be sufficient organisms free in the medium to allow the test to be made directly with 0·1 ml. medium. However, it is often more reliable to inoculate some cells first into freshly prepared Difco PPLO broth and incubate for four to eight days before subculturing on to PPLO agar and proceeding as already described.

Elimination of contamination

Obviously it is undesirable to have cell lines which are contaminated in the first place and, if possible, it is better not to make any attempt to rescue contaminated lines. Sometimes, however, it becomes essential to attempt to remove contamination from a valuable strain. This can occasionally be achieved, usually by a combination of washing and treatment with antibiotics. For bacteria which grow free in the medium this treatment is sometimes effective. The medium should be removed from the cells which should then be washed repeatedly with BSS containing high concentrations of antibiotics to which the organism is known to be sensitive (this demands bacteriological study). They are then suspended by trypsinisation or any other method and inoculated into fresh medium containing antibiotics at a low inoculum density. When the cell line has apparently recovered from the contamination antibiotics should be removed and the cells maintained without them for several subcultures before they can be considered safe to use.

Yeast contaminations can be treated similarly, using Mycostatin or Fungizone but this treatment is rarely fully satisfactory.

It is in relation to contamination with PPLO that serious attempts must sometimes be made to clear the cultures of infection. The most successful results have been obtained with kanamycin (Kannasyn) added to the cultures of a concentration of 100 μg. per ml. for a period of three weeks at a time. The cells should be sub-cultured in low inocula and should be transferred to fresh vessels frequently during treatment. Some kanamycin-resistant strains of PPLO have been reported and therefore this treatment cannot be relied upon entirely. It must be obvious that routine incorporation of kanamycin at low concentrations in the culture medium invites the development of resistant organisms. It should therefore be avoided. Overnight treatment with kanamycin at a concentration of 600 μg. per ml. has also been reported to clear contaminated cultures. Other antibiotics are ineffective on the whole and some, such as penicillin, actually promote the development of L forms.

Another technique for clearing contaminated cultures employs hyperthermia. Hayflick found that PPLO could be eliminated from some cultures by treating them for some hours at 41° C., a treatment which did not permanently harm the cells. This method is apparently not always successful and the precaution must be taken, as indeed after any treatment, to check by culturing that the cells have actually been cleared.

BIBLIOGRAPHY

ANTIKAJIAN. G., WRIGHT, L. T., PLUMMER, J. I. & WEINTRAUB, S. (1951). The effect of triethylene melamine, aureomycin and some 4-amino derivatives of folic acid on tissues *in vitro*. *J. nat. Cancer Inst.* **12**, 269.

BARILE, M. F. & SCHIMKE, R. T. (1963). A rapid chemical method for detecting PPLO contamination of tissue cell cultures. *Proc. Soc. exp. Biol. Med.* **114,** 676.

BARILE, M. F., MALIZIA, W. F. & RIGGS, D. (1961). Immunofluorescence of PPLO in tissue cultures. *Bact. Proc.* **44,** 83.

BARILE, M. F., YAGUCHI, R. & EVELAND, W. C. (1958). A simplified medium for the cultivation of pleuropneumonia-like organisms and the L forms of bacteria. *Amer. J. clin. Path.* **30,** 171.

CARSKI, T. R. & SHEPARD, C. C. (1961). Pleuropneumonia-like (mycoplasma) infections of tissue culture. *J. Bact.* **81,** 626.

COLLIER, L. H. (1957). Contamination of stock lines of human carcinoma cells by pleuropneumonialike organisms. *Nature (Lond.)* **180,** 757.

CORIELL, L. L. (1962). Detection and elimination of contaminating organisms. *Nat. Cancer Inst. Monograph No. 7,* 33.

CORIELL, L., FABRIZIO, D. & WILSON, S. R. (1960). Comparison of PPLO strains from tissue culture by complement fixation. *Ann. N.Y. Acad. Sci.* **79,** 574.

CORIELL, L., TALL, M. & GASKILL, H. (1958). Common antigens in tissue culture cell lines. *Science* **128,** 198.

CRUIKSHANK, C. N. D. & LOWBURY, E. J. L. (1952). Effect of antibiotics on tissue cultures of human skin. *Brit. med. J.* **2,** 1070.

DEMIS, D. J., DAVIS, M. & CAMPBELL, J. (1960). The effects of griseofulvin on epithelial cells in tissue culture. *J. invest. Derm.* **34,** 99.

FOGH, J. & HACKER, C. (1960). Elimination of pleuropneumonia-like organisms from cell cultures. *Exp. Cell Res.* **21,** 242.

HAYFLICK, L. (1960). Decontaminating tissue culture infected with pleuropneumonialike organisms. *Nature (Lond.)* **185,** 783.

HOWARD, D. H. (1960). Effect of Mycostatin and Fungizone on the growth of Histoplasma capsulatum in tissue culture. *J. Bact.* **79,** 442.

HOYT, A., CHANEY, A. L. & CAVELL, K. (1938). Studies on steam sterilization and the effects of air in the autoclave. *J. Bact.* **36,** 639.

HU, F., LIVINGOOD, C. S., JOHNSON, P. & POMERAT, C. M. J. (1953). Tissue culture studies on human skin. IV. The comparative toxic effects of antibiotics on tissue culture explants of human skin and embryonic chick spleen. *J. invest. Derm.* **20,** 357.

IKEGAKI, K. (1951). Effects of streptomycin on the growth of normal tissue cells *in vitro*. *Antibiotics* **4,** 311.

KEILOVA, H. (1948). The effect of streptomycin on tissue cultures. *Experientia,* **4,** 483.

KENNY, G. E., POLLOCK, M. E. & SYVERTON, J. T. (1960). Time and concentration of kanamycin for elimination of PPLO from mammalian cell cultures. *Bact. Proc.* p. 121.

LEPINE, P., BARSKI, G. & MAURIN, J. (1950). Action of chloromycetin and of aureomycin on normal tissue cultures. *Proc. Soc. exp. Biol. N.Y.* **73,** 252.

McCULLOCH, E. C. (1945). *Disinfection and Sterilization,* 2nd ed. Philadelphia: Lea & Febiger.

MADOFF, S. (1960). Isolation and identification of PPLO. *Ann. N.Y. Acad. Sci.* **79,** 574.

MALIZIA, W. F., BARILE, M. F. & RIGGS, D. (1961). Immunofluorescence of pleuropneumonialike organisms isolated from tissue cell cultures. *Nature (Lond.)* **191,** 190.

METZGER, J. F., FUSILLO, M. H., CORNMAN, I. & KUHNS, D. M. (1954). Antibiotics in tissue culture. *Exp. Cell. Res.* **6,** 337.

MORTON, H. E. (1938). Bacterial filters and filtration technics. *Amer. J. clin. Path. Tech. Suppl.* **2**, 185.

OISHI, Y. (1954). 1. The effects of antibiotics and chemotherapeutic agents on the growth of fibroblasts from chick embryo heart in the simplified replicate tissue culture. *Jap. J. exp. Med.* **24**, 169.

OISHI, Y. (1956). II. Effects of antibiotics and chemotherapeutics on the growth of fibroblasts from chick embryo heart in the simplified replicate tissue culture. *Jap. J. exp. Med.* **26**, 159.

PERLMAN, D. & BRINDLE, S. A. (1963). Antibiotic control of contamination in tissue cultures. In *Antimicrobial Agents and Chemotherapy*—1963, p. 458.

PERLMAN, D., GIUFFRE, N. A. & BRINDLE, S. A. (1961). Use of Fungizone in control of fungi and yeasts in tissue culture. *Proc. Soc. exp. Biol. (N.Y.)* **106**, 880.

PERLMAN, D., GIUFFRE, N. A., JACKSON, P. W. & GIARDINELLO, F. E. (1959). Effects of antibiotics on multiplication of L cells in suspension culture. *Proc. Soc. exp. Biol. (N.Y.)* **106**, 880.

POLLOCK, M. E., KENNY, G. E. & SYVERTON, J. T. (1960). Isolation and elimination of pleuropneumonia-like organisms from mammalian cell cultures. *Proc. Soc. Exp. Biol. (N.Y.)* **105**, 10.

POLLOCK, M. E., TREADWELL, P. E. & KENNY, G. E. (1963). Mammalian cell cultures contaminated with pleuropneumonia-like organisms. II. Effect of PPLO on cell morphology in established monolayer cultures. *Exp. Cell Res.* **31**, 321.

POMERAT, C. M. & LEAKE, C. D. (1954). Short term cultures for drug assays : general considerations. *Ann. N.Y. Acad. Sci.* **58**, 1110.

ROBINSON, L. G., WICHELHAUSEN, R. H. & ROIZMAN, B. (1956). Contamination of human cell cultures by pleuropneumonialike organisms. *Science* **124**, 1147.

ROTHBLAT, G. (1960). PPLO contamination in tissue cultures. *Ann. N.Y. Acad. Sci.* **79**, 340.

ROTHBLAT, G. H. & MORTON, H. E. (1959). Detection and possible source of contaminating pleuropneumonialike organisms (PPLO) in cultures of tissue cells. *Proc. Soc. Exp. Biol. (N.Y.)* **100**, 87.

SCHIMKE, R. T. & BARILE, M. F. (1963). Arginine breakdown in mammalian cell culture contaminated with pleuropneumonia-like organisms (PPLO). *Exp. Cell Res.* **30**, 593.

SHEPARD, M. C. (1958). Growth and development of T-strain pleuropneumonialike organisms in human epidermoid carcinoma cells (HeLa). *J. Bact.* **75**, 351.

WIGMORE, J. O. & HENDERSON, W. M. (1955). Control of yeast contamination by " Mycostatin " in cultures of foot and mouth disease. *Nature (Lond.)* **176**, 516.

CHAPTER IX

PREVENTION OF CONTAMINATION

II. ASEPTIC TECHNIQUE

THE discussion so far has dealt entirely with the preliminary preparation of materials and apparatus in such a way that bacteria and toxic chemical substances are excluded. The following section will deal with the handling of the materials in such a manner that no contamination is introduced during experimental manipulations.

Contamination from tissue

First of all, it is essential to ensure that no bacteria are introduced with the tissue. Contamination from tissue may be avoided by collecting it aseptically or sterilising it after removal. Most internal tissues of animals are already sterile except those that have direct communication with the exterior, *e.g.* the respiratory passages and the alimentary tract. Hence, with the majority it is only necessary to remove them from the animal in such a way that contamination is avoided. This technique is particularly applicable to embryonic material. The contents of a fertile egg are normally sterile and if precautions are taken to remove the embryo without contamination, then one starts the experiment with clean material. In the same way, the contents of the uterus of a mammal are normally sterile and if they are removed by careful operating technique no problem of contamination should be encountered.

In the case of adult tissues, bacteria are occasionally found even when they are removed from internal organs. This does not happen very frequently and it is rarely necessary to take special precautions. If the specimens are particularly valuable, however, or if there is a risk that they may have been contaminated during removal, as is often the case with surgical specimens before they have reached the tissue culture laboratory, then they must be sterilised. This can be done effectively by means of antibiotics, the tissue being washed in a solution of very high concentration before being grown in a medium containing the usual concentrations. A useful antibiotic mixture is balanced salt solution containing 1,000 units of penicillin per ml. and 0·5 mg. of streptomycin per ml. Neomycin (0·5 mg. per ml.) is also highly effective. If the tissues are washed in this solution before they are cut up for explantation, very few organisms will survive.

The elimination of micro-organisms is a particularly big problem in growing tissues from cold-blooded organisms and invertebrates. However, the development of antibiotics has greatly facilitated this and a procedure such as that described for surgical specimens is suitable. Other means of sterilisation have also been used, *e.g.* 1 in 1,000 merthiolate, ultra-violet light and 10 per cent. hexylresorcinol.

Contamination from the air

If no mistakes in technique have been made in preparation of the tissue, media and apparatus, then subsequent contamination can only arise from the air in the room in which the operations are carried out, or from the operator. Contamination from these sources can be avoided in almost all cases by adhering to a few simple rules of aseptic technique. Only rarely is it necessary to use a specially fitted room and the desirability of doing so depends on the problem to be undertaken. For instance, many experimental programmes involve the use of short-term cultures, that is to say, cultures grown for a period of some days only. In these cases, it is unnecessary to take special precautions since with careful technique it is perfectly possible to carry out short-term tissue culture in an ordinary laboratory. When this is done there may be occasional losses due to contamination by dust or spores from the air, but these cultures can be discarded with no great loss of time or results.

On the other hand, moderately long-term experiments, *i.e.* experiments lasting two to three weeks, make an aseptic room desirable. This room need not be specially fitted out. It need only be a room kept apart for carrying out tissue culture procedures. It should be kept particularly clean and only operators should be permitted in the room while tissue cultures are being handled. If this is done and careful aseptic technique employed, other precautions are not necessary.

When an aseptic room is regularly used by a number of people, it is desirable to have a set of rules concerning its use. The following set of rules has been found adequate.

1. The room must be kept clean and tidy at all times.
2. No material known to be contaminated may be opened in it.
3. When aseptic work is being performed nobody may enter the room or open the door without obtaining permission from the person working there.
4. All working areas should be swabbed with alcohol before use.
5. If discarded medium is placed in the sink it must be washed down thoroughly with water for several minutes.
6. After use the table must be cleared and cleaned. All materials must be removed. All marks due to drops of medium etc. must be washed off.
7. Pipettes and test-tubes must be removed from the rack immediately after use. Unused materials must be removed for re-sterilisation.
8. Used pipettes must be placed in a jar of water. Other glassware which has been in contact with medium or other proteinaceous solutions should be placed in a pail of water. The last person to use the room each day must ensure that the jar and pail are removed to the washing up bench. Each morning the jar and pail must be refilled with water and replaced in the aseptic room first thing.
9. Clean, used glassware should be collected in a wire basket and removed to the washing up bench.
10. Only articles actually belonging in the aseptic room may be left there.

Long-term experiments with very valuable materials may require more rigorous precautions. Thus it may be desirable to sterilise the air in the aseptic room. The normal practice is to circulate it through a series of filters but it may also be passed through an ultra-violet irradiation chamber where all organisms are killed, while a further refinement, sometimes introduced, is an electrostatic dust remover. In the absence of a circulating system, the air can be partially sterilised by keeping an ultra-violet light on continuously. It must be so situated that it does not play on the operators who might otherwise suffer injury. This can be done by mounting it above head level in such a position that all radiation is directed upwards.

In this way all the air above the light is sterilised, so that no bacteria-laden dust can fall in the operation zone.

Further precautions that should be taken in operating an aseptic room are aimed at the laying of dust. Floors must be carefully cleaned at regular intervals and both they and the walls should be treated with a light oil which will cause dust to adhere.

Contamination from the operator

If all the preceding sources of contamination have been eliminated then the one source left is the operator himself. Contamination as a result of the presence of an operator can arise from three sources:

(1) Direct contamination of instruments or cultures from non-sterile objects during operation.

(2) Bacteria carried in expired air.

(3) Organisms carried by dust raised by the operator's movements.

Direct contamination may arise from :

(1) Contact of apparatus, particularly pipettes, with non-sterile surroundings or with the hands.

(2) The entry of organisms present at the lip of containers.

For the beginner, the most difficult part of aseptic technique is the mastery of various manipulations without contaminating pipettes by bringing them into contact with non-sterile objects. The only way to learn to avoid this is to perform the manipulations repeatedly under the supervision of an experienced technician who will point out each fault. During the handling of cultures, if there should ever be any doubt as to whether a pipette touched a non-sterile object, it should invariably be discarded. Contamination from the hands may be minimised by sterilising them before commencing work. This can be done fairly efficiently by thorough washing in soap and water. Some people prefer to rinse them with a little alcohol.

One particular point to watch is ' double transfer ' of contaminating organisms, *i.e.* contamination of a culture with an instrument which has itself been contaminated by contact with the hands. There are two very common examples of this. A frequent mistake is to hold a pipette too low down while fixing a rubber tube or teat to the end. If this pipette is subsequently inserted into a bottle or container, it will contaminate the inside of the neck. When a pipette is again inserted, bacteria may be carried right

10

into the medium. A second example of this type of contamination is that commonly encountered in the handling of knives. These instruments are usually grasped well forward when used. If they are then placed inside sterile tubes or other containers and subsequently withdrawn, the tips of the blades will be contaminated as they pass over the area which has been in contact with the contaminated part of the knife handles.

These errors can be avoided by practice and meticulous attention to technique, which ultimately becomes quite automatic. There are, in addition, a number of simple routine precautions that can be taken to avoid some of the errors described. Thus all pipettes should be discarded immediately after use. This avoids the possibility of contamination due to using pipettes which have been rendered non-sterile by being placed in contaminated holders and is well worth the extra outlay and labour. Also it is often desirable to use a system for instruments which involves their re-sterilisation immediately before use. Two methods are commonly used. In one, the instruments are placed in a boiling water bath after use and removed again just before they are required. In the other technique, the instruments are dipped in spirit and this is burned off before they are re-used.

On opening culture vessels there is always a great danger of contaminating the contents with organisms from the lip. This happens because the vessels accumulate a little dust in the incubator. Also on cooling to room temperature a negative pressure is created within them so that when the stopper is removed, there is an inrush of air which carries the dust with it. This can largely be avoided by flaming the necks of all vessels before removing the stoppers. The flaming need only be brief since its function is simply to fix the dust in place but it should be noted that all parts of the neck of the vessel must be flamed. It is not sufficient just to place the neck briefly in the flame. It should be rotated while it is there.

If the medium comes in contact with the neck of the vessel, as may happen if the contents are removed by pouring, then this cursory type of flaming is not enough since bacteria will be washed back into the flask with the last drop or two remaining. In such cases, the neck of the vessel must be very carefully flamed till it is hot enough to kill any bacteria present. The contamination of cultures by dust from the lip of the vessel can be minimised by covering the stopper and neck. A brown paper cover secured with a rubber band is adequate or alternatively an aluminium foil or parafilm cover can be used. Screw-caps have an advantage over stoppers in this respect since they cover a small area of the neck.

Many people regard contamination from the breath of the operator as one of the main causes of infection of cultures. In fact, this is not so. During ordinary quiet breathing very few bacteria are exhaled. The number increases very greatly, however, during speech or coughing. Therefore, contamination from exhaled bacteria can be prevented in one of two ways, either by using a mask or by refraining from talking. There is some danger in using a mask inasmuch as it tends to create a sense of false security. A mask is quite efficient so long as the operator is breathing quietly but if he speaks or coughs it becomes filled with organisms and subsequently even quiet breathing forces them out of the cloth. Instead of a thick cloth mask, it may therefore be preferable to use a baffle made of X-ray film. Alternatively, a glass plate may be interposed between the operator and the material on which he is operating. This is particularly desirable if conditions make it necessary for him to lean over his work. Otherwise, this problem is best handled by refraining from talking and by keeping the mouth and nose well away from the cultures.

Contamination from dust can be avoided by (a) preventing dust from being raised in the room, and (b) preventing dust in the air from entering the culture vessel.

Dust normally arises from three sources:

    (1) The floor and operating table.
    (2) The clothes.
    (3) The operator's hair and body.

The raising of dust from the floor and table can be prevented by coating them with a layer of light oil. Dust adheres to this and is prevented from spreading about the room. Sometimes it is undesirable to oil the table top and in that case it can be swabbed with 70 per cent. alcohol before use to kill off most of the organisms present. Even when these precautions have been taken, it is highly desirable to avoid all unnecessary movement in the room and all draughts should be excluded.

Clothes, particularly street clothes, carry a great deal of dust and any movement within the room is likely to set up a cloud of germ-laden particles. To a large extent this can be prevented by wearing a clean laboratory coat over the street clothes. For particularly careful work a clean, sterile gown should be used on each occasion, although for ordinary work this is not necessary. If a laboratory coat is not worn, at least the sleeves should be rolled up and the arms washed up to the elbows. While working with cultures it should always be assumed that dust will fall from the arms so that care should be taken to avoid passing the hands and arms over open dishes.

One of the most dangerous sources of dust is the operator's hair. If the procedures employed necessitate bringing the head over the working table or near it, it is better to wear a cap. Also, the operator should try to keep as far away from his work as is convenient.

Despite all these precautions, it is still possible that there may be some dust in the air and one must, therefore, continuously employ a technique which will prevent it from settling into the culture vessels. This can be achieved by keeping all vessels covered as much as possible and it is often desirable to perform all manipulations under a glass plate. When bottles and flasks are handled they should be held at an angle when open so that dust cannot drop straight down into the bottom.

CHAPTER X

DESIGN AND EQUIPMENT OF A TISSUE CULTURE LABORATORY

THE design and equipment of a tissue culture laboratory are mainly governed by the research programme contemplated and in view of the great variety of fields in which tissue culture is applied it is difficult to generalise. However, there are certain basic facilities which must be introduced into any laboratory where these techniques are to be used. For some research projects these involve very minor outlay and little organisation whereas in others considerable expense may be involved and it may be desirable to plan special accommodation.

The basic requirements can be considered under these headings :
1. Sterilisation and cleaning facilities.
2. Sterile working area.
3. Storage for media.
4. Incubator facilities.
5. Special glassware and other apparatus.

Sterilisation and cleaning facilities

For the cleaning of glassware, the first essential is a large sink with a plentiful water supply and adequate bench space for the handling of materials. For washing glassware itself, there are a number of mechanical aids, ranging from motor-driven rotary brushes to fully automatic dish-washing machines. Certain simple items are very useful in cutting down drudgery and, in particular, it is worthwhile to acquire a pipette-washer and a bottle-washer. The former is a siphon arrangement which rinses pipettes automatically when attached to the tap. The latter is a simple apparatus, again attached to the tap, which injects a strong jet of water into a bottle pressed down over it. With these the time spent on rinsing is materially reduced and the job is usually done more thoroughly.

For boiling glassware, an ordinary domestic wash-boiler is inexpensive and suffices for most purposes. For soaking glassware, there is a large variety of plastic vessels, mostly used for other purposes.

Before drying by other means, it is desirable to drain glassware and a large drainage rack is almost essential. These are available commercially or they can be made from galvanised large-mesh wire netting (2-in. square mesh) supported on a Dexion frame.

For the sterilisation of apparatus a sterilising oven and an autoclave are required. A wide variety of these are available and can be found in any supply company's catalogue. However, for the small laboratory it should be mentioned that domestic electric ovens make very useful sterilising ovens and are excellent value for money. Similarly, practically all small items and most solutions can be sterilised conveniently in a pressure cooker instead of an autoclave. Even in a well-equipped laboratory, a pressure cooker is a useful item for the rapid sterilisation of small amounts of material by moist heat.

For the sterilisation of solutions it is necessary to purchase filters and filter apparatus. These have already been discussed in Chapter VIII.

Sterile working area

For some kinds of work nothing special is required and the manipulations can be performed on a clean bench in a clean laboratory, relatively free from draughts. Some precautions that can be taken to prevent dust from contaminating cultures have already been discussed.

If much work is to be done which involves prolonged risk of exposure to infection, a simple shield or sterile cabinet may be employed. The easiest type of shield consists simply of a sheet of glass or plastic supported over the working area. A rather more elaborate version of this type of apparatus is the sterile operating cabinet of a type similar to that used for handling radio-active compounds. For tissue culture purposes the table illustrated in Figure 21 has been found particularly convenient. Its special feature is a glass shelf supported over the working area. This shelf not only pre-

vents dust from settling on the material but also effectively doubles
the readily available bench surface. It can be made very easily from

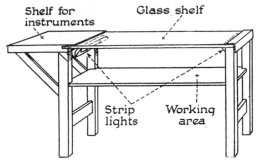

Fig. 21
A useful type of table for tissue culture work.

slotted angle alloy and a sheet of
plate glass. The lights are convenient
and easily fitted also.

    If a substantial part of the
laboratory's activities are to be devoted to tissue culture work indefinitely, it is well worth while fitting up
a sterile room. This need only be a
clean room with a door which can
be closed to isolate it from the rest
of the laboratory while sterile work
is in progress. A fresh coat of paint
from time to time will provide clean

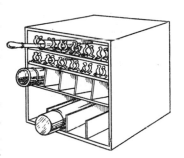

Fig. 22
A convenient pipette rack made
from aluminium sheet.

sterile walls. In designing a new department, many refinements
may be introduced such as glass walls and sliding doors. The room
need only be 4 or 5 ft. square, but where conditions allow it is
better to have large sterile rooms, at least 10 ft. square.

Storage for media

    Practically all tissue culture media are best stored in the cold
and a few items should be stored in the solid frozen state. For a
small laboratory storage of these items can be adequately managed
with a domestic refrigerator having a rather large freezing compartment. When more extensive storage facilities are required, it
is usually desirable to add a deep-freeze cabinet to run at -10
to $-20°$ and, if possible, a freezer operating at $-70°$ C. Some

laboratories are equipped with cold rooms and these may, of course, be used for the storage of stock media, but it is usually convenient to have a small service refrigerator near the tissue culture room also.

Incubator facilities

All cells from warm-blooded animals have to be grown at temperatures near the normal temperature for the animal in order to get the best growth. There are many incubators on the market which can be used for this purpose. In general, water-jacketed incubators are more suitable than the anhydric variety since there is less likelihood of ' hot spots ' which are common over the heaters in the bottom of anhydric incubators. Also the rate at which the temperature changes is dampened to some extent by the water jacket. Unfortunately very few incubators have thermostatic controls which can be relied on never to go wrong and extreme temperature swings may particularly occur during the night when the temperature of the building changes and the incubator is completely closed. In purchasing an incubator for tissue culture purposes it is particularly important to ensure that the best possible thermostatic control is fitted and it is desirable to have two thermostats fitted in series so that if one goes wrong the other will take over. An incubator for tissue culture purposes should be fitted with wire mesh shelves rather than perforated metal shelves since the latter do not permit adequate air circulation and areas of poor growth are often found over the holes in the shelves. For the same reason forced circulation by means of a fan is a desirable feature.

If tissue culture is being conducted on a large scale, it is desirable to have a walk-in incubator or hot room. Such a room is easily constructed by fitting a windowless room with tubular electric heaters switched on and off by a thermostatic control switch. It is desirable to place a strong fan in the room if the temperature is to be kept uniform but for some experiments it is useful to omit the fan, in which case a temperature gradient of several degrees is established between the floor and the ceiling. This gradient is often remarkably uniform so that shelves at different levels can be relied on to give reproducible temperatures.

For some purposes, special incubators are sometimes required, *e.g.* gas-tight incubators with a gas inlet and outlet for maintaining a constant partial pressure of CO_2 in the atmosphere. These can be constructed with a little ingenuity according to requirements and need no special description.

Special glassware and apparatus

The actual items required in a tissue culture laboratory and the amounts of each vary with many individual factors—the programme of research, scale of research and personal taste, to mention only a few. In order to provide a rough guide to purchasing equipment, it has been assumed that one person will be working with an assistant and that he will have no access to shared facilities.

General equipment

The following major items are essential or highly desirable:
    One refrigerator with deep-freeze compartment.
    One or more incubators.
    One centrifuge.
    One rough and one sensitive balance.
    One sterilising oven.
    One autoclave or pressure cooker.
    One pipette-washer.
    One bottle-washer.
    One deioniser for water.
    One all-glass still.
    Buckets, pans, etc., for collecting and soaking used glassware.
    Microscopes (for large-scale work an inverted microscope is
        particularly desirable).

Requirements for glassware and special apparatus are bound to vary very greatly. The following list of initial requirements is reasonably representative for most purposes.

		Quantity
Flasks (conical)	1 litre	1
	500 ml.	4
	250 ml.	6
Beakers	50 ml. to 1 litre	1 each
Measuring cylinders	1 litre	1
	500 ml.	1
	250 ml.	2
	50 ml.	4

General equipment (*contd.*)

		Quantity
Volumetric flasks	1 litre	1
	500 ml.	1
	250 ml.	2
	100 ml.	2
Petri dishes	85 mm.	4 dozen
	60 mm.	4 dozen
Cans for sterilising Petri dishes		2
Universal containers		6 dozen
Medical flat bottles	16 oz.	6 dozen
	12 oz.	6 dozen
Test-tubes	$6'' \times \frac{5}{8}''$	2 gross
	$3'' \times \frac{1}{2}''$	1 gross
Stoppers for above (red rubber)		2 gross each size
Centrifuge tubes		6 dozen
Test-tube baskets		6
Test-tube racks		6
Pipettes, graduated	10 ml.	6 dozen
	5 ml.	6 dozen
	1 ml.	6 dozen
Pipettes, bulb	100 ml.	1
	50 ml.	2
	20 ml.	2
Pipettes, Pasteur (or glass for making pipettes)		2 gross
Rubber teats	5 ml.	6 dozen
Cans for sterilising pipettes		10
2 ml. syringes		2
14 gauge needles		6 dozen
$3'' \times 1''$ microscopic slides		1 dozen boxes
$\frac{7}{8}''$ square No. 0 coverslips		6 oz.
Watchglasses (embryological)		1 dozen
Coplin dishes		1 dozen
Cotton-wool		2 lbs.
Gauze		10 yd.
Filter funnels (assorted sizes)		6

Instruments

Instruments	Quantity
Bard-Parker knife handles	4
Knife blades No. 11	2 dozen
No. 23	1 dozen
Dissecting forceps	2
Dissecting scissors	2
Fine straight forceps	2
Fine curved forceps	4
Fine scissors	2
Barber's scissors	1
Platinum wire in mounts	4
Coverslip forceps	4

Special apparatus

For certain techniques special glassware and apparatus is required. Since the amounts needed are entirely dependent on the research programme no amounts are stated.

Coverslip techniques

Depression slides, large and small coverslips, racks for slides, double boiler, camel-hair brushes.

Roller-tube techniques

Roller-drum, racks for roller-tubes.

Organ culture

Embryological watchglasses.

Special instruments—cataract knives and watchmaker's forceps, dissecting microscope.

Handling of strains

Magnetic stirrer, Cornwall pipettes.

Sources of materials

There follow some lists of suppliers of tissue culture materials in Europe and the United States. These are by no means complete and while the products of the manufacturers mentioned have been found generally satisfactory, this is not to imply that goods manufactured by other firms are necessarily inferior. In the following lists the full address of a supplier has only been given when it is first mentioned, an abbreviated address being given subsequently.

General suppliers of laboratory apparatus

Baird & Tatlock (London) Ltd., 14-17 St. Cross Street, London, E.C.1.
Fisher Scientific Company, 717 Forbes Street, Pittsburgh 19, Pa., U.S.A.
A. Gallenkamp & Co. Ltd., 17 Sun Street, Finsbury Square, London, E.C.2.
Griffin & George Ltd., Ealing Road, Alperton, Wembley, Middx.
The Laboratory Glassblowers Company, 63 Lowlands Road, Harrow, Middx.
A. H. Thomas Company, 230 South 7th Street, Philadelphia 5, Pa., U.S.A.
J. W. Towers & Co., Ltd., Victoria House, Widnes, Lancs.

General glassware (in addition to above firms)

Bellco Glass Inc., 413 North Fourth Street, Vineland, New Jersey, U.S.A.
Chance Bros. Glassworks, Smethwick 40, Birmingham.
Clay-Adams, Inc., 141 East 25th Street, New York 10, N.Y., U.S.A.
Corning Glass Works, Corning, N.Y., U.S.A.
H. G. Elliott Ltd., E-Mil Works, Treforest Industrial Estate, Pontypridd, Glamorgan.
Albert A. Henning & Company, 16 East 23rd Street, New York 10, N.Y., U.S.A.
James A. Jobling & Co. Ltd., Wear Glass Works, Sunderland.
Kontes Glass Company, Vineland, New Jersey, U.S.A.
Labglass Inc., 514 West 147th Street, New York 31, N.Y., U.S.A.
Quickfit & Quartz Ltd., ' Quickfit ' Works, Stone, Staffs.

General biological products and biochemicals

Armour & Co., Research Division, Chicago 9, Ill., U.S.A.
The Armour Laboratories, Hampden Park, Eastbourne.
Bios Laboratories, Inc., 17 West 60th Street, New York 23, N.Y., U.S.A.
British Drug Houses Ltd., West Quay Road, Poole, Dorset.
Burroughs Wellcome & Co., The Wellcome Building, Euston Road, London. N.W.1.
California Corporation for Biochemical Research, 3408 Fowler Street, Los Angeles 63, Calif., U.S.A.
    (British agents—V. A. Howe & Co., 46 Pembridge Road, London, W.11.)
Cudahy Laboratories, The Cudahy Packing Company, Omaha 7, Nebraska, U.S.A.
General Biochemicals Inc., 677 Laboratory Park, Chagrin Falls, Ohio, U.S.A.
Glaxo Laboratories, Greenford, Middx.
H.M. Chemical Company Ltd., Santa Monica, Calif., U.S.A.
Hoffman-LaRoche Inc., LaRoche Park, Nutley 10, New Jersey, U.S.A.
Hyland Laboratories, 4501 Colorado Boulevard, Los Angeles 39, Calif., U.S.A.
Koch-Light Laboratories Ltd., Poyle Trading Estate, Colnbrook, Bucks.
Nutritional Biochemicals Corp., Cleveland 28, Ohio, U.S.A.
    (British agents—V. A. Howe & Co., 46 Pembridge Road, London, W.11.)
Pabst Laboratories, 1037 West McKinley Ave., Milwaukee 3, Wis., U.S.A.
    (British agents—V. A. Howe & Co., 46 Pembridge Road, London, W.11.)
Parke, Davis & Co., Detroit 32, Michigan, U.S.A.
Parke, Davis & Co., Staines Road, Hounslow, Middx.
Roche Products Ltd., Broadwater Road, Welwyn Garden City, Herts.
Sigma Chemical Company, 4648 Easton Avenue, St. Louis 13, Missouri, U.S.A.
    12 Lettuce St., London, S.W.6.
Worthington Biochemical Corp., Freehold, New Jersey, U.S.A.
    (British agents—V. A. Howe & Co., 46 Pembridge Road, London, W.11.)

SOURCES FOR SPECIAL APPARATUS AND EQUIPMENT

Item	*Supplier*
Cataract knives	Albert A. Henning & Co., New York. George Tieman & Co., 107 East 28th Street, New York, N.Y., U.S.A. John Weiss & Son, 281 Oxford St., London, W.1.
Cell counting equipment (Earle)	Kontes Glass Co., New Jersey, U.S.A. District Scientific Co., 10046 La Tijera Blvd., Los Angeles 45, Cal.
Cell counters (electronic)	Casella (Electronics) Ltd., 46/48 Osnaburgh St., London, N.W.1. Coulter, 590 W. 20th St., Hialeah, Florida. 2-4 Ashwell St., St. Albans, Herts., England. Evans Electroselenium Ltd., Harlow, Essex.
Columbia staining dishes	A. H. Thomas Company, Philadelphia. Albert A. Henning & Co., New York. Standard Scientific Supply Corp., 34 West Fourth St., New York 12.
Cornwall syringe	Becton Dickinson & Company, Rutherford, New Jersey, U.S.A. (British agents—V. A. Howe & Co.) Arnold R. Horwell, 17 Cricklewood Broadway, London, N.W.2.
Coverslips	Corning Glass Works, N.Y., U.S.A. Chance Bros., Birmingham.
Coverslips—'Gold Seal'	Clay-Adams, Inc., New York, U.S.A.
Coverslip forceps	Clay-Adams, Inc., New York, U.S.A. Vicarey Davidson Co., 162 Bath St., Glasgow, C.2, Scotland.
Culture tubes, Leighton	Microbiological Associates Inc., Washington 14, D.C., U.S.A. Bellco Glass Inc., New Jersey, U.S.A. Scientific Glass Apparatus Co., Inc., 100 Lakewood Terrace, Bloomfield, New Jersey, U.S.A. Camlab (Glass) Ltd., 50 Burleigh Street, Cambridge.

SOURCES FOR SPECIAL APPARATUS AND EQUIPMENT
(*contd.*)

Item	Supplier
Culture tubes—screw-capped with inert teflon or silicone liners	Kimble Glass Company, Toledo 1, Ohio, U.S.A. The Virtis Company, 160 Ashburton Ave., Yonker, N.Y., U.S.A. Bellco Glass Inc., Vineland, New Jersey. Esco (Rubber) Ltd., 2 Stothard Place, London, E.C.2.
Depression slides (Maximow type)	A. H. Thomas Company, Philadelphia, Pa., U.S.A.
Depression slides (similar to Maximow type)	S. Rampling, 3 Market Street, Cambridge.
Depression slides (with flat concavity for phase microscopy)	Paul Rosenthal, 505 Fifth Ave., New York 17, N.Y.
Flasks—Carrel	Corning Glass Works. Clay-Adams, Inc. Albert A. Henning & Co. Kontes Glass Company. Labglass Inc.
Flasks—Carrel type (optically unsuitable)	James A. Jobling & Co. Ltd.
Flasks—Disposable plastic	Falcon Plastics, Culver City, Calif., U.S.A.
Flasks—Earle T-flasks	Kontes Glass Company.
Flasks—Roux (specially selected for tissue culture)	Esco (Rubber) Ltd.
Incubators	Wyble Engineering Development Corp., P.O. Box 223, Silver Spring, Md., U.S.A. Laboratory Thermal Equipment Ltd., Greenfield, Nr. Oldham. A. Gallenkamp & Co., Ltd., 17-29 Sun Street, London, E.C.2. Chas. Hearson & Co. Ltd., 68 Willow Walk, London, S.E.1. Gainsborough Engineering Co. Ltd., Park Works, Middleton, Lancs.
Incubators, carbon dioxide	Hotpack Corporation, Cottman Ave. & Melrose St., Philadelphia, Pa.
Liquid nitrogen refrigerators	Cryenco, 200 West 48th Ave., Denver 16, Colorado. Linde Co., B2-30 43rd Ave., Long Island City 1, N.Y. Union Carbide Ltd., Alloys Division, 8 Grafton St., London, W.1.

SOURCES FOR SPECIAL APPARATUS AND EQUIPMENT
(*contd.*)

Item	*Supplier*
Millipore filters	Millipore Filter Corp., Bedford, Mass., U.S.A.
McIlwain chopper	H. Mickle, Mill Works, Gomshall, Surrey.
Patapar	A. J. Buck & Son, 1515 E. North Ave., Baltimore, Md., U.S.A.
Perfusion chambers	Wahlberg - McCreary, Inc., 2112 Pease Ave., Houston 2, Texas. W. R. Prior & Co. Ltd., London Rd., Bishop's Stortford, Herts., England. Electro - Mechanical Development Co., 2337 Bissonnet, Houston, U.S.A.
Plastic trays (for metabolic inhibition test)	Linbro Chemical Co. Inc., 681 Dixwell Ave., New Haven, Conn., U.S.A. R. B. Turner & Co. Ltd., " Inocular House ", Church Lane & Hobbs Green, E. Finchley, London, N.2.
Roller-tube rotors	Wyble Engineering Development Corp. Standard Scientific Supply Corp. Aloe Company, 5655 Kingsbury St., St. Louis 12, Mo., U.S.A. Matburn Ltd., 83 Lamb's Conduit Street, London, W.C.1. New Brunswick Scientific Co., Somerset St., P.O. Box 606, New Brunswick, N.S.
Seitz filters	Corning Glass Works. Fisher Scientific Company. A. H. Thomas Company. A. Gallenkamp & Co. Ltd.
Selas filters	Selas Corpn. of America, Dresher, Pa.
Silicone stoppers and liners	Esco (Rubber) Ltd.
Sintered glass filters	Corning Glass Works. A. H. Thomas Company. The Virtis Company. James A. Jobling & Co. Ltd. A. Gallenkamp & Co. Ltd.

SOURCES FOR SPECIAL APPARATUS AND EQUIPMENT
(*contd.*)

Item	*Supplier*
Spinner culture vessel	Bellco Glass Inc.
Stainless steel "expanded metal" (for organ culture)	The Expanded Metal Co., Burwood Ho., Caxton St., London, S.W.1.
Still, double distillation, all glass	Quickfit & Quartz Ltd., 'Quickfit' Works, Stone, Staffs.
Still, glass	Barnstead Still and Sterilizer Co., 2 Lanesville Terrace, Boston 31, Mass., U.S.A. Loughborough Glass Co., Willows Works, Loughborough, Leics. Bellco Glass Inc.
Time-lapse cinemicrographic apparatus	Electro - Mechanical Development Co. Gillett & Sibert Ltd., 417-419 Battersea Park Rd., London, S.W.11. Sage Instruments Inc., 2 Spring St., White Plains, N.Y. W. Vinten Ltd., 715 North Circular Rd., London, N.W.2. Carl Zeiss, Oberkochen/Württ, West Germany. (British agents—Degenhardt & Co. Ltd., 32 Maddow Street, London, W.1.)
Trypsinising flask	Bellco Glass Inc.
Watch-glasses, embryological	A. H. Thomas Company. A. Gallenkamp & Co. Ltd.

General chemicals

J. T. Baker Chemical Co., Phillipsburg, New Jersey, U.S.A.
British Drug Houses Ltd., West Quay Road, Poole, Dorset.
Fisher Scientific Company, 717 Forbes Street, Pittsburgh 19, Pa., U.S.A.
Hopkin & Williams Ltd., 16-17 St. Cross Street, Hatton Garden, London, E.1.
Koch-Light Laboratories Ltd., Poyle Trading Estate, Colnbrook, Bucks.
May & Baker Ltd., Dagenham, Essex.
Merck & Company, Inc., Rahway, New Jersey, U.S.A.

Special tissue culture media

Burroughs Wellcome & Co., The Wellcome Building, Euston Rd., London, N.W.1.
Cappel Laboratories, Westchester, Pa., U.S.A.
Connaught Medical Research Laboratories, Toronto 5, Ontario, Canada.

Colorado Serum Products, Denver, Colo.
Hyland Laboratories, 4501 Colorado Boulevard, Los Angeles 39, Cali-
    fornia, U.S.A.
Difco Laboratories, 920 Henry Street, Detroit 1, Michigan.
    (British agents—Baird & Tatlock (London) Ltd., 14-17 St. Cross Street,
    London, E.C.1.)
Flow Laboratories Inc., 1710 Chapman Ave., Rockville, Md., U.S.A.
Microbiological Associates Inc., 4856 Bethesda Avenue, Washington 14,
    D.C., U.S.A.
Oxoid Division, Oxo Ltd., Thames House, Queen St. Place, London, E.C.4.
Pentext Inc., P.O. Box 248, Kankakee, Illinois, U.S.A.

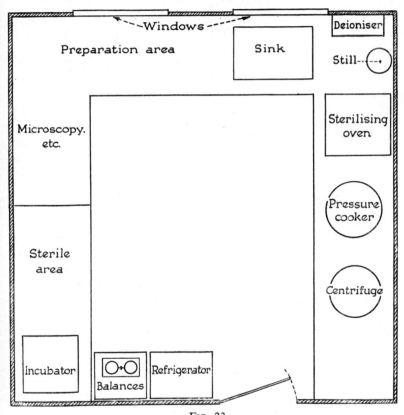

FIG. 23
A suitable layout for tissue culture work in a small room.

LABORATORY DESIGN

The minimum accommodation desirable for a tissue culture
laboratory is a single room. Because of the special nature of the
work it is undesirable to share a room with people doing research

11

of a different kind, although occasionally this may be feasible, particularly if the simplest tissue culture techniques are being used.

Many workers will be content to have a single room but it is occasionally possible to plan a special suite of rooms for tissue culture purposes and between the two extremes the accommodation available may vary widely. Experience has shown that certain basic principles of design are particularly convenient and the following descriptions of a single-room unit and a special suite are merely intended to offer some suggestions to those who are setting up a laboratory for the first time.

A single-room unit

Assuming that one has been allocated a small room, about twelve feet square, with a window-bench containing a sink and two wall benches, a reasonable arrangement is shown in Figure 23. The special features are as follows.

The position of the sink dictates the disposition of such things as the deioniser, still and buckets for glassware. It is desirable to reserve an area near the sink for all preparative work and an area with good light—in front of a window is best. It is also convenient to have the sterilising oven and autoclave or pressure cooker fairly near the preparation area. Since there will be a good deal of movement on this bench, it is a suitable place for a centrifuge but unsuitable for optical instruments or balances. The 'sterile area' is situated as far as possible from any draughts and as far as possible from areas where there is much movement, *e.g.* the preparation area. For some purposes the 'sterile area' may merely be a clean bit of bench. Alternatively, it may be fitted with a sterile cabinet and if the room already contains a fume cupboard this may easily be converted to such a purpose. It is convenient to have the incubator near this area. In a small room the remaining piece of wall bench can be used for microscopical examination of material or other special purposes. The blank wall behind the door is a convenient place for the refrigerator and the balances can be accommodated on a strong table on the same wall where they are relatively free of draughts and vibration.

Laboratory suite for tissue culture

Many features of the design of a special suite of rooms depend on the purpose for which the tissue culture method is to be used.

For this reason it is unnecessary here to discuss the layout of chemical or virology laboratories or of offices, instrument rooms, etc. The parts of a suite which may require to be designed specially with tissue culture work in mind are the preparation and sterilisation rooms, incubator room, aseptic rooms and cubicles, and possibly a special dark room. It has been found a useful principle to design the suite round the incubator room, with ready access from one unit to another. An example of such an arrangement is shown in Figure 24. The suite can be constructed at the back of a large laboratory on the wall away from the windows. Some special features of this design may be commented on.

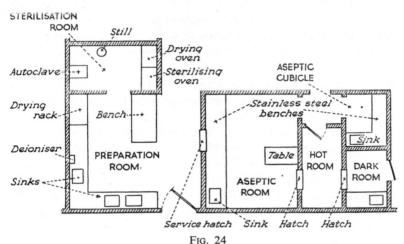

FIG. 24

Plan of a suite of rooms designed for tissue culture work.

Sterilisation room

This should contain all driers, hot-air sterilisers, autoclaves, furnaces and stills and it should be particularly well ventilated. For this reason it is usually desirable to have it on an outside wall with sufficient exhaust fans to the exterior.

The preparation room

This should be of ample size with benches for cleaning and packing materials, sinks (preferably two or three), drying racks, storage cupboards and so on. For convenience it should be situated fairly near the aseptic rooms and an arrangement similar to that shown in Figure 24 is recommended. A service hatch between the main aseptic room and the preparation room makes it easy to move materials in and out at the commencement and end of the day's work.

The aseptic room

This should be designed so as to have the minimum of fixed furnishings. A built-in stainless steel bench and sink unit on one wall is all that is necessary. The floors should preferably be of terrazzo or tile and a drain should be fitted so that the room can be washed down. For the same reason it is best to have tiled walls or walls of other waterproof material. Corners should be rounded so that they can be easily cleaned. It is useful to have one wall made of glass from bench height upwards. This provides good light and permits easy observation of work in progress in the room so that teaching is facilitated and the individual in the room can sign to assistants outside if necessary. The room should, of course, have the usual services. It is desirable that it should be fitted with a filtered air supply and air-conditioned. This latter requirement is essential in hot climates and almost essential even in relatively cool climates since the temperature in a closed room with several individuals in it can rise very quickly. Not only is this uncomfortable for people working in the room but it can cause serious damage to cultured cells. Removable furnishings include a table and chairs. Comfortable typist's or draughtsman's chairs are preferable to stools if the work involves prolonged sitting. A working table of the type described (p. 151) is particularly useful. In planning a new suite of rooms with unlimited space available the aseptic room should be made fairly large and a suitable size is 12 ft. square. This permits all manipulations to be carried out comfortably, although a great deal can be done in much more limited accommodation.

Aseptic cubicle

In planning a very large suite of rooms for several workers, it may be desirable to include several aseptic rooms of the type described above. This is not often necessary but it is useful to have at least one extra area for people who want to do some aseptic work while the main aseptic room is in routine use. A small cubicle, incorporating most of the important features of an aseptic room, suffices for most purposes. This can be a small room about six feet square with an L-shaped bench on two walls carrying the services.

Entry to both aseptic room and aseptic cubicle is best obtained by sliding doors since these can be opened and shut without causing an influx of air to the room. Instead of a handle they can be operated by a foot-bar about three inches from the floor. This is a very convenient arrangement and permits material to be carried in and out in both hands. Also, if completely sterile work is being done with scrubbed hands the door can be opened and shut without contaminating them. It is useful to arrange entry to the aseptic areas by an air-lock to cut down further on the movement of dust-laden air.

Hot room

In any permanent tissue culture suite, it is desirable to have a hot room with the air temperature at 36 - 37° C. A good arrangement is to have this centrally placed and in the suite illustrated the aseptic rooms, etc., have been built round it. This permits direct access from the aseptic room to shelves in the hot room by means of small doors in the wall. The same air-lock as is used for the aseptic cubicles serves as an air-lock for the hot room. This prevents excessive variations of temperature due to movement of people out and in. The door should be fitted with an automatic closing spring so that it cannot be left open inadvertently. It is also convenient to have a microscopic observation box projecting from the hot room into a room outside to permit observation of cells without any alteration of their temperature. This warm microscope box may be situated in a small dark-room so that photography can be carried out and the films developed with the maximum of convenience.

General facilities

The facilities which have been described are essential in any tissue culture unit working on a large scale. Other facilities—for histochemistry, microbiology, biochemistry, etc.—can be fitted on as required. However, in designing them it is important to avoid having certain units in close proximity to the tissue culture unit. In particular, animals should be kept as far away as possible. Not only do they give rise to spore-laden dust in their vicinity, but they frequently carry small animals, such as mites and lice, which may gain entry to sterile packages and contaminate them. Mites, from animal sources, may establish themselves in the area and prove extremely difficult to eradicate.

Care should also be taken in situating chemical laboratories nearby, particularly laboratories in which fumes are likely to be produced (as in the digestion of biological materials by strong acids). These can poison cells. Similarly it should be remembered that formalin and phenol, which are often continuously present in the air of pathology laboratories, may prove harmful. The danger in these cases does not actually arise from the amount of the materials which may gain access to the cells during the brief periods when they are open to the atmosphere. It is mainly due to the fact that they can be absorbed into stored water or media in bottles stoppered with cotton-wool plugs. For reasons of this kind it is always necessary to consider the arrangement of tissue culture rooms in relation to the disposition of laboratories for other purposes in the vicinity.

It should be emphasised that this consideration of the design of a suite of rooms for tissue culture aims at the ideal. It will rarely be possible for the average worker to design rooms exactly as he wants them and it will frequently be unnecessary to consider some of the refinements mentioned. However, the principles remain the same whether a large or small unit is being planned.

BIBLIOGRAPHY

COMAN, D. R. & STABLER, N. G. (1941). An apparatus for roller tube culture. *Science* **94**, 569.

EARLE, W. & HIGHHOUSE, F. (1954). Culture flasks for use with plane surface substrate tissue cultures. *J. nat. Cancer Inst.* **14**, 841.

LISHER, W. C. & DORÉ, C. F. (1953). Roller tube tissue culture apparatus. *Exp. Cell Res.* **5**, 542.

CHAPTER XI

PRIMARY EXPLANTATION TECHNIQUES

I. TISSUE CULTURES

PRIMARY explantation denotes the cultivation of pieces of tissue fresh from the organism. The primary explantation techniques are the traditional techniques of tissue culture and, with very few exceptions, they were almost the only techniques in use until about 1945. These methods are still widely employed and will obviously continue to be for a very long time to come. Most of the techniques are similar in principle, the main differences being in the vessels used for growing the tissue. The main groups of methods are those using depression slides, Carrel flasks and roller tubes, of which there are many variations. Organ cultures, which logically fall into the same general category, actually require a highly specialised collection of techniques which separate them from the ordinary tissue culture methods. Methods employing the same principles as those which were developed for vertebrate tissues have also been employed for the cultivation of insect and plant tissues.

SLIDE CULTURES

Slide cultures or coverslip cultures are made by explanting a very small fragment of tissue on to a coverslip which is subsequently inverted over the cavity of a depression slide. This, the oldest and the traditional form of tissue culture, is still quite widely employed in some fields and still has its place. It has a number of advantages. Thus, it is simple and relatively inexpensive. Also, the cells spread out in a manner which is favourable for microscopic examination and photography in the living state. Finally, the cells grow directly on the coverslip so that they are easily fixed and stained and made into permanent preparations. The disadvantages of the technique are that the small supply of oxygen and nutrients is very rapidly exhausted so that the medium quickly becomes acid and this necessitates that rapidly grown tissues must be transferred frequently. In addition, it is difficult by this technique to maintain sterility for long periods and, finally, only very small amounts of tissue can be cultured; consequently the application of the method is limited. From the foregoing it will be appreciated that the main place of slide culture is in morphological studies. Modifications of the method are particularly valuable in time-lapse cinemicrographic investigations.

There are six general types of slide cultures:

(1) Single coverslip with plasma clot (Harrison).
(2) Double coverslip with plasma clot (Maximow).
(3) Single coverslip with fluid hanging drop (Lewis and Lewis).
(4) Double coverslip with perforated cellophane (Schilling and Earle).
(5) Thin drilled metal or glass slide with plasma and fluid medium (Gey).
(6) Special slide with a circulating fluid medium-perfusion chamber (Pomerat).

THE PREPARATION OF SLIDE CULTURES

Single coverslip with plasma clot

This technique is still commonly employed and is probably the one that has been used most in tissue culture during the past fifty years. Details of the technique are as follows:

(1) Set out all the instruments required, including a rack with sterile test-tubes for holding Pasteur pipettes. Prepare the constituents of the medium. Usually this is made up in two parts, one part containing plasma and the other part containing embryo extract. Typically, one solution would contain 50 per cent. plasma in balanced salt solution and the other one would contain 50 per cent. embryo extract in serum.

(2) With a pair of sterile forceps, place one or two coverslips (22 mm.) on a clean, sterile surface (a bench top which has been wiped with 70 per cent. alcohol and allowed to dry). Use a capillary pipette to place one drop of the plasma-containing solution in the centre of each coverslip.

(3) Transfer one or two explants to this drop, either by means of the knife blades or by a fine pair of forceps, taking care not to crush the tissue.

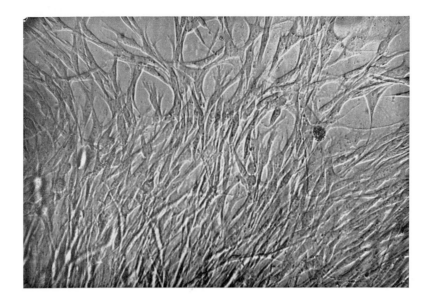

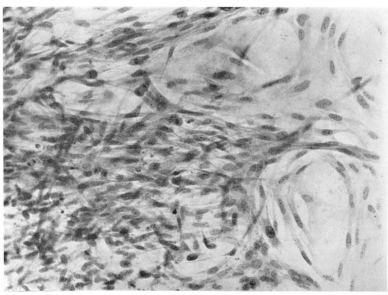

PLATE 5

Top: Adult rat subcutaneous fibroblasts, four days in culture. Phase contrast. ×175. (Courtesy of Mrs. H. Benitez.) *Bottom*: Endothelial outgrowth from a foetal rat rib, six days in culture. Stained Masson-Mallory trichrome. ×200. (Courtesy of Dr. M. R. Murray.)

facing p. 168

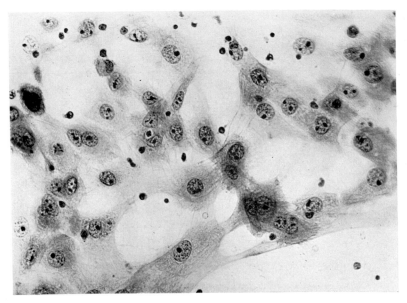

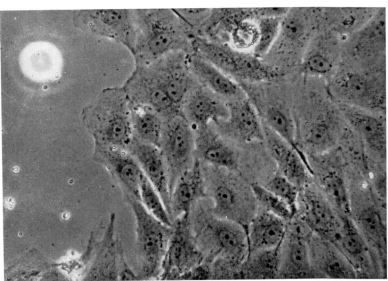

PLATE 6

Top: Human thymus epithelium, four days in culture. Stained Masson-Mallory trichrome. ×300. (Courtesy of Dr. M. R. Murray.) *Bottom*: New-born rat liver epithelium, six days in culture. Phase contrast. ×300. (Courtesy of Mrs. H. Benitez.)

(4) Add to this a drop of the embryo extract-containing solution. Immediately mix thoroughly before clotting starts and spread out into an area of approximately 15 to 20 mm. diameter. Locate the explants in this according to the desired arrangement.

(5) With a glass rod, place two small spots of petroleum jelly near the concavity of a depression slide in such a position that they will be covered by the coverslip. Invert the slide over the coverslip preparation and press down in such a way that the petroleum jelly sticks the coverslip to the slide. Place the culture aside to permit the medium to clot.

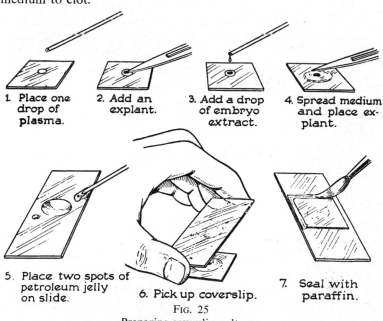

1. Place one drop of plasma.

2. Add an explant.

3. Add a drop of embryo extract.

4. Spread medium and place explant.

5. Place two spots of petroleum jelly on slide.

6. Pick up coverslip.

7. Seal with paraffin.

Fig. 25
Preparing coverslip cultures.

(6) Turn the cultures over and seal the margins of the coverslips with hot paraffin. Label and incubate at 37° C. Sealing the slide with paraffin must be done with care. It is better to use a rather thick seal since, apart from being more effective, this is easier to remove. The wax is conveniently kept in a double saucepan and should be thinned with about 25 or 30 per cent. petroleum jelly before use. A wax based on beeswax is more satisfactory than one based on paraffin wax. Instead of wax a useful sealing material for short-term cultures is rubber solution (as used for repairing bicycle tyres).

Maximow double coverslip method with plasma clot

This technique is very similar to that already described. One or two large (40 mm.) square coverslips are placed on a sterile surface

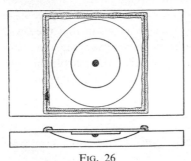

FIG. 26

The Maximow double coverslip method.

and a small drop of balanced salt solution is put on each. A square or round 22 mm. coverslip is then placed in the centre of each large one, being held in position by surface tension of the balanced salt solution. The culture is then prepared on the small coverslip exactly as before. A large depression slide is used and the entire preparation is attached to it by petroleum jelly and wax in such a way that the small coverslip is not in contact with the slide at any point.

Single coverslip with liquid medium. Lying and hanging drop cultures

This is an extremely simple technique but its applications are very limited. The prepared explants are placed in culture medium in a watch glass. Coverslips are laid out on a sterile surface, the explants drawn into the tip of a capillary pipette and deposited, one in the centre of each coverslip. Fluid can be drawn off and carefully remeasured (1 drop for a 1-in. slide, 2 to 3 drops for a large slide). The fluid must then be spread out in a very thin circular film with the explant protruding above its surface. A depression slide bearing 2 drops of petroleum jelly, as described above must be applied immediately and the preparation turned over with a quick flip to prevent the fluids from running into the crevice between the slide and coverslip. After labelling and paraffining, slides may be incubated in either the upright or inverted position. The cells grow directly on the glass of the coverslip.

AFTER-CARE OF SLIDE CULTURES

Single coverslip cultures are very useful for short-term studies but they are difficult to handle subsequently except by a process of transfer. Carrel's immortal strain was kept going for over 30 years by this technique but it is really extremely tedious and is not recommended. The Maximow double coverslip technique was developed to facilitate handling of long-term coverslip cultures where it was desirable to leave the explant in its original location.

Washing and feeding double coverslip cultures

(1) By means of a razor blade, remove the paraffin seal, then with the finger and thumb remove the large coverslip with small one attached. Flip it over so that the culture is uppermost and lay it on a clean surface.

(2) With a needle in the left hand and forceps in the right, detach the small coverslip and transfer it to a Columbia staining dish containing balanced salt solution. Usually four coverslips are washed in one dish. Instead of using a special needle to prise up the small coverslip, a pointed (No. 11) Bard-Parker knife may be used in the same way. If Columbia staining dishes are not available, watch glasses or Petri dishes will serve the same function.

(3) After treating several explants in this way select a large clean coverslip for each culture and place it on a sterile surface. Remove a small coverslip from a washing dish and place it, culture up, on the large coverslip. Two to four cultures may be handled at a time. It will be found that by controlling the rate of withdrawal of the small coverslip from the balanced salt solution, the amount of fluid left adhering to it can be regulated fairly precisely. If too much remains, difficulties will be incurred subsequently in feeding the culture. If there is too little, air bubbles will appear between the two coverslips making observation difficult.

(4) Feed the culture by adding a drop of feeding solution (e.g. 1 part of balanced salt solution, 1 part of serum, 1 part of 50 per cent. embryo extract) to the small coverslip and attach a clean depression slide, as before, with petroleum jelly.

Patching

Sometimes it is necessary to patch the plasma clot if there is any evidence of liquefaction. The procedure is as follows. First, wash the cultures as before. Then in a watch glass place two drops of a mixture of plasma and balanced salt solution. To this add two drops of a mixture of serum and embryo extract. Mix these quickly and place a drop of the mixture on each coverslip before coagulation begins. The pipette and watch glass must be discarded after each patching. A clean petroleum jellied slide may then be attached. *Note.*—Never place a pipette contaminated with embryo extract in the tube of plasma.

FIG. 27
Cutting an explant for transfer to a new clot.

Transferring coverslip cultures

Coverslip cultures have to be transferred by cutting away the excess plasma from the explant and then dissecting it and re-explanting each of the resulting pieces on a new coverslip. Place the coverslip on a raised block. With a Bard-Parker knife and a small curved blade make a cut through the outgrowth (Fig. 27). Note that uninfiltrated plasma must not be included since otherwise further growth from the explant will not occur. Lift the knife cleanly away after cutting so as not to tear the clot. The square of tissue may then be cut into two or four pieces and each of these transferred to new coverslips and treated as new explants.

In setting up slide cultures the main mistakes made by beginners are as follows:
(1) Damage to the explant by excessive crushing or tearing during preparation.
(2) Inadequate washing of the explant with the result that erythrocytes and debris cloud the clot.
(3) Opacity of the clot from other causes such as bubbles or dirty embryo extract.

CARREL FLASK TECHNIQUE

This technique is now used very much less than formerly but it still has its proponents and therefore merits a description. Its main use nowadays is in the establishment of strains from fresh explants of tissue, by the technique described by Earle *et al.* For many purposes, other types of flask are quite satisfactory, *e.g.* Erlenmeyer flasks. A good Carrel flask, however, has excellent optical properties and this is an advantage if it is desired to follow growth of the cells microscopically. The design of the Carrel flask is of importance since those available commercially are very variable. It is particularly important that the neck should be as wide as possible since a narrow neck makes manipulations almost impossible. It is also desirable to have a flask which has excellent optical properties but very few of these are available since the manufacture of an

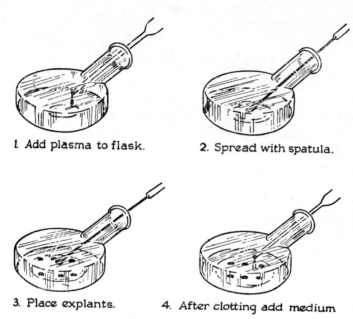

1 Add plasma to flask.   2. Spread with spatula.

3. Place explants.   4. After clotting add medium

FIG. 28
Preparing Carrel flask cultures.

optically-perfect Carrel flask is a highly skilled operation. The 30 ml. polystyrene culture flasks made by Falcon Plastics have all the properties of good Carrel flasks and can be recommended for these techniques.

The main advantages over coverslip cultures are as follows : The tissue can be maintained in the same flask for months or even years. Large numbers of cultures can be prepared comparatively easily and fairly large amounts of tissue can be grown. Large amounts of medium can be used and this makes it possible for the medium to be removed for assay. In flask cultures the gaseous phase can be readily controlled and the amount of medium can be measured accurately.

There are two types of Carrel flask techniques, thick and thin clot cultures. The thick clot encourages rapid growth and is particularly suitable for short-term cultures. The clots can be removed intact from the flask for staining. On the other hand, thin clot cultures are best for maintaining cultures over a considerable period of time and they are better suited for testing the effects of materials added to the medium.

PREPARATION OF CULTURES

(1) Place some D 3·5 (diameter of 3·5 cm.) Carrel flasks in a rack with their necks pointing to the right. A convenient number to handle is up to six at any one time. The necks should be flamed.
(2) Place one drop of plasma on the floor of each flask. Using a platinum spatula spread this plasma out in a circle extending just short of the edge of the floor of the flask.
(3) With the spatula, transfer the desired number of explants to the plasma and allow clotting to occur. The explants can be arranged according to a desired pattern by manipulation with the spatula. Dr. Parshley uses a convenient planting guide which is placed under the flask and which shows where the explants should be situated.
(4) After the plasma has clotted and the explants are fixed in position, extra medium can be added. In the case of thick clot cultures 1·2 ml. of dilute ($\frac{1}{4}$) plasma are placed on top of the explants and the whole is then left to clot. For thin clot cultures, 1·2 ml. of dilute ($\frac{1}{4}$) serum is added instead of the plasma.
(5) Finally, the flasks should be gassed with an appropriate gas phase, usually 5 per cent. of carbon dioxide in air.

Renewal of medium
(1) The old fluid is drawn off by means of a pipette.
(2) 1·2 ml. fluid medium is added to replace this.
(3) The flask is again gassed.

In the case of thick clot cultures, the flask should be inverted and allowed to drain for several hours before replacing the used plasma. In either case, if there is any liquefaction of the clot a patch should be made by adding a drop of fresh plasma and allowing it to clot.

The transfer of tissue

If it is desired to transfer the tissue from these flasks to other vessels it has to be removed and cut into suitable pieces before being replanted. In the case of thin clot cultures the explant can be scraped off with a spatula and removed for cutting. On the other hand, in dealing with thick clot cultures the entire clot must be carefully loosened with a spatula and slid out entire on to a glass plate before cutting up the explants.

A common use of the Carrel flask technique, as has been mentioned previously, is the establishment of cell strains. For this purpose, a strip of tissue 5 to 10 mm. long and 1 to 2 mm. wide is planted in a thick clot. After it has begun to grow well the tissue is removed and replanted. It is a common practice to trypsinise the entire clot after the culture has become established and to use the suspension to seed new vessels. In this way, the cells can be transferred from a plasma substrate to a glass substrate. The procedure to be used for trypsinisation is described in Chapter XIII.

TEST-TUBE CULTURES

Ordinary test-tubes form very cheap and convenient vessels for the cultivation of cells and tissues. They can be used for preparing large numbers of cultures and can be set up either in roller drums or in stationary racks. They have the advantage of being cheap and easy to handle in large quantities. There are, however, a number of disadvantages in the use of test-tube cultures. The optical conditions are very poor. Also it is very difficult to quantitate accurately due to the curvature of the inside of the tube. There is a definite risk of contamination of ordinary stoppered tubes due to a slight leak of air or medium between the stoppers and the tubes. This may particularly occur on opening tubes which have been removed from the incubator when there is almost invariably an inrush of air. This is likely to carry with it any organisms which may have settled between the stopper and the lip of the tube. If a small drop of medium has been left there during a previous transfer the region is almost certain to be heavily contaminated. This complication must always be kept in mind in handling test-tube cultures.

The actual techniques of test-tube culture resemble closely those employed with other vessels. Cultures may be grown in plasma clots, in which case the technique is very similar to the

Carrel flask technique. They may also be grown directly on the glass wall of the vessel without a plasma clot and this technique requires a little more consideration. Lastly, cell suspensions may be allowed to settle and grow on the inside of test-tubes and this technique is exactly the same as that employed with other types of vessels. This is described in Chapter XV.

Plasma clot technique

(1) With a Pasteur pipette, place a drop of plasma near the bottom of each tube and spread it over the lower third of the tube.

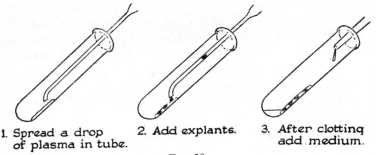

1. Spread a drop of plasma in tube.   2. Add explants.   3. After clotting add medium.

FIG. 29
Preparing roller-tube cultures.

(2) Transfer the explants, usually about four, to the plasma and leave to clot.
(3) After they are fixed in position, add medium, usually 0·5 to 1 ml. per tube.
(4) Stopper and label the tubes and place them in a stationary rack or in a roller drum in the incubator.

Feeding test-tube cultures

Feeding test-tube cultures is simply achieved by removing the supernatant fluid and replacing it with fresh medium.

Patching test-tube cultures

If there is evidence of liquefaction of the plasma clot then, after removal of the supernatant fluid, one drop of plasma mixed with one drop of culture medium should be added to the tube and it should be rotated slightly to ensure that the culture area is covered. After the plasma has clotted, fresh fluid medium may be added.

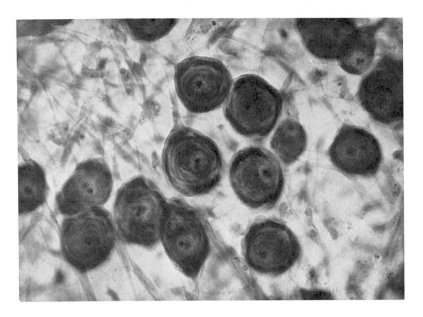

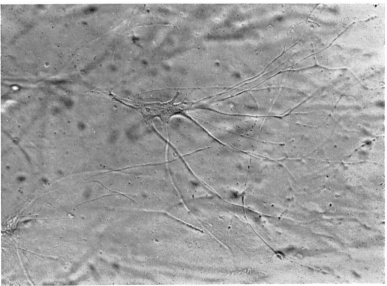

PLATE 7

Top: Chick embryonic dorsal root ganglion cells, 15 days in culture.
Stained eosin-thymol blue. × 350. (Courtesy of Mrs. E. Peterson and Dr.
M. R. Murray.) *Bottom*: Adult human lumbar sympathetic ganglion cell.
23 days in culture. Phase contrast. × 175.

facing p. 176

Transfer of cultures from test-tubes

Cultures can very readily be removed from test-tubes by means of a bent Pasteur pipette. With the tip a small circular cut is made in the plasma surrounding the chosen colony. By gently pushing on the margins of the dissected plasma the small disc containing the colony is freed from the glass vessel. It is then transferred to a glass plate and trimmed to remove the peripheral plasma in the

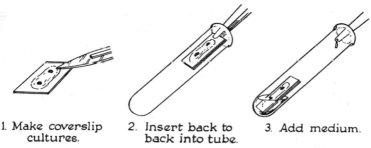

| 1. Make coverslip cultures. | 2. Insert back to back into tube. | 3. Add medium. |

Fig. 30

Preparing flying coverslip cultures in roller tubes.

same way as for coverslip cultures. Note that in all procedures involving the opening of test-tubes which contain cultures, great care should be taken to flame the mouth of the tube very thoroughly indeed. If the stopper has become wet by contact with medium, it is best to discard it and use a new one.

Culture of primary explants in roller tubes without plasma

It is possible to grow fragments of tissue direct on glass without the use of a coagulum, and this technique has been used quite commonly with roller tubes. In order to prevent the explants from falling off the wall of the tube, particularly when it is being washed by fluid continuously in a roller drum, it is necessary to allow them to adhere by partial drying. The fragments of tissue are taken up into a Pasteur pipette along with some medium and are transferred to the tube. This is rolled around gently as the liquid containing the explants is added. The fragments may thus be left adhering to the tubes and after they have all been placed the excess medium is removed. The tubes are then stoppered and left to dry for 10 to 15 minutes; 0·5 to 1 ml. of medium is added and the tubes are placed on a rack or in a roller drum. The cells grow directly on

12

the glass wall of the tube. A similar technique to the one described has been used in biochemical studies with large numbers of explants (Gerarde, Jones and Winnick).

Flying coverslips in test-tubes

A very convenient way of preparing coverslip cultures for histological examination or for mounting in perfusion chambers is by means of so-called 'flying coverslips' in test-tubes. Flying coverslips are small narrow coverslips (11 mm. wide, 40 or 22 mm. long). These can be inserted into ordinary $6'' \times \frac{5}{8}''$ test-tubes. Cultures are prepared on them in the standard manner for coverslip cultures but instead of mounting them on depression slides, they are slid into test-tubes. A fluid medium is added to the tubes (1 to 2 ml. each) which may then be placed in a stationary rack or in a roller drum. Feeding is simply performed by removing the fluid medium and replacing it with fresh material. Large numbers of cultures can be conveniently prepared in this way.

THREE-DIMENSIONAL SUBSTRATES

In those techniques which have been described, the cells are allowed to migrate and grow in an essentially two-dimensional environment. This produces very flat cells spread over a large area. As a result the internal structures are beautifully displayed but, on the other hand, many of the characteristic morphological appearances are lost. Also, the size of the population is limited by the extent of the surface which can be managed. This latter difficulty has now been overcome by growing cells in suspension but it was with the object of increasing the surface area that most three-dimensional substrates were developed. Their main application at present is, however, in providing a three-dimensional matrix in which the cells may develop structures similar to those which exist *in vivo*.

Three-dimensional substrates which have been used are glass wool, glass cloth, glass helices, cellulose sponge and gelatin sponge. Of these, cellulose sponge, particularly in combination with plasma, is the only one used to any extent.

The material used by Leighton (1951) is fine-pore cellulose sponge, manufactured by Dupont. This is used for removing excessive moisture from photographic plates and is available from Ilford

Ltd. It is prepared by first cutting it into strips of about 5 × 10 mm. cross-section. These are then held between glass slides and sliced with a razor blade. Slices about 0·5 mm. thick should be used and any that happen to be thicker should be rejected. They are prepared by boiling for a total of one hour in two changes of distilled water and then washed for 30 minutes each in acetone, ether and absolute alcohol. After a final boiling in distilled water the slices can be autoclaved and are ready for use.

Cultures are prepared according to any of the standard procedures already described, the cellulose sponge being incorporated in a plasma clot along with the explant. The migrating cells invade the interstices of the sponge. These cultures are not very satisfactory for direct examination and are usually fixed and sectioned first. Leighton recommends fixation in Zenker-formalin for 30 minutes, followed by washing in water for two hours. The sponges can then be stored as required in 80 per cent. alcohol. Before sectioning they are taken through alcohols and toluol (15 minutes each change) to paraffin and sectioned at 6 microns.

BIBLIOGRAPHY

CARREL, A. (1929). La technique de la culture des tissus en goutte pendante. *C.R. Soc. Biol. (Paris)* **106**, 7.

CARREL, A. & BURROWS, M. T. (1911). Cultivation of tissues *in vitro* and its technique. *J. exp. Med.* **13**, 387.

CARREL, A. & EBELING, A. H. (1922). Pure cultures of large mononuclear leucocytes. *J. exp. Med.* **36**, 365.

EARLE, W. R. (1939). Use of strip-shaped explants in tissue cultures. *Arch. Path. (Chicago)* **27**, 88.

EARLE, W. R., SCHILLING, E. L. & SHANNON, J. E. (1951). Growth of animal tissue cells on three-dimensional substrates. *J. nat. Cancer Inst.* **12**, 179.

EHRMANN, R. & GEY, G. O. (1953). The use of cell colonies on glass for evaluating nutrition and growth in roller-tube cultures. *J. nat. Cancer Inst.* **13**, 1099.

FRISCH, A. W. (1952). A glass wool matrix for roller tube tissue cultures. *Proc. Soc. exp. Biol. N.Y.* **81**, 545.

GERARDE, H. W., JONES, M. & WINNICK, T. (1952). Protein synthesis and amino acid turnover in tissue culture. *J. biol. Chem.* **196**, 51.

HULLIGER, LOTTE (1956). Über die unterschiedlichen Entwicklingsfähigkeiten der Zellen des Blutes und der Lymphe *in vitro*. *Virchows Arch.* **329**, 99.

LEIGHTON, J. (1951). A sponge matrix method for tissue culture. Formation of organized aggregates of cells *in vitro*. *J. nat. Cancer Inst.* **12**, 545.

LEIGHTON, J. (1954). The growth patterns of some transplantable animal tumors in sponge matrix tissue culture. *J. nat. Cancer Inst.* **15**, 275.

LEIGHTON, J. & KLINE, I. (1954). Studies on human cancer using sponge matrix tissue culture. *Tex. Rep. Biol. Med.* **12**, 847.

MAXIMOW, A. (1925). Tissue cultures of young mammalian embryos. *Contr. Embryol. Carneg. Instn.* **16**, 47.

CHAPTER XII

PRIMARY EXPLANTATION TECHNIQUES

II. ORGAN AND EMBRYO CULTURE

ALTHOUGH the organ culture technique has been used to grow intact embryonic organs, the name is actually something of a misnomer since it is usually employed to maintain small pieces of organs *in vitro*. The object of the organ culture technique is to maintain the architecture of the tissue and to direct it towards normal development such as occurs *in vivo*. In order to achieve this aim, it is essential that the tissue should never be disrupted or damaged and this requires careful handling, so that organ culture techniques generally demand more careful manipulation than tissue culture techniques. (See Chapter XIV.)

Media used for growing organ cultures are generally the same as those used for other types of tissue culture. Nowadays, synthetic or semi-synthetic media are very commonly used and, on the whole, have proved very satisfactory.

The techniques of organ culture can be divided into those employing a solid medium and those employing a fluid medium.

Organ cultures on plasma clots

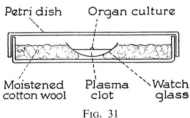

FIG. 31
The 'classical' organ culture technique.

The classical technique of organ culture consists of placing a small, carefully dissected piece of tissue on top of a plasma clot. The plasma clot is formed in a watch glass which itself rests on a pad of cotton-wool in a Petri dish. The cotton-wool is kept moist to prevent excessive evaporation from the dish. The tissue fragment invariably gives rise to some liquefaction of the plasma in its immediate vicinity and has to be transferred to a new situation every day or two. This requires some care in handling. The technique is rarely employed in the above form nowadays since it has been improved by using a raft of lens paper or rayon net on which the tissue is placed. Transfer of the tissue can then be achieved easily by moving the raft very slightly.

The clot for these cultures may be formed by mixing 15 drops of plasma with five drops of embryo extract. For best results it is recommended that the plasma should not have been stored for more than a week after collection. Embryo extract for organ culture is prepared from 12 to 14-day incubated chick embryos. The gall-bladder is first removed and the remainder of the embryo pulped by cutting repeatedly with scissors in an equal amount of BSS. After standing at room temperature for one hour the extract is centrifuged and the supernatant is used as embryo extract. This product is sometimes referred to as embryo juice (EJ).

Cultures on agar

Wolff and Wolff (1952) have used media solidified with agar as supports for organ cultures. In much of their work they have used a medium composed of seven parts 1 per cent. agar (Difco) in Gey's BSS, three parts chick embryo extract and three parts horse serum. In other studies a defined medium has been incorporated in the agar. This method has the advantage that the support does not liquefy and no additional mechanical support is required. The source of the agar is important since not all products are satis-factory.

Embryonic organs generally grow well on this medium but tumours from adult animals will not normally survive. However, Wolff and Schneider have shown that tumours can be grown parasitically on chick embryonic mesonephros which itself grows satisfactorily on it.

Fluid media

The use of solid substrates limits the experimental value of the method since sampling and analysis of the medium is difficult. Chen (1954) first grew organ cultures on a fluid medium by placing them on a raft made of lens paper which floated on a synthetic medium. Cellulose acetate net has proved more satisfactory and is used by some workers but the techniques employing a platform of perforated metal gauze, introduced by Trowell (1954), are now tending to replace 'raft' techniques, which are rather more trouble-some to use.

PREPARING AN ORGAN CULTURE ON A CELLULOSE ACETATE RAFT
(Shaffer)

1. A suitable cellulose acetate fabric with holes 0·5 - 1 mm. square is selected and cut into pieces of suitable size. Shaffer (1956) used voile, Silene V. V. & Co. but this is no longer obtainable. The essential property of a suitable rayon is solubility in acetone. The

Preparing explant
on gauze raft.

Transferring culture
to watch-glass.

FIG. 32
Preparing an organ culture on a rayon raft.

pieces are prepared by three successive washes in glass-distilled water, two in absolute alcohol and two in ether, over a period of some hours. They are immersed in a silicone solution, *e.g.* Siliclad (Clay-Adams) 1 part in 100 parts water or MS 1109, drained, allowed to dry and left in a damp atmosphere overnight. They are washed with several changes of glass-distilled water, rinsed with absolute alcohol, cut into pieces of suitable size (2×1 cm.) and sterilised by dry heat at 130° C. (not to be exceeded).

2. The raft is placed on a very small drop of balanced salt solution (only enough to fill the interstices of the net) and the tissue is placed on it. The net is lifted from the drop of saline and excess fluid is removed by touching it against dry glass momentarily. It is gently placed in the surface of 0·5 ml. of medium in a watch glass.

3. Feeding of the culture is performed by removing the net, with its culture, removing excess fluid as before and placing it on top of a fresh pool of medium.

Note.—If the siliconed fabric is wetted with a proteinaceous solution it will no longer float so that care must be taken in handling to prevent this.

The techniques so far described have been applied almost entirely to the cultivation of embryonic organs or embryonic organ fragments. The cultivation of fragments of adult tissues as organ cultures has proved a particularly difficult problem and Trowell has adduced evidence that this is because of the much greater requirement of adult tissues for oxygen. Using the special medium T8 referred to in Chapter VI and special apparatus permitting the use of 95 per cent. O_2 in the gas phase, Trowell has successfully cultured a variety of adult organs, including liver. In these studies he found that serum was toxic and it should be noted that his experiments were done with serum-free media.

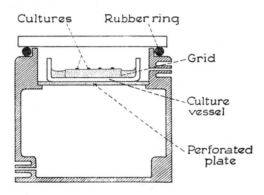

FIG. 33
Trowell's type II culture chamber.

Trowell's Type II culture chamber is illustrated in Figure 33. It consists of an aluminium chamber which can be sealed by a glass plate and which can be gassed with a mixture of 95 per cent. O_2 and 5 per cent. CO_2. The chamber is divided into upper and lower chambers by a perforated plate. The upper chamber contains a culture dish (Trowell used fused silica) and the lower chamber serves as a gas reservoir. Within the culture dish is a square metal grid made of stainless steel expanded metal. This is made by taking a strip 25×33 mm. and bending it about 4 mm. from the ends to form a grid 25 mm. square, standing on 4 mm. legs.

The culture vessel is filled with medium so that it just comes up to the top of the grid and a piece of lens paper (Green's C105) 27 mm. square is placed on top so that it just becomes wet. The organ fragments are planted on this. Squares of agar gel (2 per cent. in 0·7 per cent. NaCl, 1-3 mm. thick) may be substituted for lens paper if so desired. The tissue fragments should not exceed 2 mm. in diameter: otherwise central necrosis occurs.

In setting up the apparatus it should first be gassed at 37° C. After placing the organ fragments in position the apparatus should be gassed again before incubating. The tissues may be removed for sectioning after six to nine days of cultivation.

Many modifications of the Trowell apparatus have now been developed and these are used for the culture of both embryonic and adult material. When embryonic material is cultured a gas phase of air is generally used. In the simplest type of apparatus 50-60 mm. Petri dishes are used as culture vessels. Stainless steel gauze grids, of the type described above, are placed in these and the cultures are set up in them in exactly the same way. The culture vessels are placed in a desiccator, with water in the bottom to maintain the humidity. If necessary a gas phase of 5 per cent. CO_2 in air or 5 per cent. CO_2 in oxygen can be passed into the desiccator before sealing it. The cultures are incubated by placing the desiccator in a 37° C. incubator. Instead of a desiccator, a Filde's anaerobic jar, a plastic ' sandwich box ' sealed with sellotape, or a more specialised vessel such as the modified Kilner jar used by Lasnitzki or Trowell's original apparatus may be used. The nature of the container is rather unimportant.

Since success in growing organ cultures often depends on the rapid but gentle manipulation of the material a detailed description of setting up a culture is outlined below. Dissection of the material is necessarily prolonged and it is desirable to work with it under some kind of hood. Fell uses a simple shield made of perspex (plexiglass). This is simply a box about 8 in. long, 3 in. high and 4 in. deep with the front open. A similar, smaller shade can be placed under the dissecting microscope when it is being used. A description of a dissection of limb bones for use in this exercise will be found in Chapter XIV.

SETTING UP AN ORGAN CULTURE OF EMBRYONIC LIMB BONES ON A GRID
(Based on an exercise designed by Dame Honor Fell)

Set up apparatus

A binocular dissecting microscope with a perspex shield is required. A sterile museum jar placed on its side may be used for holding sterile instruments; it is propped up so that its floor slants, thus preventing the sterile tips of the instruments from making contact with the glass. A beaker of boiling water is needed for re-sterilising instruments. A long perspex shade (as described above) is used for shielding the material while it is being manipulated. The instruments required are a mounted needle and a knife preferably a well-honed cataract knife, but a No. 11 scalpel blade can often be used). Some pasteur pipettes and 2 ml. graduated pipettes are also needed. Suitable culture vessels are glass capsules 30 mm. in diameter contained in 3 in. Petri dishes. The smaller dish is surrounded with a ring of cotton-wool, to be moistened in order to maintain high humidity. It is often convenient to set up two 30 mm. culture vessels in a single 10 cm. Petri dish. If this is done it is important to separate the two vessels by a siliconed glass rod to prevent ' creep ' of saline from the cotton wool. The platform is made of such a size that when a given volume (say 1·5 ml.) of medium is added to the capsule it will just come up to the level of the grid. Parker's 858 medium of medium 109 containing 10 per cent. calf serum makes a suitable medium for many experiments.

Prepare dishes
1. Put 10 ml. sterile 0·9 per cent. saline in each Petri dish. (Open the dish just wide enough to admit the pipette; push the end of the pipette into the cotton-wool and release the saline gently to avoid flooding the capsule.)
2. Add 1·5 ml. of medium to each culture dish; drop six drops on the middle of the grid, then add the rest of the medium on to the floor of the dish. (When the medium on the floor makes contact with the large drop on the grid, the latter will pass through the mesh leaving a large circular wet patch.
3. Cover the culture dishes with a piece of board, e.g. a slide tray. (This prevents the lids from misting over.)

Prepare explants (see Chapter XIV)

Set up explants (e.g. chick limb bones)
1. Place the culture dish on the left of the Petri dish containing the explants. both under a shield.
2. Suck off BSS from the explants in the hollow of the slide with a fine pipette (but leave a drop of BSS on the flat part of the hollow-ground slide).

3. Rinse the knife and needle in boiling water, then in the drop of BSS on the hollow-ground slide.

4. Push the bundle of bones on to the tip of the knife with the needle, then lay the needle across the top of the perspex shield with the point projecting into the air (to avoid contamination).

5. Raise the lid of the culture dish and deposit the bones on the wet patch in the middle of the grid.

6. Place the culture dish under the shield on the dissecting microscope, remove the lid and, with the knife and needle, distribute the bones on the grid so that they do not touch one another.

7. Replace the lid of the dish and lay it on one side beneath a slide tray.

8. When all the culture dishes are ready place them in a desiccator jar. Pass a gentle current of 5 per cent. CO_2 in air into the desiccator for three to four minutes.

9. Close the jar tightly and incubate.

Subculture (The medium should be changed every 48 hours.)

1. Place the culture dish on the bench beneath the long perspex shield, propping it up on one side with any convenient object, so that the fluid medium drains towards you.

2. Raise the lid and insert the tip of an angled pipette beneath the grid. (This will cause the grid to tilt.)

3. Suck off all the old fluid.

4. Place the Petri dish flat on the bench.

5. Fill a pipette with 1·5 ml. fresh medium, lift the culture dish lid just enough to admit the pipette and drop the fresh medium on top of the explants. (To avoid trapping bubbles beneath the grid drop the fluid first near the two closed sides of the grid.)

6. For bones (but not necessarily for other types of explants): place the Petri dish under the dissecting microscope and turn the explants over. (Two angled needles are particularly convenient for this.)

7. Replace in the desiccator, gas and incubate.

The essential feature of the organ culture technique is the prevention of migration of cells from the tissue fragments. This is achieved either by moving the tissue fragments frequently or by dissecting the tissue with great care so that no damage is done such as would promote migration, or by using a substrate such as agar or rayon-acetate on which cells will not normally migrate.

A kind of organ culture can be achieved by growing fragments of tissue in suspension. This technique has been in use for many years and, as the Maitland culture, is well-known in virology. A similar technique has also been used by Parker for immunological studies and by Paul and Pearson for biochemical studies.

BIBLIOGRAPHY

BIGGERS, J. D. & HEYNER, S. (1961). Studies on the amino acid requirements of cartilaginous long bone rudiments *in vitro*. *Proc. Soc. exp. Biol. (N.Y.)* **108**, 616.

BORGHESE, E. (1950). Explantation experiments on the influence of the connective tissue capsule on the development of the epithelial part of the submandibular gland of Mus musculus. *J. Anat. (Lond.)* **84**, 303.

BORGHESE, E. (1950). The development *in vitro* of the submandibular and sublingual glands of the Mus musculus. *J. Anat. (Lond.)* **84**, 287.

CARPENTER, E., BEATTIE, J. & CHAMBERS, R. D. (1954). The uptake of I^{131} by embryonic chick thyroid glands *in vivo* and *in vitro*. *J. exp. Zool.* **127**, 249.

CHEN, J. M. (1952). Studies on the morphogenesis of the mouse sternum. I. Normal embryonic development. *J. Anat. (Lond.)* **86**, 373.

CHEN, J. M. (1952). Studies on the morphogenesis of the mouse sternum. II. Experiments on the origin of the sternum and its capacity for self-differentiation *in vitro*. *J. Anat. (Lond.)* **86**, 387.

CHEN, J. M. (1952). Studies on the morphogenesis of the mouse sternum. III. Experiments on the closure and segmentation of the sternal bands. *J. Anat. (Lond.)* **87**, 130.

CHEN, J. M. (1954). The cultivation in fluid medium of organized liver, pancreas and other tissues of foetal rats. *Exp. Cell Res.* **7**, 518.

CHEN, J. M. (1954). The effect of insulin on embryonic limb-bones cultivated *in vitro*. *J. Physiol. (Lond.)* **125**, 148.

CHLOPIN, A. (1922). Ueber *in vitro* kulturen der embryonalen gewebe der Saugetiere. *Arch. mikr. Anat.*, **96**, 435.

DAMERON, F. (1961). L'influence de divers mésenchymes sur la différenciation de l'epithelium pulmonaire de l'embryon de poulet en culture *in vitro*. *J. Embryol. exp. Morph.* **9**, 628.

DICKSON, J. A. & LESLIE, I. (1963). A filter-well technique for studying the metabolism of reaggregating cell populations. *Exp. Cell Res.* **31**, 214.

FELL, HONOR B. (1951). Methods for study of organized growth *in vitro*. Techniques of bone cultivation. In *Methods in Medical Research*. Ed. M. B. Visscher. Chicago: Year Book Publishers.

FELL, HONOR B. (1953). The effect of vitamin A on organ cultures of skeletal and other tissues. In *Connective Tissue*. Ed. C. Rogan. New York: Macy.

FELL, HONOR B. (1953). Recent advances in organ culture. *Sci. Progr.* **162**, 212.

FELL, HONOR B. (1954). The effect of hormones and vitamin A on organ cultures. *Ann. N.Y. Acad. Sci.* **58**, 1183.

FELL, HONOR B. (1956). Effect of excess vitamin A on organized tissues cultivated *in vitro*. *Brit. med. Bull.* **12**, 35.

FELL, HONOR B. & MELLANBY, E. (1955). The biological action of thyroxine on embryonic bones grown in tissue culture. *J. Physiol. (Lond.)* **127**, 427.

FELL, HONOR B. & MELLANBY, E. (1956). The effect of 1-triiodothyronine on the growth and development of embryonic chick limb-bones in tissue culture. *J. Physiol. (Lond.)* **133**, 89.

GAILLARD, P. J. (1950). Sex cell formation in explants of the foetal human ovarian cortex. *Proc. Acad. Sci., Amst.* **53**, 1300, 1337.

GAILLARD, P. J. (1951). Methods for study of organized growth *in vitro*. Organ culture technique using embryologic watch glasses. In *Methods in Medical Research*. Ed. M. B. Visscher. Chicago: Year Book Publishers. **4**, 241.

GAILLARD, P. J. (1953). Growth and differentiation of explanted tissues. *Int. Rev. Cytol.* **2**, 331.

GAILLARD, P. J. (1955). Parathyroid gland tissue and bone *in vitro*. I. *Exp. Cell Res.* **3**, 154.

GAILLARD, P. J. (1957). Morphogenesis in animal tissue cultures. *J. nat. Cancer Inst.* **19**, 591.

GROBSTEIN, C. (1953). Epithelio-mesenchymal specificity in the morphogenesis of mouse submandibular rudiments *in vitro*. *J. exp. Zool.* **124**, 383.

GROBSTEIN, C. (1953). Morphogenetic interaction between embryonic mouse tissues separated by a membrane filter. *Nature (Lond.)* **172**, 869.

GROBSTEIN, C. (1953). Analysis *in vitro* of the early organization of the rudiments of the mouse submandibular glands. *J. Morph.* **93**, 19.

GROBSTEIN, C. (1955). Tissue interaction in the morphogenesis of mouse embryonic rudiments in vitro. In *Aspects of Synthesis and Order in Growth*. Ed. D. Rudnick. Princeton: University Press.

GROBSTEIN, C. (1956). Trans-filter induction of tubules in mouse metanephrogenic mesenchyme. *Exp. Cell Res.* **10**, 424.

KEUNING, F. J. (1948). Histogenesis and origin of the autonomic nerve plexus in the upper digestive tube of the chick. *Acta Neerl. morph.* **6**, 1.

LASNITZKI, I. (1954). The effect of estrone alone and combined with 20-methyl cholanthrene on mouse prostate glands grown *in vitro*. *Cancer Res.* **14**, 632.

LASNITZKI, I. (1955). The effect of testosterone propionate on organ cultures of the mouse prostate. *J. Endocr.* **12**, 236.

LASNITZKI, I. (1956). The effect of 3:4 benzpyrene on human foetal lung grown *in vitro*. *J. Path. Bact.* **71**, 262.

LASNITZKI, I. (1961). Effect of excess vitamin A on the normal and oestrone-treated mouse vagina grown in chemically defined media. *Exp. Cell Res.* **24**, 37.

MARTINOVITCH, P. (1951). Culture of infantile endocrine glands of rats by watch glass technique in a moist chamber. In *Methods in Medical Research*. Chicago: Year Book Publishers, Inc.

MARTINOVITCH, P. N. (1953). A modification of the watch glass technique for the cultivation of endocrine glands of infantile rats. *Exp. Cell Res.* **4**, 490.

MARTINOVITCH, P. N. (1955). Infantile rat adrenal transplanted into the anterior eye chamber of adrenalectomized hosts after cultivation *in vitro*. *J. exp. Zool.* **129**, 99.

NITZIMA, M. (1956). Tissue culture studies on amphibian metamorphosis. I. Growth patterns of tadpole tissue. *Folia anat. japon.* **28**, 59.

NIU, M. C. (1954). Further studies on the origin of amphibian pigment cells. *J. exp. Zool.* **125**, 199.

NIU, M. C. & TWITTY, V. C. (1950). The origin of epidermal melanophores during metamorphosis of Triturus torosus. *J. exp. Zool.* **113**, 633.

NIU, M. C. & TWITTY, V. C. (1953). The differentiation of gastrula ectoderm in medium conditioned by axial mesoderm. *Proc. nat. Acad. Sci. (Wash.)* **39**, 985.

PETERSON, E. R. & MURRAY, M. R. (1960). Modification of development in isolated dorsal root ganglia by nutritional and physical factors. *Develop. Biol.* **2**, 461.

PROP, F. J. A. (1959). Organ cultures of total mammary glands of the mouse. *Nature (Lond.)* **184**, 379.

SCHABERG, A. (1955). Regeneration of the adrenal cortex *in vitro. Anat. Rec.* **122**, 205.

SCHABERG, A. (1955). Observations on the adrenal cortex of 5-day old rats. *Transplant. Bull.* **2**, 145.

SHAFFER, B. M. (1956). The culture of organs from the embryonic chick on cellulose-acetate fabric. *Exp. Cell Res.* **11**, 244.

STRANGEWAYS, T. S. P. & FELL, H. B. (1926). Experimental studies on the differentiation of embryonic tissues growing *in vivo* and *in vitro.* II. The development of the early embryonic eye of the fowl when cultivated *in vitro. Proc. R. Soc.* **B100**, 273.

THOMSON, D. (1914). Some further researches on the cultivation of tissues *in vitro. Proc. R. Soc. Med.* **7**, Marcus Beck Lab. Reps. (2), 15.

TROWELL, O. A. (1952). The culture of lymph nodes *in vitro. Exp. Cell Res.* **3**, 79.

TROWELL, O. A. (1954). A modified technique for organ culture *in vitro. Exp. Cell Res.* **6**, 246.

TROWELL, O. A. (1959). The culture of mature organs in a synthetic medium. *Exp. Cell Res.* **16**, 118.

WOLFF, EM. (1953). Sur la croissance et la différenciation en milieu synthétique de la syrinx de l'embryon de poulet. *C.R. Soc. Biol. (Paris)* **147**, 864.

WOLFF, EM. (1955). Les besoins spécifiques en acides aminés de la syrinx de l'embryon de poulet cultivée *in vitro* sur un milieu entièrement synthétique. *C.R. Acad. Sci. (Paris)* **240**, 1016.

WOLFF, ET. (1952). La culture d'organes embryonaires *in vitro. Rev. sci. (Paris)* **90**, 189.

WOLFF, ET. (1954). Analyse de l'action des substances tératogènes par la méthode des cultures d'organes in vitro. *Rev. Path. comp.* **53**, 1057.

WOLFF, ET. (1960). Sur une nouvelle modalité de la culture organotypique. *C.R. Acad. Sci. (Paris)* **250**, 3881.

WOLFF, ET. & BRESCH, D. (1955). Sur les parabioses heterogenes d'organes embryonaires *in vitro. Tex. Rep. Biol. Med.* **10**, 463.

WOLFF, ET. & HAFFEN, K. (1952). Sur une méthode de culture d'organes embryonnaires *in vitro. Tex. Rep. Biol. Med.* **10**, 463.

WOLFF, ET. & WOLFF, EM. (1952). Le déterminisme de la différenciation sexuelle de la syrinx du canard cultivée *in vitro. Bull. Biol.* **86**, 325.

CHOPPED TISSUE TECHNIQUE

In the techniques described so far, each fragment of tissue is individually manipulated and planted. While this generally provides the best circumstances for controlled growth of an intact tissue, it severely limits the amount of tissue that can be handled and consequently for the large-scale cultivation of viruses or for biochemical investigations, these techniques have a restricted application. To overcome this, a number of methods have been developed.

Trypsinisation of fresh tissues to obtain uniform cell suspensions and the use of strains are elegant methods of handling large numbers of cells but they are limited to a few tissues. A somewhat cruder technique employing suspensions of minced tissue has been in use for many years for the cultivation of large amounts of fresh tissue, both for virus growth and biochemical investigations. It is of particular importance since it has been widely used for growing viruses in the manufacture of vaccines. With some refinements it can be used quantitatively with a fair measure of reproducibility.

The technique was first used by Maitland and Maitland in 1928 for the cultivation of vaccinia virus in suspensions of minced kidney in a mixture of serum and Tyrode's solution. Parker used it for a study of antibody formation in spleen, and an essentially similar technique has been used by Chen and ourselves for morphological studies on the one hand and biochemical studies on the other.

Cultivation of poliomyelitis virus in minced tissue suspensions

This represents at once the simplest and most important application of the method to date. Fresh monkey kidneys are decapsulated and halved. The pelvis of the kidney is removed, leaving mainly the outer cortex. This is cut into small pieces and then chopped rather finely (usually with scissors) in Morgan and Parker's medium 199. The chopped tissue is transferred to 1 litre Roux flasks, along with some medium 199. The flasks are placed in a rocker which keeps the tissue agitated by rocking it back and forth through an angle of about 45° about twenty times a minute. After 24 hours the culture is inoculated with virus. The material is ready for harvesting in another four to seven days and is then processed for vaccine manufacture. Further details of vaccine preparation are given in Chapter XXI.

If it is desired to obtain more quantitative results, the following procedure is recommended, using the McIlwain tissue chopper (Plate 8) to cut uniform explants.

CUTTING CHICK EMBRYONIC HEART EXPLANTS BY MEANS OF THE McILWAIN TISSUE CHOPPER

1. Remove the metal cutting table and sterilise it by dry heat. Also sterilise a number of razor blades for the instrument and a supply of filter-papers (9 cm.). Swab the cutting arm, the moving platform and all other accessible parts with 80 per cent. ethanol and allow to dry.

2. Remove the hearts from chick embryos of up to 15 days. With a pair of scalpels cut off the atria and large vessels. Discard these.

3. Split the remaining ventricles in their greatest plane to give two halves from each heart. Wash in BSS.

4. Replace the metal cutting table (handling in the paper in which it was sterilised to avoid contamination). By means of forceps, place a razor blade in the holder and adjust it, screwing the clamp for the blade very tight. Place a sheet of filter-paper on the platform and moisten with about 0·5 ml. BSS. Start the machine. Add other filter-papers and readjust the blade if necessary until it is cutting evenly into the top filter-paper but not through it.

5. Place the halved hearts on the cutting table with the inside down and the rather tough pericardium up. Press them down into the moist filter-paper with the forceps used to handle them.

6. Having set the chopper to cut slices of 0·25 to 0·75 mm., set the machine in operation. When all the tissue has been sliced turn the cutting table at right angles to the previous direction. Re-set the platform and repeat the cutting in this direction.

7. Remove the diced tissue by means of a sterile platinum wire with the end flattened to form a spatula. Transfer this tissue to a container with growth medium and, by rotating the wire rapidly, ensure that the fragments are separated from each other.

8. The fragments may be pipetted by means of a wide-mouthed pipette or handled individually, according to the purpose for which they are to be used.

BIBLIOGRAPHY

McILWAIN, H. & BUDDLE, H. L. (1953). Techniques in tissue metabolism. 1. A mechanical chopper. *Biochem. J.* **53,** 412.

MAITLAND, H. B. & MAITLAND, M. C. (1928). Cultivation of vaccinia virus without tissue culture. *Lancet* **215,** 596.

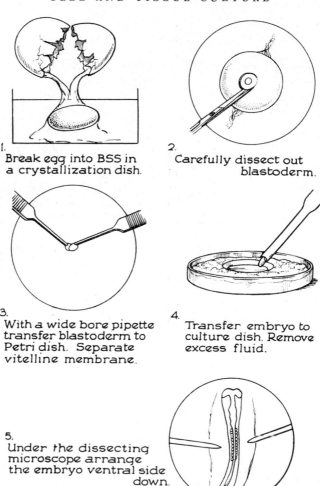

1. Break egg into BSS in a crystallization dish.

2. Carefully dissect out blastoderm.

3. With a wide bore pipette transfer blastoderm to Petri dish. Separate vitelline membrane.

4. Transfer embryo to culture dish. Remove excess fluid.

5. Under the dissecting microscope arrange the embryo ventral side down.

FIG. 34
Culture of the whole chick embryo.

WHOLE EMBRYO CULTURE

It will be remembered that probably the first recorded successful explantation was performed by Wilhelm Roux in 1885 when he maintained the medullary plate of a chick embryo for some time in saline. The technique was developed by Spratt (1956, 1957) for testing the effect of metabolic inhibitors on embryonic development.

PLATE 8

The McIlwain Tissue Chopper. A razor blade (B) mounted in an arm (A) impinges on the tissue which is supported on a platform, advanced by a ratchet and pawl arrangement (Courtesy of Professor H. McIlwain and the *Biochemical Journal.*)

In the form he developed it constitutes a fairly straightforward technique which, however, requires considerable care in manipulation. 40-hour embryos are used and development can be followed for a further 24-48 hours *in vitro* before the embryo dies. The method is as follows.

Materials.—1. *Medium.* Rothfel's modification of Spratt's medium is prepared by thoroughly mixing the supernatant from a centrifuged whole egg with an equal amount of saline-agar, which is prepared by adding 1·5 g. 'Difco' standardised agar to 100 ml. chick saline (0·7 g. NaCl; 0·024 g. $CaCl_2$; 0·042 g. KCl on 100 ml. distilled water). The saline-agar is liquefied by autoclaving and is allowed to cool to about 45° C. before mixing with the egg supernatant. 1 ml. aliquots of this medium are added to sterile watch glasses placed on moist absorbent cotton-wool pads in Petri dishes (as for organ culture). These plates can be stored in the refrigerator till required.

2. *Eggs.* Fertile hen's eggs are incubated at 38°C. for 40-42 hours to provide 11-13 somite embryos.

Explantation procedure.—The shell is wiped with alcohol and when this has evaporated the egg is broken into a sterile evaporating dish containing 50 ml. chick saline or BSS. A circular cut is made into the vitelline membrane around the blastoderm (using very fine scissors). The blastoderm is then transferred by means of a wide-bore (5 mm.) pipette to a Petri dish containing BSS. The adherent vitelline membrane is removed with the aid of forceps and the embryo is examined with a dissecting microscope to determine the stage of development. The blastoderm is then transferred to the top of the medium in the watch-glass by a large-bore pipette. It is spread out on the agar gel (ventral side down) and the excess BSS is removed with a small-bore pipette. The culture is then placed in the incubator at 37·5° C.

Rough handling of the embryo will result in death or at least in malformation. It is necessary to practise the technique until normal development can always be achieved.

Synthetic media have also been introduced for the cultivation of chick embryos. The general technique for cultivation of the embryos is the same as the one described above; the medium is also solidified by the inclusion of agar. Instead of egg centrifugate,

13

however, a synthetic mixture of amino-acids, salts, vitamins and carbohydrate is included. A suitable mixture is the one devised by Klein, McConnell and Buckingham, which is a modification of that developed by Hayashi and Herrmann. It contains in grams per litre: L-arginine-HCl, 0·075; L-histidine HCl, 0·075; L-lysine HCl, 0·16; L-tryptophan, 0·04; L-phenylalanine, 0·05; L-methionine, 0·05; L-threonine, 0·075; L-leucine, 0·05; DL-iso-leucine, 0·05; L-valine, 0·1; L-glutamic acid, 0·15; L-aspartic acid, 0·06; L-proline, 0·05; glycine, 0·2; glutamine, 0·4; L-tyrosine, 0·08; L-cystine, 0·015; L-hypoxanthine, 0·025; thiamine HCl, 0·005; riboflavine, 0·0005; pyridoxine HCl, 0·0005; folic acid, 0·0001; biotin, 0·0001; choline, 0·003; calcium pantothenate, 0·003; nicotinamide, 0·003; inositol, 0·001; $NaHCO_3$, 2·24; NaCl, 3·02; KCl, 0·42; $CaCl_2$, 0·24; glucose, 1·0; phenol red, 0·01; dihydro-streptomycin sulphate, 0·66; penicillin G potassium, 0·006. With this medium it is necessary to incubate the cultures in an atmosphere of 5 per cent. CO_2 in air.

Culture of mammalian embryos and ova.—Surprisingly little work has been done with cultured mammalian embryos, perhaps because of the technical difficulty of obtaining young viable embryos. Some of the most interesting studies have involved the culture of very young embryos indeed, usually 2-8 cell fertilised ova. The rabbit and mouse have been used for this work since it is relatively easy to syringe the ova out of the Fallopian tubes up to three days after fertilisation. By this means it has been shown that considerable development can take place *in vitro* and, for instance, 8-cell mouse ova have developed to blastocysts. It has also been shown that ova cultured in this way may be reimplanted and can go on to form healthy animals. The media used have generally been of a rather simple kind and have varied from 100 per cent. serum through the common types of plasma-embryo extract media to simple Krebs-Ringer solutions supplemented with 1 per cent. of thin egg-white or bovine albumin.

Culture of pre-implantation mammalian embryos

Mammalian embryos, from single cell stage to blastocyst, have been cultured with more-or-less success and in the past few years considerable progress has been made. Most of these studies have been carried out with mouse and rabbit material. The mouse has theoretical advantages since it is easy to induce superovulation by injection of hormones so that a large number of embryos can be obtained at a known stage in development. However, the rabbit embryo has proved much easier to culture and, whereas the 2-4 cell mouse embryo proceeds to form a blastocyst with difficulty, the fertilised rabbit egg will develop to a blastocyst in a very simple medium without any special care. Techniques for growing this material are still at an experimental stage and it is recommended that original papers on the subject should be consulted.

Culture of post-implantation mammalian embryos

Post-implantation mammalian embryos can be regarded as in many respects similar to the young chick embryos described earlier in this chapter. The main technical problem is the removal of the embryos in an undamaged state. This requires careful dissection. The embryos can then be grown as organ cultures in the usual manner. A detailed account of the technique will be found in the paper by New and Stein.

BIBLIOGRAPHY

BIGGERS, J. D., GWATKIN, R. B. L. & BRINSTER, R. L. (1962). Development of mouse embryos in organ cultures of fallopian tubes on a chemically defined medium. *Nature (Lond.)* **194,** 747.

BRINSTER, R. L. (1963). A method for *in vitro* cultivation of mouse ova from two-cell to blastocyst. *Exp. Cell Res.* **32,** 205.

BRITT, L. G. & HERRMANN, H. (1959). Protein accumulation in early chick embryos grown under different conditions of explantation. *J. Embryol. exp. Morph.* **7,** 66.

BUTROS, J. (1963). Differentiation of explanted fragments of early chick blastoderm. II. Culture on protein-deficient medium enriched with RNA. *J. exp. Zool.* **154,** 125.

CHANG, M. H. (1948). Transplantation of fertilized rabbit ova: the effect on viability of age, *in vitro* storage period and storage temperature. *Nature (Lond.)* **161,** 978.

GRAU, C. R., KLEIN, N. W. & LAU, T. L. (1957). Total replacement of the yolk of chick embryos. *J. Embryol. exp. Morph.* **5,** 210.

HAMMOND, J. (1949). Recovery and culture of tubal mouse ova. *Nature (Lond.)* **163,** 28.

KLEIN, N. W., McCONNELL, E. & BUCKINGHAM, B. J. (1962). Growth of explanted chick embryos on a chemically defined medium and effects of specific amino acid deficiencies. *Develop. Biol.* **5,** 296.

MAXIMOW, A. (1925). Tissue cultures of young mammalian embryos. *Contr. Embryol. Carneg. Instn.* **16,** 49.

NEW, D. A. T. & STEIN, K. F. (1963). Cultivation of mouse embryos *in vitro*. *Nature (Lond.)* **199,** 297.

NICHOLAS, J. S. & RUDNICK, D. (1938). Development of rat embryos of egg-cylinder to head-fold stages in plasma cultures. *J. exp. Zool.* **78,** 205-232.

196 CELL AND TISSUE CULTURE

O'Brien, B. R. A. (1961). Development of haemoglobin by de-embryonated chick blastoderms cultured *in vitro* and the effect of abnormal RNA upon its synthesis. *J. Embryol. exp. Morph.* **9,** 202.

Pincus, G. (1936). *The Eggs of Mammals.* New York: Macmillan.

Rudnick, D. (1938). Differentiation in culture of pieces of the early chick blastoderm. I. The definitive primitive streak and head process stages. *Anat. Rec.* **70,** 351.

Rudnick, D. (1938). Differentiation in culture of pieces of the early chick blastoderm. II. Short primitive streak pieces. *J. exp. Zool.* **79,** 399.

Spratt, N. T., Jr. (1946). Formation of the primitive streak in the explanted chick blastoderm marked with carbon particles. *J. exp. Zool.* **103,** 259-304.

Spratt, N. T., Jr. (1947b). Development *in vitro* of the early chick blastoderm explanted on yolk and albumen extract saline-sugar substrata. *J. exp. Zool.* **106,** 345-365.

Spratt, N. T., Jr. (1948). Development of the early chick blastoderm on synthetic media. *J. exp. Zool.* **107,** 39-64.

Waddington, C. H. (1932). Experiments on the development of chick and duck embryos, cultivated *in vitro*. *Phil. Trans.* **B 221,** 179.

Waterman, A. J. (1933). Development of young rabbit blastocysts in tissue culture and in grafts. *Amer. J. Anat.* **53,** 317-345.

Whitten, W. R. (1956). Culture of tubal mouse ova. *Nature (Lond.)* **177,** 96.

CHAPTER XIII

PRIMARY EXPLANTATION TECHNIQUES

III. DISAGGREGATION METHODS

PREPARATION OF CELL SUSPENSIONS FROM FRESH TISSUES

ROUS and Jones, in 1916, described the use of trypsin to digest away the plasma clot in which a tissue culture was grown and showed that the cells could be replated on coverslips after they had been dispersed in this way. At that time the method seemed to have little application. Many years later, in 1952, a paper was published by Moscona, in which he described the disaggregation of embryonic limb-buds by treating them with trypsin. The cell suspensions could subsequently be cultured. In the same year Dulbecco described a method for the preparation of replicate cultures of chick embryonic tissues by digesting the whole embryo with trypsin. The technique has now been applied to very many embryonic and adult tissues.

Intercellular materials differ in different tissues from muco-polysaccharides to fibrous proteins and include, in addition to carbohydrate and protein elements, inorganic salts as in bone. Thus it might be expected that different tissues would require different treatment in order to obtain disaggregation. In adult tissues this is generally true probably due to the development of large amounts of intercellular materials of a specialised nature. However, embryonic tissues and adult and neoplastic tissues with little matrix can very often be disaggregated by one of three techniques or a combination of these. These are:

1. Physical disruption.
2. Enzymatic digestion.
3. Treatment with chelating agents.

Physical disruption is not often used alone, mainly because it is difficult to obtain uniform suspensions without cell damage. Sometimes, however, it can be used by itself. Thus viable crude suspensions of chick embryonic tissue can be obtained by expressing the embryo through the nozzle of a syringe. Also

Lasfargues and Ozzello have obtained viable suspensions of cells from human breast carcinomas by slicing and chopping tissue fragments with a very sharp knife to release the cells from the fibrous stroma. However, physical disruption is usually combined with one of the other methods mentioned below. For instance, before treating tissues with enzymes or chelating agents they are usually cut up into very small fragments while the treatment itself is usually accompanied by fairly vigorous agitation to help break up the tissue.

Enzymatic digestion.—Of the many enzymes that have been employed to disaggregate tissues, trypsin is by far the most commonly used. Others which have been tried successfully are collagenase, elastase, a mucase, pancreatin, papain, pronase and a preparation from snail livers.

Reports concerning the effectiveness of collagenase are contradictory and this is almost certainly because of the difficulty of obtaining a standard preparation. Lasfargues used it successfully to obtain cultures of normal mammary epithelium from the mouse although it should be noted that complete tissue disaggregation was not obtained in this instance.

In his exhaustive investigation of enzymes capable of disaggregating tissues, Rinaldini found highly purified elastase generally ineffective except in the unkeratinised skin of the young (13-day) chick embryo. He also found hyaluronidase to be almost completely ineffective. However, good disruption of various embryonic tissues was obtained with a crude elastolytic preparation from pancreas containing a mucolytic and a proteolytic fraction.

With regard to trypsin and pancreatin (a crude extract of pancreatic enzymes) Rinaldini found purified trypsin more effective for separating cells in established cultures but pancreatin more effective for disaggregating tissues from the animal. When pure crystalline trypsin is used for this purpose the cells tend to become stuck together with long mucinous strings. Pancreatin probably contains some mucases which digest this material. Auerbach and Grobstein, on the basis of independent observations, recommend a mixture of trypsin and pancreatin. Some investigators have maintained that much of the mucinous material is DNA from damaged cells and have recommended the use of deoxyribonuclease to disperse it. (Most crude pancreatic extracts also have nuclease activity.)

Papain, a mixture of proteases from the papaya plant which is commonly used as a beef tenderiser by virtue of its ability to digest intercellular proteins, has been used effectively as a 1/1,000 solution in BSS containing 0·02 per cent. cysteine hydrochloride (which is necessary to activate the enzyme preparation).

Bacterial proteases, notably pronase and nagarse, have also been used successfully for dispersing cells from cell sheets.

For the disaggregation of insect tissues Martignoni, Zitcer and Wagner have prepared an enzyme extract from the livers of snails. This extract contains many proteolytic enzymes, including chitinases and viable cell suspensions have been obtained after treatment with it.

Chelating agents.—Certain tissues, especially epithelial tissues, seem to require divalent cations, particularly calcium and magnesium, for their integrity. If these ions are removed by substances which bind them (chelating agents) the tissue may disrupt very easily. Chelating agents most commonly used are citrate and ethylene-diamine-tetra-acetic acid (E.D.T.A., Versene or sequestrene). Although Melnick has used Versene to disaggregate fresh kidney tissue these agents are rarely used for fresh tissues, their main application being the production of cell suspensions from established cultures of epithelial type. A notable exception to this, however, is the technique devised by Anderson for obtaining suspensions of liver cells. He perfuses the liver with citrate and then completes the disruption by forcing the tissue through gauze. This technique has not yet been used with complete success in producing cell-strains but it holds promise for the future.

Trypsin is the only substance used very extensively for disaggregating tissue and some of its applications will be described. It has to be emphasised that not all tissues are attacked by it. Most embryonic organs are easily disaggregated but adult organs with a high content of fibrous tissue are refractory. However, adult tissues with a rather low fibrous tissue content, such as the kidney, are quite easily treated. The original technique described by Moscona is as follows.

Disaggregation of embryonic limb-buds (Moscona, 1952)

Limb-buds from 4 - 5 day chick embryos are washed repeatedly in balanced salt solution and then in salt solution lacking calcium and magnesium (NaCl—8·00 g., KCl—0·20 g., NaH_2PO_4, H_2O—0·005 g., $NaHCO_3$—1·00 g., glucose—2·00 g. in 1 litre water). They are transferred to a solution of 3 per cent. trypsin (B.D.H.) in this BSS and left for 10 - 12 minutes at 38° C. The epidermis can then be separated from the underlying tissue and the myogenic from the chondrogenic blastema. The separated parts are cut into smaller pieces and replaced in trypsin solution. By means of 1 per cent. KOH solution the pH is raised to 8·4 - 8·6. The cells become dis-aggregated after 15 - 20 minutes, requiring only a little pipetting to complete the process. After washing by taking up in salt solution and centrifuging they are suspended in growth-promoting medium and allowed to settle on glass.

The process described involves fairly rough treatment for the cells and most of the procedures used now are decidedly gentler. Thus, for chick embryonic disaggregation Auerbach and Grobstein recommend using a 3 per cent. solution of a mixture of three parts trypsin (Difco 1/250) and one part pancreatin (4×USP) in Tyrode's solution from which calcium and magnesium salts have been omitted. Ten to twelve minutes swirling at 37·5° is enough to obtain disaggregation. In particular, when trypsinisation procedures are used as a preliminary to cloning cells it is recom-mended that they should be as gentle as possible. The following procedure is employed successfully for some biochemical studies.

Preparation of trypsinised embryonic ' carcass '

Fourteen- to fifteen-day chick embryos are decapitated and eviscerated. The skin, wings and feet are removed. The remaining tissue is chopped up quite finely with scissors and washed repeatedly with balanced salt solution to remove erythrocytes. Four or five volumes of 0·5 per cent. trypsin (1/250 Difco) are added to the tissue pulp. This is conveniently placed in a roller-tube and left to rotate at 38° C, the pH having been adjusted to about 7·6. After about twenty minutes the tube is removed from the roller drum and the contents sucked up and down once or twice by means of a wide-bore pipette. The contents are allowed to settle for a minute to allow the bigger pieces of débris to separate out. The crude supernatant is transferred to a tube. The tube is then centrifuged and the trypsin discarded. After resuspending in a growth medium the material is inoculated into suitable vessels. The resulting culture contains a great deal of débris. After 48 hours the medium is removed and replaced with 0·5 per cent. trypsin. In about ten minutes the cells are again suspended. This time the suspension is filtered through a fine stainless steel gauze screen before centrifuging, resuspending and reinoculating into fresh vessels. The resulting culture consists mainly of muscle cells.

The most general application of this type of technique is in the preparation of monolayers of amnion or kidney epithelium cells for virus studies. Since very large numbers of cells are required, the technique has been modified mainly by the introduction of mechanical devices to carry out some or all of the process automatically. As in the preceding techniques, disaggregation of the cells is usually achieved by means of trypsin (0·25 - 0·5 per cent.

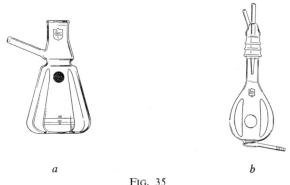

a   b

FIG. 35

Trypsinisation vessels (a) for intermittent trypsinisation, (b) for continuous trypsinisation (Bellco Glass Inc.)

Difco 1/250) but versene, a strong chelating agent, has been shown to be equally effective by Melnick's group and is sometimes preferred. Versene is diamino-ethane-tetra-acetic acid and it is also called E.D.T.A. (ethylene-diamine-tetra-acetic acid). It is used at a concentration of 200 mg. per litre in a buffered solution free of calcium and magnesium ions. A suitable solution is described on page 230, where its use is described for the transfer of cell strains. The disodium salt is soluble. In the procedure to be described it can be substituted for trypsin but it should be noted that, if this is done, all washings must be performed with calcium and magnesium-free salt solutions.

The mechanical devices referred to above are all based on the use of an Erlenmeyer flask with indentations in each side to

promote turbulence when the contents are agitated by a magnetic
stirrer (Fig. 35). A further improvement in the flask consists of
either a transverse ridge on one side near the neck or a belly blown
out on one side. These devices are intended to retain large particulate matter when the cell suspension is decanted off. The fully

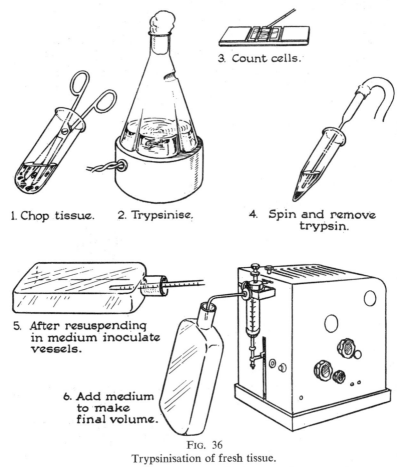

3. Count cells.

1. Chop tissue.   2. Trypsinise.   4. Spin and remove
trypsin.

5. After resuspending
in medium inoculate
vessels.

6. Add medium
to make
final volume.

FIG. 36
Trypsinisation of fresh tissue.

developed vessel consists of a flask with indentations as before and
with an outlet tube coming off underneath in the centre of the floor.
A perforated disc at this outlet prevents large particles from falling
through into the tube and the centrifugal motion of the stirrer
throws most of the particles away from it and towards the
periphery. A constant flow of trypsin solution is allowed to enter

the flask while a constant flow of cell suspension leaves through the outlet tube. For very large-scale working, as in the production of vaccines, completely automatic continuous tissue trypsinising devices have also been developed.

Trypsinisation of monkey kidney tissue

1. The kidneys are removed aseptically either immediately after death or by nephrectomy under anaesthesia before the animal is killed. They are immediately decapsulated and the pelvis is dissected away. The kidney tissue is then chopped up in BSS by means of long-handled scissors until the pieces have a size of 3 - 5 mm.

2. The BSS is decanted off, replaced with more BSS and this is again decanted off. 5 - 10 g. of tissue fragments are placed in a 500 ml. Erlenmeyer flask of the type discussed above and about 100 ml. of prewarmed trypsin solution added. A sterile silicone-covered magnet is inserted and the flask placed over a magnetic stirrer (magmix) arranged to run fairly slowly.

3. After about 20 minutes the supernatant fluid is discarded and a further 100 ml. of warm trypsin solution are added. After another 20 minutes the next harvest is decanted into sterile centrifuge tubes.

4. Three or four harvests are obtained in this way until only fibrous material is left. Specimens of the pooled cell suspensions are removed for counting and the suspensions are then centrifuged at 1,000 g. for five minutes and suspended in growth medium (2 per cent. calf serum in medium 199). When the cell count is known the volume is made up with medium so that the cell concentration is about 300,000 cells/ml.

5. The cell suspension is inoculated into flasks (15 ml. per T60 flask or 16 oz. medicine bottle, 50 ml. per penicillin culture flask, 80 ml. per Roux bottle, 400 ml. per diphtheria toxin bottle) and placed in the incubator.

Preparation of primary human amnion cells

Arrange if possible to have the afterbirth delivered into a sterile container in conditions such that no contamination with disinfectants occurs. Within 12 hours separate the amnion from the chorion and wash in several changes of calcium and magnesium-free balanced salt solution containing 100 units of penicillin and 100 µg.

of streptomycin per ml. This can be stored for up to 24 hours in BSS or processed immediately.

Trypsinisation procedure (Dunnebacke and Zitcer)

1. Spread the membrane out in a large Petri dish with 50 ml. of 0·25 per cent. trypsin (Difco 1/250) in calcium- and magnesium-free BSS.

2. After one hour transfer the membrane to a 750 ml. Erlenmeyer flask containing 200 ml. of 0·25 per cent. trypsin solution. Shake manually or mechanically.

3. After 2 - 4 hours the cells are freed from the membrane, which should be washed with two or three changes of buffer.

4. Combine the cell suspensions from stages 2 and 3 and centrifuge at 1,000 r.p.m. for ten minutes. Resuspend in medium and count the cells (a membrane yields $2 - 6 \times 10^8$ cells).

5. Dilute the cells with growth medium (20 per cent. human serum in medium 199) to give 10^6 cells/ml. and inoculate growth vessels.

6. Cultures are confluent after 5 - 10 days incubation.

The medium requires to be changed every 7 days. Secondary cultures can be prepared by treatment with trypsin or versene (Chapter XV) but these cells only rarely give rise to permanent strains.

Cloning of primarily disaggregated cells

If a suspension of cells, obtained by trypsinisation, is diluted adequately and inoculated into culture vessels colonies may develop from single cells. This technique, which is described more fully for cell strains on page 236 has been used by some investigators to determine the kinds of cells which survive in culture conditions. The plating efficiency (p. 325) is very low for primarily disaggregated cells and from many tissues is of the order of 10^{-5} to 10^{-6}.

BIBLIOGRAPHY

AUERBACH, R. & GROBSTEIN, C. (1958). Inductive interaction of embryonic tissues after dissociation and reaggregation. *Exp. Cell Res.* **15**, 384.

BISHOP, L. W. J., SMITH, M. K. & BEALE, A. J. (1960). An apparatus for producing trypsinized monkey kidney cell suspensions. *Virology* **10**, 280.

BODIAN, D. (1956). Simplified method of dispersion of monkey kidney cells with trypsin. *Virology* **2**, 575.

DULBECCO, R. & VOGT, M. (1954). Plaque formation and isolation of pure lines with poliomyelitis viruses. *J. exp. Med.* **99**, 167.

KONIGSBERG, I. R. (1961). Cellular differentiation in colonies derived from single cell platings of freshly isolated chick embryo muscle cells. *Proc. nat. Acad. Sci. (Wash.)* **47**, 1868.

LEHMAN-GRUBE, F. (1961). Preparation of cell cultures from human amniotic membranes. *Arch. Ges. Virusforsch.* **11**, 258.

MADDEN, R. E. & BURK, D. (1961). Production of viable single cell suspensions from solid tumors. *J. nat. Cancer Inst.* **27**, 841.

LASFARGUES, E. Y. (1957). Cultivation and behaviour *in vitro* of the normal mammary epithelium of the adult mouse. II. Observations on the secretory activity. *Exp. Cell Res.* **13**, 553.

MARTIGNONI, M. E., ZITCER, ELSA M. & WAGNER, R. P. (1958). Preparation of cell suspensions from insect tissues for *in vitro* cultivation. *Science* **128**, 360.

MOSCONA, A. (1952). Cell suspensions from organ rudiments of chick embryos. *Exp. Cell Res.* **3**, 535.

MOSCONA, A. (1956). Development of heterotypic combinations of dissociated embryonic chick cells. *Proc. Soc. exp. Biol. (N.Y.)* **92**, 410.

MOSCONA, A. & MOSCONA, H. (1952). The dissociation and aggregation of cells from organ rudiments of the early chick embryo. *J. Anat. (Lond.)* **86**, 287.

MELNICK, J. L., RAPPAPORT, C., BANKER, D. D. & BHATT, P. N. (1955). Stabilized suspensions of monkey kidney cells suitable for intercontinental shipment. *Proc. Soc. exp. Biol. (N.Y.)* **88**, 676.

RAPPAPORT, C. (1956). Trypsinization of monkey kidney tissue: an automatic method for the preparation of cell suspensions. *Bull. Wld Hlth Org.* **14**, 147.

RINALDINI, L. M. (1958). The isolation of living cells from animal tissues. *Int. Rev. Cytol.* **7**, 587.

RINALDINI, L. M. (1959). An improved method for the isolation and quantitative cultivation of embryonic cells. *Exp. Cell Res.* **16**, 477.

ROSS, G. T. & BAHN, R. C. (1961). Preparation and properties of suspensions of anterior pituitary cells of adult male rats. *Lab. Invest.* **10**, 636.

ROUS, P. & JONES, F. S. (1916). A method for obtaining suspensions of living cells from the fixed tissues and for the plating out of individual cells. *J. exp. Med.* **23**, 549.

THIEDE, H. A. & RUDOLPH, J. H. (1961). A method for obtaining monolayer cultures of human fetal cells from term placentas. *Proc. Soc. exp. Biol. (N.Y.)* **107**, 565.

WALLIS, C., LEWIS, R. T. & MELNICK, J. L. (1961). Preparation of kidney cell cultures. *Tex. Rep. Biol. Med.* **19**, 194.

YOUNGNER, J. S. (1954). Monolayer tissue cultures. I. Preparation and standardization of suspensions of trypsin-dispersed monkey kidney cells. *Proc. Soc. exp. Biol. (N.Y.)* **85**, 202.

ZITCER, ELSA M., FOGH, J. & DUNNEBACK, THELMA H. (1955). Human amnion cells for large-scale production of polio virus. *Science* **122**, 30.

ZAROFF, L., SATO, G. & MILLS, E. E. (1961). Single-cell platings from freshly isolated mammalian tissue. *Exp. Cell Res.* **23**, 565.

CHAPTER XIV

PRIMARY EXPLANTATION TECHNIQUES

IV. SPECIAL CONSIDERATIONS FOR DIFFERENT TISSUES

VERTEBRATE TISSUES

TISSUES from animals are usually obtained from two fundamentally different sources, embryos on the one hand and
adults on the other. The distinction is made between these
two because they require somewhat different treatment. Embryonic
tissues are sterile from the beginning and have merely to be handled
with aseptic technique in order to obtain usable material. They also
tend to grow easily, migrate rapidly and undergo mitosis very soon
after explantation. On the whole, fibroblasts tend to grow out from
them more rapidly than other types of cells. Adult material, on
the other hand, has often to be specially treated to ensure its sterility
before culturing. Many adult tissues grow *in vitro* with difficulty
and there is often a latent period of several days before any outgrowth becomes apparent. There is less tendency for fibroblasts
to grow out from adult tissues and very often other cell types, in
particular epithelial cells, grow rather well from adult material.
Tumour tissues from adult animals behave in many ways like
normal adult tissue, but, on the whole, they tend to grow more
readily and to grow more rapidly in the first few days.

Embryonic tissues

Embryonic tissues may, of course, be obtained from any source.
The most readily available are those from the chick, the mouse
and the human. Tissues from all these grow well although those
from avian sources tend to cease to grow after several generations
whereas tissues of mammalian origin frequently become permanently established.

The classical source of tissue for culture studies is the chick embryo. It is particularly convenient inasmuch as it provides a sterile source of material, readily accessible when required. Since it is very widely used, the dissection of the chick embryo will be described in detail.

DISSECTION OF THE CHICK EMBRYO

1. Select an egg which has been incubated for 7-14 days (for general purposes 10-12 days is a good age to provide tissues).

2. Check that the egg contains a healthy embryo by candling. (Hold the egg in front of an aperture in a piece of cardboard in front of a bright light. The shadow of the embryo should be readily discerned, with a clear airspace at the blunt end of the egg. The blood vessels should be easily distinguished but there should not be a sharp line of demarcation at the margin of the vascular zone.)

3. Wipe the eggshell with alcohol and allow it to dry. Crack the shell over the airspace and remove it, taking care not to allow pieces to fall on the membrane below. With a pair of sterile forceps lift up the opaque white membrane to expose the embryo. Lift the embryo out very gently with a pair of curved forceps placed under the neck and place it on a Petri dish (Fig. 14).

4. Lay the embryo on its back and with an open pair of forceps in the left hand spread out the wings. Insert a curved pair of forceps under the abdominal skin and rip it open up to the sternum (Fig. 37). Insert the forceps just under the sternum and pluck out the *heart*. Place it in a drop of BSS in a Petri dish.

5. The *liver* can be recognised as a reddish-purple, soft object. The curved forceps are carefully closed behind it and it is then plucked out also.

6. The remainder of the abdominal viscera, mainly crop, stomach and *intestines* are plucked out and transferred to a Petri dish.

7. Work the forceps round behind each *eyeball* and pluck them out of their sockets (Fig. 37). Place one blade of a pair of forceps under the ridge of the eyebrow, close the forceps and pull out the *frontal bone* (Fig. 37).

8. Cut off the head. Commencing near the tail of the embryo apply two pairs of (preferably wide and blunt) forceps. Work these forward, one after the other, so as to squeeze out the *spinal cord—*

rather like toothpaste from a tube (Fig. 37). The same manoeuvre can be applied to the head.

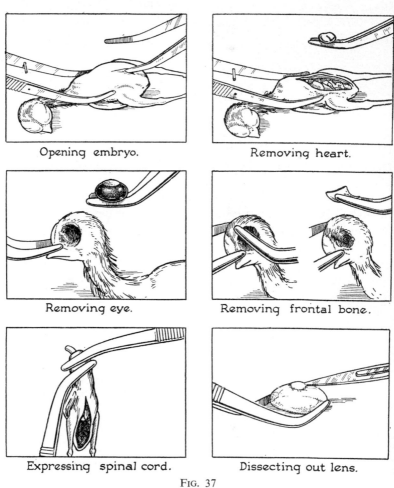

Opening embryo.

Removing heart.

Removing eye.

Removing frontal bone.

Expressing spinal cord.

Dissecting out lens.

FIG. 37
Dissection of the chick embryo.

9. *Skin* is gently peeled from the top of the head, the back or the thighs.

10. *Skeletal muscle* is obtained from the thighs.

11. The various organs are subsequently treated as follows before explantation:

HEART.—With two knives, fitted with No. 11 Bard-Parker blades, cut off the atria and great vessels. Wash the ventricles in BSS and cut up into explants of suitable size (0·5 mm. cubed).

LIVER.—Remove the gall-bladder (a small olive-green sac) and cut up the remainder into explants after washing with BSS.

INTESTINE.—Discard the crop and stomach. Stretch out the intestine and slice it into slices about 0·5 mm. wide. A large number of uniform explants can be obtained very easily in this way.

EYEBALL.—Carefully slit open the eyeball and express the contents. The viscous humour forms a semi-solid jelly and the *lens* forms a minute, more solid structure at the front of this. It is surrounded by a fringe of pigmented iris in older embryos. Remove the *lens* (Fig. 37) and dissect off the *iris*. Returning to the collapsed eyeball the pigmented *retina* can be separated from the white sclera with a little care. All these structures can be cultured.

FRONTAL BONE.—Cut into explants of convenient size with No. 11 blades.

SPINAL CORD.—Slice in the same way as intestine to give a large number of very similar explants.

SKIN.—Cut into rather large explants.

MUSCLE.—Cut into rather large explants.

Chick embryonic limb-bones for organ culture

In Chapter XII it was emphasised that the first essential in most organ culture studies is a clean and careful dissection of the organ to be cultured. Hence each study requires its own special techniques, depending on the organ concerned. It would be impractical to outline many of the dissections but the embryonic limb-bone is a classical subject of study and its preparation provides a good illustration of the type of technique used. Seven-day embryos are suitable.

The embryo is removed from the egg as described above. (At seven days it is extremely fragile and should be withdrawn very gently, allowing the membranes to fall away from it. Any compression of the neck or strong traction will decapitate it.) It is placed in a depression slide and washed with BSS (by means of a pipette) till no blood remains. The legs are then removed by cutting them

14

close to the spine so as to avoid amputating the ends of the femora. Each leg is placed in a depression slide and washed with several changes of BSS. The femur and tibia are gently dissected from each leg. Great care must be taken to remove all muscle tissue, if possible, without damaging the periosteum. Very sharp knives are essential and well-honed cataract knives are best, although satisfactory dissections can be performed with No. 11 scalpel blades. Wash the tissue several times with BSS, removing the debris with a Pasteur pipette until only the clean bones are left in the BSS.

MAMMALIAN EMBRYONIC TISSUES

As sources of mammalian embryonic tissues the mouse and rat are most commonly used. The procedure for removing the embryos is straightforward. A pregnant female is killed (by decapitation or dislocation of the neck in mice). The animal is then submerged in water and its fur is thoroughly moistened (to prevent loose hairs contaminating the field of operation). The skin is cut round the animal's thorax, just under the forelegs. It can then be stripped back in much the same way as a glove or sock might be removed, to expose the abdominal wall (Fig. 38) which is thus obtained in a completely uncontaminated condition. It is easy then to open up the abdomen and remove the uterine horns containing the embryos. Care must be taken, of course, not to puncture the intestine. The uterus, placed in a sterile Petri dish, is opened and the embryos removed. Dissection of the mouse embryo can be conducted in a manner similar to dissection of the fowl embryo. It is, however, smaller and more skill is required.

Embryos of large mammals can be obtained from the slaughter-house and both pig and cow embryos provide excellent culture material. It is best to obtain the entire uterus containing the embryo. This is slung up from a hook and the outer surface of the uterus liberally swabbed with tincture of iodine (it is almost certainly very heavily contaminated). With a trocar and cannula most of the amniotic fluid is removed (to be used as a supplementary medium if desired). The uterus is then placed in a large, clean tray, swabbed with iodine once more and opened by a large incision. It is best to have an assistant retract the walls of the uterus as soon as the incision is made. The embryo can then be removed and transferred to a sterile container.

The human embryo also provides excellent material for tissue culture studies and embryos are readily available in some hospitals. Occasionally a hysterectomy specimen will become available and in

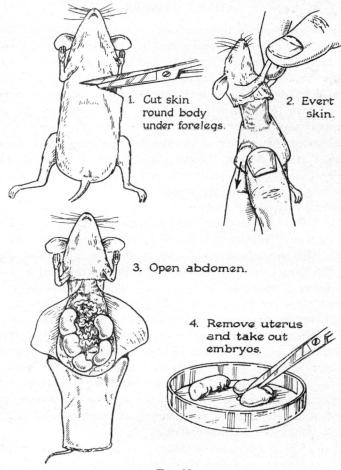

1. Cut skin round body under forelegs.

2. Evert skin.

3. Open abdomen.

4. Remove uterus and take out embryos.

Fig. 38
Aseptic removal of embryos from a pregnant mouse.

that case it can be treated in exactly the same way as pig and cow uteri. More usually the embryo or foetus is likely to be obtained some time after death, almost certainly contaminated and possibly macerated. In this event it should be treated exactly as any other surgical specimen. Internal tissues can be obtained readily by aseptic technique but if skin is required for culturing it is necessary to try to sterilise it by exposing it to high concentrations of antibiotics as described in Chapter IX.

ADULT TISSUES

For the purposes of tissue culture all specimens obtained from animals in the post-natal phase can be considered adult tissues. They have to be treated similarly and, in general, they behave similarly. Tissues from old animals are often more difficult to grow than tissues from young animals and exhibit a longer lag period before growth commences. However, thereafter the growth rate and general behaviour are indistinguishable. The differences between old and young tissues seem to be related to the amounts of connective tissue matrix present. Tissues, such as kidney, in which there is little fibrous tissue, behave in practically the same manner irrespective of the age of the donor, whereas fibrous tissues grow much better from young animals.

Many adult tissues have been successfully cultured and the main difficulty encountered is, of course, the maintenance of sterility. This problem is least acute in the case of surgical specimens and tissues removed aseptically from experimental animals. Even tissues from inside the body can contain bacteria, however. Generally, this can be ignored and contaminated cultures can be rejected later as they occur, but occasionally valuable material has to be grown where there exists some doubt about sterility. When this is the case an attempt must be made to sterilise it and the most satisfactory method is first to wash it thoroughly with balanced salt solution containing a high concentration of antibiotics as described in Chapter IX. Then, when the tissue is dissected into explants it can be trimmed, the outer edges being rejected and the explants being taken from the interior.

Among the classical adult tissues for cultivation is the central nervous system of the kitten which provides very suitable material for some morphological studies and has been intensively used for this purpose. The subcutaneous fibroblast of the adult rat is another tissue that has been commonly employed, particularly in studies of mitosis. Bone marrow from many animals, especially rabbits, has been particularly used in studies of haemopoiesis. Human surgical specimens, in particular lymphatic tissue, nasal epithelium, bone marrow and tumours, have provided material for many studies also.

Two adult tissues are of particular importance in virology— the kidney and the amnion. Kidneys are obtained, usually from monkeys, by an aseptic operation. Human amniotic membranes are obtained from normal births, the midwifery staff being asked to collect them in sterile basins with the minimum of handling and the minimum of exposure to disinfectants. As soon as possible after delivery, the membranes are dissected free of the placenta and umbilical cord and are washed in sterile BSS containing strepto- mycin and penicillin. The detailed handling of these materials is described in Chapter XIII.

One other tissue, the leucocytes of the blood, requires to be considered separately. The buffy coat is of interest since it provides a sample of cells which can be repeatedly obtained from the same individual, its behaviour is particularly reproducible and the phases of development of these cultures has been thoroughly described. The culture of mononuclear cells from the blood, after stimulation by antigen or phytohaemagglutinin is of particular interest since it has become a standard method for the study of chromosomes, especially in humans. The migration and growth of cells from the buffy coat of many animals has been examined but those most commonly used have been the fowl, the rabbit and the human. The procedure is as follows.

PREPARATION OF EXPLANTS OF THE BUFFY COAT

1. Coat several centrifuge tubes, test-tubes, Pasteur pipettes and serum needles with silicone (Repelcote, Hopkins and Williams). Similarly, prepare one or two 20 or 50 ml. syringes, depending on the amount of blood required. Sterilise all the glassware. Place the centrifuge tubes and test-tubes in an ice-bath.

2. Remove the blood by venepuncture (or cardiac puncture in small animals) and immediately place 10 ml. in each of the centrifuge tubes, avoiding frothing. Seal the centrifuge tubes with a sterile cotton-wool plug turned down over the edge and secured with a rubber band, or with aluminium foil, and centrifuge at 1,800 g. for 10 minutes (preferably in a refrigerated centrifuge at 2 - 4°).

3. By means of a siliconed Pasteur pipette, transfer almost all the clear supernatant layer of plasma to a siliconed test-tube. Store this in an ice-bath or in the refrigerator.

4. To the surface of the packed cells remaining in the centrifuge tube add one drop of 1/10 dilution of embryo extract. Stir the surface very carefully with the end of the pipette and immediately centrifuge at 1,800 g. for another two or three minutes.

5. Handling them carefully so as not to disturb the cell layers, place the centrifuge tubes in an incubator. The surface will have clotted firmly in 10-15 minutes. With a sterile platinum wire manoeuvre the clot out of the tube into a Petri dish containing about 10 ml. of BSS. Wash it twice more in 10 ml. amounts of BSS to remove most of the red blood cells and then place it on a Petri dish with a few drops of BSS and cut it into explants in the usual manner.

6. These explants develop best in a plasma clot and they can be implanted in the autologous plasma which has been stored in the ice-bath. A suitable clot is formed with 25 per cent. plasma in Eagle's medium with a very small amount of dilute (1/10) embryo extract added to initiate coagulation.

Note.—It is sometimes difficult to prevent premature coagulation of blood, particularly if it has been collected by an unpractised operator by cardiac puncture. Coagulation can be further inhibited in this case by adding to each of the centrifuge tubes 0·1 ml. of 25 mg. per cent. heparin before adding the blood. If this is done it is necessary to use a higher concentration of embryo extract to coagulate the plasma and undiluted EE_{50} should be used instead of a 1/10 dilution. Although perfectly satisfactory results can be obtained by this technique, it is better to avoid it if possible since both heparin and embryo extract are harmful to cultures of peripheral blood cells and the best results are definitely obtained when anticoagulants are avoided.

Culture of peripheral blood leucocytes

Although numerous reports concerning the cultivation of leucocytes from the peripheral blood by the above technique have appeared in the literature the results, especially with some mammals including man, have been somewhat erratic. The use of phytohaemagglutinin (originally in order to facilitate separation of erythrocytes from leucocytes) seems to stimulate a burst of mitosis in these cells and hence provides a very convenient way of obtaining samples of human cells in mitosis. These are particularly useful in the study of chromosomal abnormalities, such as Mongolism and Klinefelter's Syndrome. The following method is adapted from that of Hungerford *et al.* which is itself a modification of the method proposed by Osgood.

1. To a volume of aseptically collected heparinised venous blood add phytohaemagglutinin (Difco) in the proportion of 0·25 ml. per 10 ml. blood. Leave to stand in ice water for 30-60 minutes.

2. Centrifuge at 350 r.p.m. for 10 minutes at 4° C. Pipette off the supernatant containing the leucocytes.

3. Centrifuge at 2,000 r.p.m. for 3-4 minutes, remove the supernatant and resuspend the cells in a medium consisting of 20 per cent. of the donor's plasma plus 80 per cent. medium 199, containing antibiotics. The initial cell concentration should be about 1-2 × 10^6 cells per ml.

4. Inoculate test-tubes with about 2 ml. each of the cell suspension and incubate at an angle at 37·5° C.

5. After 3-4 days the mitotic index is at its maximum. If it is desired to accumulate mitoses colchicine should be added to give a final concentration of 10^{-7} M and the cells should be harvested 8-18 hours later and prepared by a chromosome-spreading technique (Chapter XIX).

BIBLIOGRAPHY

BAKER, LILLIAN E. (1933). The cultivation of monocytes in fluid medium. *J. exp. Med.* **58,** 575.

BERMAN, L. & STULBERG, C. S. (1962). Primary cultures of macrophages from normal human peripheral blood. *Lab. Invest.* **11,** 1322.

CHEN. H. P. & PALMAR. G. K. (1958). A method of isolating leukocytes. *Amer. J. clin. Path.* **30,** 567.

DAVIDSON. R. G., BRUSILOW. S. W. & NITOWSKY, H. M. (1963). Skin biopsy for cell culture. *Nature (Lond.)* **199,** 296.

FAWCETT, D. W. & VALLEE, B. L. (1952). Studies on the separation of cell types in serosanguinous fluids. blood, and vaginal fluids by flotation on bovine plasma albumin. *J. Lab. clin. Med.* **39,** 354.

HARNDEN, D. G. (1960). A human skin culture technique used for cytological examinations. *Brit. J. exper. Path.* **41,** 31.

HSU, T. C. (1957). A material for rapid cultivation of epithelial cells. *Cytologia* **22,** 12.

HULLIGER, LOTTE (1956). Über die unterschiedlichen Entwicklingsfähigkeiten der Zellen des Blutes und der Lymphe in vitro. *Virchows Arch.* **329,** 289.

LAJTHA, L. G. (1952). Culture of human bone marrow in vitro. *J. clin. Path.* **5,** 67.

OSGOOD, E. E. & BROOKE, J. H. (1955). Continuous tissue culture of leukocytes from human leukemic bloods by application of 'gradient' principles. *Blood,* **10,** 1010.

OSGOOD, E. E. & KRIPPAEHNE, M. L. (1955). The gradient tissue culture method. *Exp. Cell Res.* **9,** 116.
PUNNETT, T. & PUNNETT, H. H. (1963). Induction of leucocyte growth in cultures of human peripheral blood. *Nature (Lond.)* **198,** 1173.
SIMINOVITCH, L., McCULLOCH, E. A. & TILL, J. E. (1963). The distribution of colony-forming cells among spleen colonies. *J. Cell. comp. Physiol.* **62,** 327.

CULTIVATION OF TISSUES FROM COLD-BLOODED VERTEBRATES

The techniques for growing these tissues are identical with those for warm-blooded animals. The one important detail in which they differ is the incubation temperature. In many cases it is important to ensure that this does not rise too high, *e.g.* for many fish tissues it should be kept below 18° C.

A very beautiful demonstration of the migratory activity of epithelial cells can be seen in explants obtained from the tail of a fish, particularly one of the fan-tailed varieties of goldfish. The tail is disinfected with a mild disinfectant (70 per cent. alcohol) and washed with sterile BSS before snipping off a piece. This can be explanted in a chick plasma clot in a medium containing 10 per cent. chick embryo extract. If the temperature is kept at about 18° considerable migration is already visible in four or five hours.

Amphibian tissues can be treated in a very similar manner and the usual incubation temperature is 26° C.

One of the main problems in obtaining tissues from cold-blooded vertebrates is the exclusion of contaminating organisms. Often sterile tissue can be obtained from internal organs after sterilising the exterior with iodine or merthiolate. However, parasitic organisms are not infrequently found in the internal organs of these animals and recourse must then be had to antibiotics, as already described.

BIBLIOGRAPHY

BARTH, L. G. & BARTH, L. J. (1959). Differentiation of cells of the *Rana pipiens* gastrula in unconditioned media. *J. emb. exp. Morph.* **7,** 210.
CAMERON, GLADYS (1950). *Tissue Culture Technique.* 2nd ed. New York : Academic Press.
CARY, L. R. (1933). Growth of some tissues of Ptychodera behamensis *in vitro. Publ. Carneg. Instn.* **28,** 125.
CLEM, L. W.. MOEWUS, L. & SIEGEL, M. M. (1961). Studies with cells from marine fish in tissue culture. *Proc. Soc. exp. Biol. (N.Y.)* **108,** 762.

DEDERER, PAULINE H. (1921). The behavior of cells in tissue culture of fundulus heteroclitus with special reference to the ectoderm. *Biol. Bull.* **41**, 221.

FLICKINGER, R. A. (1949). A study of the metabolism of amphibian neural crest cells during their migration and pigmentation *in vitro*. *J. exp. Zool.* **112**, 465.

GATENBY, J. B. (1932). A technique for studying growth and movement in explants from Helex Aspersa (snail). *Arch. exp. Zellforsch.* **13**, 665.

GRAND, C. G. & CAMERON, GLADYS (1948). Tissue culture studies of pigmented melanomas: fish, mouse and human. *In* The Biology of Melanomas. *Spec. Publ. N.Y. Acad. Sci.* **4**, 171.

HOLMES. S. J. (1914). The behavior of the epidermis of amphibians when cultivated outside the body. *J. exp. Zool.* **17**, 281.

HOLTFRETER, J. (1931). Über die Aufzucht isolierter Teile des Amphibienkeimes. *Arch. EntwGesch.* **124**, 404.

MOSER, C. & FLICKINGER, R. A. (1963). Effects of nutrient media on gastrula ectoderm of Rana pipiens cultured *in vitro*. *J. exp. Zool.* **153**, 219.

NITZIMA, M. (1956). Tissue culture studies on amphibian metamorphosis. I. Growth patterns of tadpole tissue. *Folia anat. jap.* **28**, 59.

NIU, M. C. & TWITTY, V. C. (1950). The origin of epidermal melanophores during metamorphosis of Triturus torosus. *J. exp. Zool.* **113**, 633.

NIU, M. C. (1954). Further studies on the origin of amphibian pigment cells. *J. exp. Zool.* **125**, 199.

PRESTON, M. M'E. (1948). Amphibian tissue culture for biophysical research. *Nature (Lond.)* **161**, 203.

PRESTON, M. M'E. (1949). The cultivation *in vitro* of various amphibian tissues. *J. R. micr. Soc.* **69**, 65.

UHLENHUTH, E. (1914). The cultivation of the skin epithelium of adult frog Rana pipiens. *J. exp. Med.* **20**, 614.

UHLENHUTH. E. (1916). Changes in pigment epithelium and iris pigment cells of Rana pipiens induced by changes in environment. *J. exp. Med.* **24**, 689.

WOLF. K. & QUIMBY, M. C. (1962). Established eurythermic line of fish cells *in vitro*. *Science* **135**, 1065.

CULTURE OF INVERTEBRATE TISSUES

Throughout the years attempts have been made to culture tissues of insects and other invertebrates. Recently interest in this field has increased and attention has been turned particularly towards the culture of arthropod cells. The general principles and methods are the same as those for vertebrate tissues, the major difference being in the nature of the medium used. The advances in insect tissue culture of recent years have followed the detailed analysis of samples of insect haemolymph, upon which many media have been based. On the other hand it is striking that, quite recently, there has been a decided tendency to adopt the same principles, and even media, as have proved successful in culturing vertebrate tissues.

Few invertebrate tissues other than insect tissues have been cultured but some successful attempts have been made to grow coelenterate cells; the media used have again been similar to those employed in vertebrate tissue culture.

The basal salt solution would seem to be the only component that requires to be specially adapted for each kind of organism. In particular pH, osmotic pressure and the ratios of certain ions may be important. Otherwise there are strong indications that the same kind of nutritional supplements can be used for most animal cells.

Arthropods

Cells and tissues have been cultured mainly from Diptera, Lepidoptera and Ixodidae. Cultures have usually been made from pupal or larval tissues; these have included brain, optic lobe, eye, intestinal tract, the fat body, Malpighian tubules, ovarioles, spermatocytes and blood cells. Greatest success has been achieved with cultures from blood and ovarioles.

Media.—Steady progress in the culture of arthropod tissues has followed the introduction of Wyatt's medium which was based on an analysis of haemolymph from Bombyx mori. Grace's medium (page 105) was developed from it by the addition of a group of B vitamins. Both of these media are usually supplemented with 10 per cent. homologous haemolymph, treated in the manner described on page 70. These media differ from media used for vertebrate tissues in three major respects.

1. pH. The pH of arthropod tissue fluids is more acid than that of vertebrate tissues. The usual range is pH 6·3 to 6·9. Opinions differ about the tolerance of arthropod tissues to variation in pH. Martignoni considers moderate pH changes to be harmful while Jones suggests that insect tissues tolerate wide pH variations.

2. Osmotic pressure. The osmotic pressure of insect tissue fluids varies from just below that of vertebrate tissues to more than twice as great. Generally the osmotic pressure of insect blood is high and a major contribution to it is made by amino acids which are present at rather high concentrations. These also contribute to the buffering capacity of insect blood.

3. The ratios of ions in the medium. These vary from insect to insect but, in general, the Na/K ratio is low as is also the Ca/K

ratio. The phosphate concentration of insect blood is also high and most of the phosphate is in the form of organic phosphates.

When due allowance is made for these factors it is obvious that the kinds of media which support the growth and maintenance of insect tissues are very similar to those used for vertebrate cells. Indeed some success has been obtained with modifications of medium 199. It has also been found that media supplemented with lactalbumin hydrolysate, peptone, casein hydrolysate or yeast extract (yeastolate) are useful. Lactalbumin hydrolysate has been used at a concentration of 1 per cent. (w/v) and cascin hydrolysate as high as 5 per cent. (w/v). Yeastolate has been added at a concentration of 0·1 per cent. (w/v). These concentrations are very much higher than would be tolerated by vertebrate cells. Wyatt found high concentrations of trehalose in haemolymph and it was presumed that this was the main carbohydrate. However, it is by no means certain that it is metabolised extensively whereas glucose, fructose and maltose are all utilised. Glucose is usually included in media as the main energy source.

Insect plasma, in which the polyphenol-polyphenol oxidase system has been inactivated as described in Chapter V, is usually included in the medium. However, vertebrate sera of different kinds and vertebrate embryo extracts have also been added. Indeed, most of the requirement for insect plasma can apparently be met by calf serum but there is always a residual requirement for a large molecular component from insect blood.

A typical medium for culture of insect tissue would contain 10-20 per cent. of serum (either wholly insect haemolymph or at least 1/5 haemolymph, the rest being, for example, calf serum). The rest of the medium would usually be one of the media for culture of insect tissues, described in Chapter VI. Best results have been claimed for Grace's medium.

Sources of tissues and techniques.—Although very many kinds of insect tissues have been used pupal tissues are particularly suitable since it is easy to sterilise the outside of the pupa by immersing it in a mild antiseptic and treating it with strong solutions of antibiotics. The ovaries, which are found dorsally in the region of the fifth and sixth abdominal segments of Bombycidae and Saturnidae are one of the most suitable tissues for culturing. After removal they are cut into explants about 1 mm^3 and explanted, often as hanging-drop cultures. These tissues can also be disaggregated, as described in Chapter XIII, and explanted on to glass.

Other invertebrates

Numerous attempts have been made to culture other invertebrate tissues and possibly the most interesting, since they indicate that the principles used in the culture of mammalian and avian tissues may be generally applicable, are those which have used coelenterate cells. Philips was first successful in growing Hydra cells. Since then Martin and Tardent have grown cells of a marine coelenterate in a medium composed of sea-water to which had been added serine, glycine and tyrosine as well as glucose and Yeastolate yeast extract, the whole being supplemented with lobster blood plasma. Li and his colleagues grew cells from a fresh-water Hydra. These authors used a medium composed of a modified salt solution (Table XIV) with added horse serum and Eagle's medium. They used large amounts of antibiotics to eliminate microorganisms.

The actual techniques were standard hanging-drop and roller-tube preparations.

BIBLIOGRAPHY

ARVY, L. & GABE, M. (1946). Sur la multiplication *in vitro* des cellules sanguines de *Forficula auricularia. C.R. Soc. Biol. Paris* **140**, 787.

BUCK, J. B. (1953). Physical properties and chemical composition of insect blood. In *Insect physiology,* ed. Roeder, K. D. New York: Wiley.

CASTIGLIONI, M. C. & RAIMONDI, G. R. (1961). First results of tissue culture in *Drosophila. Experientia* **17**, 88.

DAY, M. F. & GRACE, T. D. C. (1959). Review of recent work on insect tissue culture. *Annu. Rev. Ent.* **4**, 17.

FREW, J. G. H. (1928). A technique for the cultivation of insect tissues. *J. exp. Biol.* **6**, 1.

GLASER, R. W. (1917). The growth of insect blood cells *in vitro. Psyche* **24**, 1.

GOODCHILD, A. J. P. (1954). Culture of insect tissues. *Nature (Lond.)* **173**, 504.

GRACE, T. D. C. (1958). The prolonged growth and survival of ovarian tissue of the Promethea moth, *Callosamia promethea, in vitro. J. gen. Physiol.* **41**, 1027.

GRACE, T. D. C. (1958). Effects of various substances on growth of silkworm tissues *in vitro. Aust. J. exp. Biol.* **11**, 407.

HORIKAWA, M. & KURODA, Y. (1959). *In vitro* cultivation of blood cells of *Drosophila melanogaster* in a synthetic medium. *Nature (Lond.)* **184**, 2017.

JONES, B. M. (1962). The cultivation of insect cells and tissues. *Biol. Rev.* **37**, 512.

JONES, B. M. & CUNNINGHAM, I. (1960). Growth by cell division in insect tissue culture. *Nature (Lond.)* **187**, 1072.

JONES, B. M. & CUNNINGHAM, I. (1961). Growth by cell division in insect tissue culture. *Exp. Cell Res.* **23**, 386.

LI, Y-Y FU, BAKER, F. D. & ANDREW, W. (1963). A method for tissue culture of *Hydra* cells. *Proc. Soc. exp. Biol. (N.Y.)* **113**, 259.

MARTIGNONI, M. E. (1960). Problems of insect tissue culture. *Experientia* **16**, 125.

MARTIGNONI, M. E. (1962). Insect tissue culture: a tool for the physiologist. In *Insect Physiology,* Proceedings of the 23rd Biological Congress, Oregon State University. Corvallis, Oregon: Oregon State University Press.

MARTIGNONI, M. E. & SCALLION, R. J. (1961). Preparation and uses of insect hemocyte monolayers *in vitro. Biol. Bull.* **121**, 507.

MARTIGNONI, M. E., ZITCHER, F. M. & WAGNER, R. P. (1958). Preparation of cell suspension from insect tissues for *in vitro* cultivation. *Science* **128**, 360.

MARTIN, R. & TARDENT, P. (1963). Kultur von Hydroiden-Zellen *in vitro. Rev. suisse. Zool.* **70**.

TOBIAS, J. M. (1948). The high potassium and low sodium in the body fluid and tissues of a phytophagus insect, the silkworm, *Bombyx mori,* and the change before pupation. *J. cell comp. Physiol.* **31**, 143.

VAGO, C. & CHASTANG, S. (1962). Cultures de tissus d'insectes a l'aide de serum de mammiferes. *Entomophaga* **7**, 175.

WIGGLESWORTH, V. B. (1959). Insect blood cells. *Annu. Rev. Entomol.* **4**, 1.

WYATT, G. R. & KALF, G. F. (1956). Tehalose in insects. *Fed. Proc.* **15**, 388.

WYATT, S. S. (1956). Culture *in vitro* of tissue from the silkworm *Bombyx mori. J. gen. Physiol.* **39**, 841.

WYATT, G. R. (1961). The biochemistry of insect haemolymph. *Annu. Rev. Entomol.* **6**, 75.

STORAGE OF TISSUE BEFORE CULTURING

As a general principle it is best to set up cultures as soon as practicable after the tissue has been obtained. However, it is possible to use tissues which have been stored up to two days before use. Cells may be grown from foetuses which have been dead for 24 hours but post-mortem material is usually unsatisfactory unless it is removed almost immediately after death. The main factors affecting the viability of tissue are the temperature at which it is stored and the ease with which nutrients and oxygen can diffuse to it. Thus tissue in the centre of a large organ will soon die, particularly if the temperature remains fairly high, since metabolites in the vicinity of each cell will rapidly be used up when the circulation stops and no more metabolites will become available. On the other hand peripheral tissues, such as the skin, may survive for a very long time since they cool down quickly (so that metabolism is reduced) and oxygen can diffuse in from the air while metabolites can diffuse out from dying tissues in the deeper layers.

If precautions are taken to ensure that metabolism is reduced and metabolites can diffuse to the tissue survival for many days may be obtained. These conditions are achieved by cutting the tissue into small fragments, putting them into a nutrient solution and storing at room or refrigerator temperature. This procedure should be adopted if tissue cannot be handled immediately for any reason.

Long-term storage of tissue is considered in more detail in Chapter XVIII.

CULTURE OF PLANT TISSUES

In many respects the culture of plant tissues is similar to the culture of animal cells. In general the techniques are rather simpler for the following reasons: (1) Simpler culture media can be employed. (2) The cultures can be incubated in equilibrium with room air in cotton-wool stoppered bottles. (3) The cultures are incubated at room temperature. The actual techniques can be divided into those using fluid media and those using semi-solid substrates. Fluid media are generally used for the culture of roots and for cell suspensions (discussed in Chapter XVI) while disorganised tissues are usually grown on semi-solid media on which they pile up to form a mass known as a callus. Semi-solid media are usually the same as the liquid media but contain about 0·5 per cent. agar (Difco).

Preparation of tissues from plants

The principles involved in obtaining plant tissues for culturing are exactly analogous to those used in obtaining animal tissues, *i.e.* aseptic removal or disinfection.

Aseptic removal of tissue is fairly easy with many plant tissues. For instance, it is only necessary to break a carrot to expose a sterile surface from which a piece of tissue can be removed by means of a sterile cork-borer to give an excellent subject for cultivation. Similarly, the potato, artichoke, etc., can be sterilised on the outside with disinfectant (usually a detergent followed by a hypochlorite solution) and a slice removed to expose a sterile surface.

Twigs, branches, tree-trunks, and so on can be treated similarly. After sterilisation of the outside the epithelium or bark can be removed to expose the sterile internal tissues, ready for cultivation.

In addition to tissues of the above type a good deal of plant tissue culture has been concerned with the growth of root tips. They are best obtained by removing seeds from the interior of a fleshy plant and permitting them to germinate in aseptic conditions. As a rule, the seeds are sterilised with detergents and hypochlorite, or some similar means, and then placed on moist sterile filter-paper or agar in the dark to germinate.

This subject is considered in detail by White and the reader who wishes further information is recommended to consult his textbook.

Cultivation of plant tissues

A brief description of two classical types of culture will be given to illustrate the principles.

Culture of tomato roots

Sterile tomato roots are first obtained. The seeds are removed aseptically from a ripe tomato (the skin can be thoroughly washed and then swabbed with alcohol). They are placed on moist sterile filter-paper in sterile Petri dishes and left in the dark for a few days to germinate. Healthy roots, 2 - 3 cm. long, are then cut off with scissors and transferred to 125 ml. conical flasks containing 50 ml. of White's plant medium (Chapter VI). The flasks should not be stoppered but merely covered with aluminium foil. The roots grow and can be transferred weekly by cutting off about 1 cm. from the tip of each and placing in new medium. White has maintained a strain of tomato roots for over twenty years by this method.

Culture of carrot callus

In this case the culture is grown on a solid substrate. A number of 6″ × 1″ test-tubes are prepared by inoculating each with 10 ml. of White's medium partly solidified by the inclusion of 0·5 per cent. agar. The solution is sterilised and the agar dissolved by autoclaving. After inoculating the sterile tubes they are stoppered with sterile cotton-wool or aluminium foil and placed in a rack at an angle of about 30° to form a long slope.

A large, healthy carrot is cleaned thoroughly and dried on the outside. It is then broken to expose a sterile surface and with a sterile corkborer a core about 5 mm. in diameter is removed. This is transferred to a Petri dish and sliced into discs. One or two discs are placed on the agar slope and the tube, capped with aluminium foil, is placed in a rack at an angle.

Some tissues are more demanding than others in their nutritional requirements and the preparation of some explants requires more technical skill but the principles of plant tissue culture are the same in most techniques.

BIBLIOGRAPHY

CAPLAN, S. M. & STEWARD, F. C. (1949). A technique for the controlled growth of excised plant tissue in liquid media under aseptic conditions. *Nature (Lond.)* **163**, 920.

GAUTHERET, R. J. (1939). Sur la possibilité de réaliser la culture indefinie des tissus de tubercle de carotte. *C.R. Acad. Sci. Paris* **208**, 118.

GAUTHERET, R. J. (1959). *La culture des tissus végétaux*. Paris: Masson.

GIBBS, J. L. & DOUGALL, D. K. (1963). Growth of single plant cells. *Science* **141**, 1059.

HALPERIN, W. & WETHERELL, D. F. (1964). Adventive embryony in tissue cultures of the wild carrot, daucus carota. *Amer. J. Bot.* **51**, 274.

JONES, L. E., HILDEBRANDT, A. C., RIKER, A. J. & WU, J. H. (1959). Growth senescence and rejuvenation of tobacco cells in microculture. *Plant Physiol.* Suppl. **34**, iii.

MUIR, W. H. & HILDEBRANDT, A. C. (1953). Growth of tissue cultures under several conditions of aeration. *Abst. Amer. Soc. Plant Physiol.* A.I.B.S., Madison, Wis.

MUIR, W. H., HILDEBRANDT, A. C. & RIKER, A. J. (1954). Plant tissue cultures produced from single isolated cells. *Science* **119**, 877.

NICKELL, L. G. & TULECKE, W. (1959). Responses of plant tissue cultures to gibberellin. *Bot. Gaz.* **120**, 245.

REINERT, J. (1963). Growth of single cells from higher plants on synthetic media. *Nature (Lond.)* **200**, 90.

SCHROEDER, C. A., KAY, E. & DAVIS, L. H. (1962). Totipotency of cells from fruit pericarp tissue in vitro. *Science* **138**, 595.

STEWARD, F. C. (1964). Growth and development of culture plant cells. *Science* **143**, 20.

WEATHERELL, D. F. & HALPERIN, W. (1963). Embryos dervied from Callus cultures of the wild carrot. *Nature (Lond.)* **200**, 1336.

WHITE, P. R. (1939). Potentially unlimited growth of excised plant callus in an artificial nutrient. *Amer. J. Bot.* **26**, 59.

WHITE, P. R. (1954). *The cultivation of animal and plant cells*. London: Thames and Hudson. New York: Ronald Press.

CHAPTER XV

CELL STRAINS

STATIC CULTURE METHODS

WHEN a colony of cells has been subcultured many times *in vitro* and continues to proliferate rapidly so that there is no reason to doubt that it can be carried indefinitely, it is designated a permanent cell line or permanent cell strain. Material which has been freshly explanted very rarely progresses smoothly to becoming a permanent strain. More commonly, after an initial phase of rapid growth, the cells slow down and stop growing. In many cases they die out but in some cases, after a variable static period, there is a sudden outgrowth of new cells. Thereafter they can frequently be carried indefinitely.

The initial phase of rapid growth may last only a few days or as long as many months. During this phase the strain is referred to as a primary cell line or primary cell strain. It is not always possible to make a clear distinction between primary and permanent strains if the primary phase lasts a particularly long time, as it does, for instance, with human skin fibroblasts which can commonly be carried in continuous culture for about a year after isolation before they eventually peter out. However, certain arbitrary observations may suggest whether a line is established permanently or not. For instance, primary strains are usually diploid but this is rather uncommon in permanent strains. Furthermore, the emergence of a permanent strain is often characterised by the sudden appearance of rapidly-growing colonies in a degenerating population. This phenomenon is called 'transformation'. (It probably has no connection with bacterial transformation.) However, sometimes no obvious 'transformation' can be observed.

Cells which have passed through these phases to become a permanent strain are frequently very different from the cells of the tissue from which they originated. They have a different pattern of metabolism, are capable of supporting the growth of a wide variety of viruses and are very frequently polyploid. Unusual degrees of ploidy are often encountered and many strains are, for instance, triploid.

At the present time, it is not known whether these cells arise by selection, adaptation, transformation, mutation or some other undefined process. It is almost impossible to be certain of the cells of origin of a strain arising from a piece of tissue, owing to the complexity of the cellular composition of all animal tissues and the loss of all recognisable morphological characteristics. This statement may require modification with the advance of knowledge of cell behaviour and we may ultimately be able to distinguish between them on biochemical and immunological grounds. Progress has already been made in this direction and some provisional criteria for cell identification are described at the end of the chapter.

A strain arising from a piece of tissue may consist of one or several types of cell. It is frequently the case that one cell-type outgrows all others but it has been demonstrated beyond doubt that this is not invariably true. In other cases morphologically indistinguishable cells may grow together. A great many strains are of this type. On the other hand, many have now been raised from a single cell. These are called clone strains and the method of cloning is discussed later in this chapter.

A partial list of the commoner standard permanent cell strains is given in Table XXI.

Bearing these considerations in mind, we shall now consider the methods of manipulating cell strains. They always grow uniformly, as colonies, layers or suspensions. Very few cell-strains nowadays are carried as colonies but when they are, they are usually carried in roller-tubes and the techniques described in Chapter XI are used. The original technique, used by Carrel for his immortal strain, used coverslip cultures. This highly skilful, tedious and unnecessary method is never employed now for this purpose. A very few strains of cells grow spontaneously in suspension and their manipulation is essentially identical with that of cells maintained in suspension by artificial means. They will be discussed in the next chapter.

Most cell strains are grown direct on glass surfaces. They are maintained in glass vessels having a flat surface on which the cells can settle, such as Carrel flasks, T-flasks, prescription bottles, Kolle flasks, penicillin culture flasks, Roux bottles, Erlenmeyer flasks, crystallisation dishes and Petri dishes. In fact, any vessel with a flat bottom which can be conveniently sterilised and sealed is suitable for the purpose. The actual shape of the vessel will depend on other requirements. For instance, if it is desired to examine the cells microscopically while they are growing it will obviously be desirable to use a vessel with better optical properties than a prescription bottle. But for the simple maintenance of cells the prescription bottle is perfectly satisfactory.

The essential manipulations involved in maintaining cell-strains are medium renewal or ' feeding ' and subculture or transferring. Feeding is very simple, consisting merely of removing all or part of the used medium and replacing it with fresh medium. The more fundamental manipulation in handling these cultures is transferring. This requires that the cells be obtained in suspension.

SUSPENDING CELLS FROM A MONOLAYER CULTURE

Cells growing in a monolayer on a glass surface may be brought into suspension :

(1) By physical methods—scraping from the glass ; shaking.

(2) By chemical methods—(a) proteolytic enzymes ; (b) chelating agents.

Some cell-strains are very loosely adherent to the glass surface and may be suspended simply by agitating the flask gently. There are many cells which will not leave the glass so readily but which can easily be dislodged by scraping with a rubber or plastic ' policeman ' on the end of a glass rod. When the dislodged flakes are then sucked up and down once or twice in a pipette a suspension of single cells is formed. A refinement of this technique is to place within the culture vessel a small magnet enclosed in silicone rubber. The cells can then be suspended readily without opening the vessel by placing it over a magnetic stirrer.

Many cell-strains will not yield readily to physical removal but will round up and leave the glass as single cells when treated with a dilute buffered solution of trypsin. Other proteolytic enzymes have been used for this purpose. Some workers have recommended a crude pancreatin preparation but trypsin preparations have become standard. The general method used for transferring cells is illustrated in Figure 39. The following modified technique is recommended as being both convenient and effective.

Materials.—1. BSS (warmed to 37°C.)

2. 0·5 per cent. trypsin (1/250 Difco) in citrate buffer (1·25 g. trypsin; 1·48 g. Na citrate; 3·0 g. NaCl in 500 ml. water, *p*H adjusted to 7·8) (warmed to 37° C.).

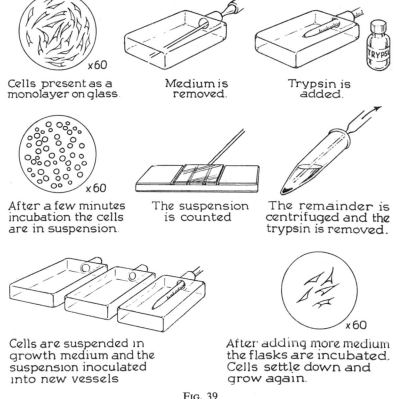

Cells present as a monolayer on glass.

Medium is removed.

Trypsin is added.

After a few minutes incubation the cells are in suspension.

The suspension is counted

The remainder is centrifuged and the trypsin is removed.

Cells are suspended in growth medium and the suspension inoculated into new vessels

After adding more medium the flasks are incubated. Cells settle down and grow again.

Fig. 39
Maintenance of cell strains.

Technique.—Unstopper the flasks to be treated and remove all the medium. Wash twice with some BSS (an amount equivalent to 1/4 to 1/2 the original volume of medium for each wash). Add some trypsin-citrate to each vessel (sufficient to cover all the cells) and replace in the incubator for about two minutes. Remove the trypsin-citrate almost completely, stopper the vessels and replace them in the incubator. The film of trypsin solution will continue its action. When the cells have separated from the glass (check with the microscope until you are accustomed to the process) return some medium to the vessel and suspend the cells in this by gentle rocking and, if necessary, by pipetting. Some of the suspension should then be taken for counting and viability determination. Dilute this suspension with medium to give a suitable inoculation density and distribute it among fresh vessels. An inoculation density of 10^5 cells per ml. is satisfactory for virtually all cells but many can be inoculated at much lower densities (10^3-10^4 per ml.). This is preferable if the strain will grow up from such low inocula but for new strains it is wise to start with higher inocula and proceed gradually to lower ones since many cells will die very rapidly if dispersed too thinly.

Trypsin is commonly used at 0·1 per cent. to 0·5 per cent. but it should be noted that many people consider a lower concentration of trypsin desirable and as low a concentration as 0·025 per cent. is used. The pH is most important during trypsinisation. Below pH 7·0 trypsin is virtually inactive. Above pH 8·0 the cells are progressively damaged in its presence. If centrifugation is used the speed is important. In a protein-rich medium little damage is done to the cells by rapid centrifugation but in a medium low in protein, they are easily destroyed and it is advisable to use very low rates of centrifugation (500-1,000 r.p.m.). With delicate cells excessive pipetting is also to be avoided though many cells can be pipetted freely without damage.

The same result may be achieved without proteolytic enzymes by the use of a chelating agent. A chelating agent is a chemical substance which will bind divalent kations. Thus it binds calcium and magnesium ions and probably its effect in causing cells to round up and leave the glass is connected with this function. The chelating agent commonly used for this purpose is diamino-ethane-tetra-acetic acid, most commonly known by one of its trade-names, Versene. Versene occurs as a free acid or as salts. The acid is insoluble but the sodium salts are quite soluble and consequently either disodium versenate should be used or free versene should be neutralised to bring it into solution. It is employed as a 1 : 5,000 solution in calcium and magnesium-free salt solution, buffered at about pH 7·4.

Reagent.—

Na versenate	0·2 g. per litre.
NaCl	8·0 g. per litre.
KCl	0·2 g. per litre.
Na_2HPO_4	1·15 g. per litre.
KH_2PO_4	0·2 g. per litre.
Glucose	0·2 g. per litre.

Procedure.—Remove the growth medium, wash with (Ca & Mg-free) BSS, and replace with versene solution, prewarmed to 37° C. Incubate the culture for 10 - 15 minutes and suspend the cells by shaking. Centrifuge at 1,000 r.p.m. for 5 minutes. Remove the supernatant and replace with growth medium. Suspend by gentle pipetting.

If large amounts of trypsin or versene are left in the vessel after the above procedures the cells may not adhere and may become damaged. Hence if cells are dispersed in large volumes of trypsin or versene solution it is usually necessary to separate them out by centrifugation. However, if the trypsin or versene is very much diluted, as in the procedure described for trypsinisation or if great dilutions are made (*e.g.* for cloning) this is not necessary. The very small amount of trypsin left is neutralised by the serum inhibitor and versene is neutralised by the excess of calcium and magnesium in the medium. If serum-free medium is being used, however, it must never be forgotten that no trypsin inhibitor will be present.

NOTE. Not all cells respond equally well to trypsin and versene treatment. In particular cells of fibroblastic type are not readily disaggregated with versene although they may be brought into suspension readily with trypsin. Cells of epithelial type respond to either treatment as a rule.

INOCULATION OF NEW VESSELS

Having obtained a cell-suspension, it is first necessary to estimate the number of cells present and this is usually done by counting them in the way described in Chapter XX. The suspension can then be diluted with more growth medium so that a suitable size of inoculum will contain a reasonable number of cells. A common practice is to inoculate sufficient cells that the final ratio of cells to medium will be of the order of 100,000 per ml. With delicate cells a much higher inoculum, as high as 500,000 cells per ml., is sometimes necessary. On the other hand with many permanent cell strains much lower inocula are often possible and 10^3-10^4 cells per ml. may be adequate. If cells grow well at low inocula it is the best procedure to use but their ability to do so must always be checked. An inoculum of the order of 1 ml. is convenient for each flask so that to achieve a ratio of 100,000 cells per ml. in a flask containing 20 ml. of medium, it would be convenient to inoculate with 1 ml. of a suspension containing 2,000,000 cells per ml. The volume would then be made up with 19 ml. of medium.

The accuracy of the aliquots depends on a number of factors.

1. Production of a uniform suspension.

2. Maintenance of a uniform suspension during dispensing.

3. The accuracy of measurement of volumes of replicates.

If the steps described above are followed, a uniform suspension will readily be obtained with most cell-types and it can be checked by microscopic examination.

The accuracy of measurement of replicate volumes is a simple matter of standard pipetting procedures. Thus the point which requires special consideration is the second one, maintenance of the cells in suspension while they are being dispensed. Most of the cell-types commonly encountered are relatively dense and tend to settle out from the medium very rapidly so that special care has to be taken to keep them in suspension. Three methods are commonly employed.

1. **Manual stirring and pipetting.**—This method is perfectly adequate for small amounts of suspensions and for routine handling of stock cultures. A careful operator can obtain a very high degree of reproducibility in replicate cultures. The cells are maintained in suspension by stirring with a pipette while holding the vessel containing the cells in the other hand. The cells are then sucked up and down once or twice in the pipette ; some suspension is

retained and the volume adjusted very rapidly before transferring it to the waiting culture vessel. For accuracy of pipetting it may be necessary to use a pipette without a rubber tube (but with a cotton-wool filter). However, an experienced operator can do equally accurate work with a rubber teat on the end of a pipette or with a rubber tube and mouthpiece attached to it. The advantage of the latter method is that the suspension can be stirred continuously while pipetting and the level of suspension in the pipette is always under observation so that a rapid adjustment can be made.

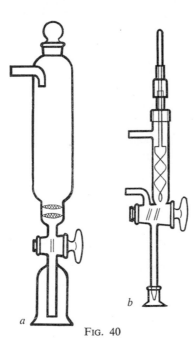

FIG. 40

Earle's apparatus for handling of replicate cell cultures. (*a*) Strainer for producing cell suspensions. (*b*) Stirrer and dispenser for delivering equal volume of a uniform cell suspension. (Kontes Glass Co.)

2. **Suspending with a magnetic stirrer.**—It takes some considerable time to acquire the skill necessary to perform the previous procedure with a high degree of accuracy. If this level of skill has not been reached, it is advisable to use a mechanical method for maintaining the cells in suspension. A magnetic stirrer provides the simplest method. The cell suspension is placed in a sterile beaker containing a sterile stainless steel or silicone-covered magnet. The beaker is placed on a magnetic stirrer so that the magnet rotates at a fairly slow rate. Aliquots of suspension can then be removed by pipette as before. It is sometimes useful to use an automatic pipetting device, such as the Lowry pipette.

3. **Special dispensing devices.**—Obviously, the above method carries a considerable risk of contamination from exposure to the atmosphere. Also, there is always a large residue of suspension left since the last few ml. tend to be whipped into a froth and the

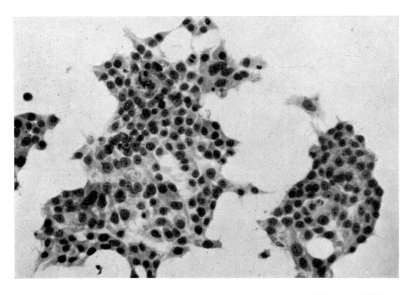

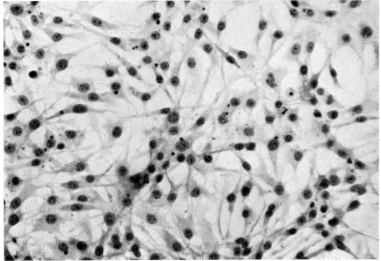

PLATE 9

Top: Cells from a strain of epithelial morphology (HLM). *Bottom*: Cells from a strain of fibroblastic morphology (strain L). Stained Ehrlich Haematoxylin. × 175.

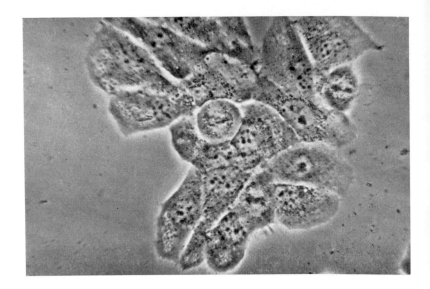

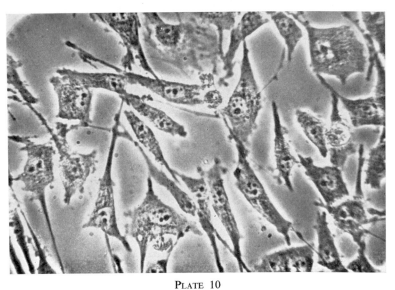

PLATE 10

Top: Cells from a strain of epithelial morphology (HeLa). *Bottom*: Cells from a strain of fibroblastic morphology (strain L). Phase contrast. ×350.

rotating magnet prevents insertion of the pipette to the bottom of the beaker. A special pipetting device has been developed at the National Cancer Institute in the United States (Fig. 40) and is now available commercially. It consists essentially of a spiral stirrer to maintain the cells in suspension and a special stopcock which measures accurate aliquots of solution. In the original model provision is made for continuous gassing of the cell suspension.

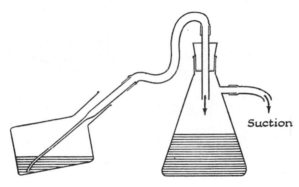

Suction

FIG. 41
Apparatus for withdrawal of medium from culture flasks.

A simplified modification was described by Syverton, Scherer and Elwood, consisting of a spiral stirrer as before and an outlet tube connected to a Cornwall pipetting unit which will dispense accurate aliquots of cell suspension. This latter apparatus works very satisfactorily provided it is operated continuously. If it is allowed to stop for any length of time cells sediment in the tube. In both cases the last few ml. should not be dispensed since stirring becomes inefficient as the reservoir empties and the aliquots cease to be exactly the same.

FEEDING AND MAINTENANCE

The feeding of cell-strains growing on glass substrates is exceedingly simple. As a rule it consists merely of removing the old medium and replacing it with new. The old medium can be either decanted or pipetted off. Since very large numbers of cells are often handled by this technique, it is desirable to employ one or two pieces of apparatus to facilitate the process. Medium can be removed very simply by means of a pipette attached to a suction pump. It is desirable to have a receiver between the pump and the pipette. A simple device of this sort is illustrated in Figure 41.

A mechanical dispenser greatly reduces the labour of adding medium to the vessels and is also convenient for making up large volumes of medium. The automatic syringe outfit illustrated and made by Becton, Dickinson & Co. is particularly convenient. Many other types of dispenser are available, such as those used in the pharmaceutical industry for filling bottles and ampoules.

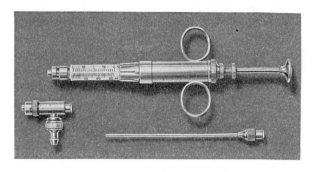

FIG. 42
Cornwall syringe for automatically pipetting aliquots of
liquids. (Becton, Dickinson & Co.)

With practically all the cell-lines known the medium can be completely exchanged at each feeding (which is usually performed every three or four days). In the case of a few delicate cell-lines it is common practice to replace only part of the old medium with new medium. Feeding should then be more frequent, every two days.

Most cells will grow to a maximum population in a vessel of given size and will increase no further, although if the medium is renewed regularly they will survive in a healthy state. Thus the rate of growth of the cultures can be controlled by varying the size of inoculum. If the numbers are reduced by half each week, the colonies will approximately double in that time. Rapidly growing cells will increase about a hundredfold in a week and it is common practice with some strains to inoculate fresh vessels with from one-twentieth to one-fiftieth of the final population. Under conditions of normal maintenance, however, one rarely anticipates an increase of more than tenfold in a week and it is a sure way of losing a strain to try to dilute it too far in the course of routine maintenance.

The medium used for maintenance depends on the strain but common media are as follows:

(1) Natural—Horse serum 20 per cent., embryo extract 10 per cent. in BSS. (Little used now.)

(2) Semisynthetic—(a) Calf serum 10 per cent., plus Eagle's medium.

   (b) Serum 5 to 10 per cent., plus medium 199 or M150.

(3) Lactalbumin hydrolysate 0·5 per cent., yeast hydrolysate 0·1 per cent., calf serum 5 per cent. in BSS.

The first medium will support most cells satisfactorily although some epithelial types will not thrive too well in the presence of a high concentration of embryo extract. The second medium will support many well-established strains satisfactorily. The third medium is commonly used in virology practice for the maintenance of HeLa cells. See also Chapters V and VI.

A convenient routine for the maintenance of cells is to handle them twice a week, feeding them on one occasion and transferring them on the other. There are, however, many other possibilities and a schedule should be developed to suit individual convenience.

Agar slope cultures

Cell strains can be grown on agar slope cultures and maintained in much the same way as bacteria. The use of semi-solid media of this kind was tried as far back as 1911 but until recently it was only used in organ culture work. One reason why agar was not commonly used was that a great many specimens are toxic to cells. In the author's experience the most reliable agar for cell culture is that prepared by Difco. The use of semi-solid media has been revived recently by Wallace and Hanks for cell-strain maintenance. Agar slopes are prepared as follows. A 3 per cent. solution of agar in water is melted and allowed to cool down to 43-44°. (It is convenient to have a water-bath at this temperature). A double strength nutrient medium is heated to about the same temperature and equal parts of it and the agar solution are mixed. 2-3 ml. aliquots are transferred to sterile test-tubes placed at an angle so that a long slope is formed. The tubes are sealed with sterile cotton-wool or other bacterial seals and left for the agar to solidify. They can then be stored for some days in a refrigerator until required. Before inoculating the slants about 0·3 ml. of medium is added to the tube and spread over the surface. Cells from another culture are picked up with a platinum loop and applied to the agar in rather large droplets. The tubes are incubated in an atmosphere of 5 per cent. CO_2 in a CO_2 incubator.

An ingenious method for maintaining cell lines has been suggested by Leighton. The cells are grown in test-tubes, each containing a glass bead about 6 mm. in diameter and the medium is replaced in these once or twice weekly. When the cultures have grown to the point where thinning is required the tube is shaken so as to dislodge most of the cells. These are discarded and the medium is renewed. The few cells remaining are enough to permit the culture to grow up again.

CLONING CELLS

For many studies it is desirable to obtain a pure strain of cells and the best way to ensure this is to grow the strain from a single cell. It should be noted that while this procedure makes certain that all the cells are of the same general type, it does not necessarily ensure that the progeny will remain genetically homogeneous.

The first technique for cloning cells was devised by Dr. Sanford in Dr. Earle's laboratory and consisted of isolating cells in capillary tubes and then growing the population in progressively larger vessels as it increased. In more detail, a very sparse suspension of cells was sucked into a fine capillary tube which was then sealed and examined under the microscope. When a single cell was seen in a length of the tube the latter was sterilised externally with chloroform and broken off so that the cell remained isolated in a section of capillary which was then implanted in a plasma clot and incubated until the cell population had grown big enough to permit transfer. This technique is not uniformly successful and is, in consequence, extremely tedious. However, it demonstrated that the growth of colonies from single mammalian cells was possible.

A considerable advance was made some years later by Puck and his colleagues who developed the method for plating single cells originally described by Rous and Jones in 1916, to enable colonies to be obtained. The method consists simply of inoculating a vessel with a very dilute suspension of cells and leaving it strictly undisturbed for about a week. The HeLa cell and a number of other epithelial cells are easily cloned by this means but some other cell-types do not form colonies readily. The essential conditions are a suitable, rich medium, scrupulously clean glassware, carefully regulated pH and careful handling of the cells so that they suffer the minimum of damage.

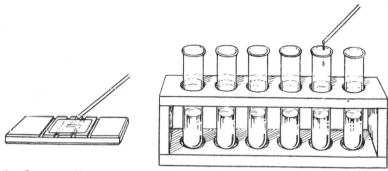

1. Count cells.

2. Make serial dilutions in medium.

3. Inoculate petri dish.

4. After 7-10 days examine colonies.

FIG. 43
Production of colonies from single cells by the dilution technique.

Cloning of HeLa cells by the dilution technique

1. Select a healthy flask of HeLa cells. The pH should be about 7·4, the medium free from débris and the microscopic appearance of the cells healthy.

2. Pour out the medium and rinse the bottle with a suitable volume of a balanced salt solution containing no calcium, magnesium or phosphate.

3. Discard the washing and add to the bottle a 0·05 per cent. solution of trypsin in citrate (see page 228). Incubate at 37° C. for 1-2 minutes, then remove the trypsin and continue incubating for another 5-10 minutes.

4. While the cell suspension is incubating, pipette 5 ml. of medium (20 per cent. human or calf serum, plus one of the synthetic media) into several 60 mm. Petri dishes and 4·5 ml. into several test-tubes. Place the Petri dishes in a CO_2 incubator (see below).

5. Add 5 ml. medium to the bottle containing the cells, agitate gently to suspend them and disperse them by gently pipetting two or three times in and out of a 10 ml. pipette.

6. Count the cells (Chapter XX). When the cell number has been determined dilute the cell suspension serially by adding 0·5 ml. of suspension to 4·5 ml. of medium in a test-tube and so on until a suspension is obtained containing 1,000 to 2,000 cells/ml. Inoculate each of the Petri dishes with 0·05 to 0·1 ml. of this suspension (to give 100 cells per dish). Agitate gently to mix the cells thoroughly, and replace the Petri dishes in the CO_2 incubator. Incubate at 37-38° C. for 7-10 days before examining.

7. If it is merely desired to count the colonies the medium can be removed and the Petri dish stained with Jenner-Giemsa stain to render the colonies visible. If the colonies are to be isolated the procedure is as follows. Having located a colony, mark its position on the outside of the dish, remove the medium and place over the colony a stainless steel or glass cylinder (5 - 6 mm. internal diameter and 10 - 12 mm. high) whose bottom edge has been coated with silicone grease. (Smear some silicone grease on the bottom of a Petri dish, apply some rings and sterilise by dry heat.) Verify that the colony is isolated by the cylinder. Wash out the inside of the cylinder twice with a few drops of salt solution and then replace it with a few drops of trypsin solution. After incubating for a few minutes mix the cell suspension by gently pipetting and remove it to the vessel in which subcultivation is to be carried out.

An alternative method for isolating colonies is as follows. Before inoculating the Petri dish cover the bottom with pieces of broken coverslip (approximately 5 mm. square). When colonies have grown examine the plate with a dissecting microscope and with sterile forceps remove any fragments of coverslip containing a single colony. Transfer these to test-tubes with 1-2 ml. medium and after they have grown farther trypsinise and passage in the usual way.

Agar suspension technique

Puck and Marcus observed that cells would grow into colonies while suspended in a medium stiffened with a low concentration of agar. Macpherson and Montagnier have developed a modification of the dilution technique on this principle. A thick agar base is first prepared in a Petri dish and the cells are then inoculated in an overlay of thin agar. Colonies, in the form of morulae, arise at the interface where they can easily be examined and, if desired, removed by pipetting. Details of the technique are as follows.

1. A stock (1 per cent.) solution of agar is made by dissolving 10 g. Difco Bacto agar in 1 litre of distilled water by boiling. It is sterilised by autoclaving.

2. The culture medium to be used is made up at double-strength. The agar stock solution is melted, then allowed to cool to 44° C. It is maintained at this temperature in a water-bath and the double-strength medium is heated to the same temperature. Before use equal quantities of double-strength medium and stock agar are mixed together to give 0·5 per cent. agar medium.

3. Base layers are prepared by pipetting 5-7 ml. of 0·5 per cent. agar medium into 60 mm. Petri dishes not more than 30 minutes before adding the overlay.

4. Cell suspensions are prepared in single-strength medium (without agar) such that 0·5 ml. contains the required inoculum of cells. The inoculum is then prepared by mixing 0·5 ml. of cell suspension and 1 ml. of 0·5 per cent. agar medium. This is quickly mixed and added to the prepared base layer.

The cultures prepared in this way are incubated in a CO_2 incubator in a humidified atmosphere in the usual way.

Some cell strains can be cloned relatively more successfully than others by this technique, which can therefore be used as a selective method.

Cloning in fibrin gels

Schindler introduced a somewhat similar technique in which cells are allowed to form colonies while embedded in fibrin gels. Fibrin is claimed to be less toxic than agar and the method is particularly useful for cells which normally grow in suspension. The medium is made up in two parts. Solution A consists of the culture medium, in which is dissolved 0·12 units of thrombin per 100 ml.

(The appearance of bubbles in the fibrin clot can be prevented by incubating this solution at 37° C. for 12-24 hours before use.) Solution B contains 250 mg. of bovine fibrinogen, 800 mg. NaCl and 25 mg. sodium citrate ($Na_3C_6H_5O_7 - 5\frac{1}{2}H_2O$). The fibrinogen is dissolved by agitation with a magnetic stirrer for 15 minutes after leaving to stand for two hours. This solution can be sterilised by ultraviolet light or by filtration through a Millipore filter. The cells are diluted and added to solution A to give a concentration of about 5 cells per ml. To 12 ml. of this in a 16 ml. culture tube are added 3 ml. of solution B and the solutions are carefully and rapidly mixed. In a few minutes a clear gel forms. The culture is incubated at 37° C. Colonies form as morulae after 5 to 10 days, depending on the rate of multiplication of the cells.

The use of a CO_2 incubator was mentioned in connection with these techniques, the point being that, in order to control the pH, a medium based on Earle's BSS should be used along with an atmosphere containing 5 per cent. CO_2. The simplest way of achieving this is to use any airtight vessel (a desiccator or anaerobic jar) and to fill it with 5 per cent. CO_2 in air from a cylinder. If much work of this nature is contemplated it is useful to have an airtight incubator with a supply of 5 per cent. CO_2 in air, either from cylinders of compressed gas or from the local compressed air supply and a cylinder of liquid CO_2 mixed by a mixing valve.

If neither of the above is available, a number of expedients is available and the easiest of these is to place a small beaker with dilute HCl in the vessel, adding a measured quantity of $NaHCO_3$, sufficient to give 5 per cent. CO_2 in the air, just before closing the vessel.

In my laboratory we have successfully cloned cells by a technique which dispenses with a CO_2 incubator. Instead of Earle's BSS the medium is based on a tris-citrate buffer containing oxaloacetate and fumarate. The following stock solutions are required: A. 0·2 M Tris; B. 0·1 M citric acid; C. Hank's BSS × 10; D. 3 M $MgCl_2$; E. 5×10^{-2} M Na fumarate; F. 5×10^{-2} M Na oxaloacetate. One litre of BSS is made by combining 80 ml. A, 50 ml. B, 65 ml C, 10 ml. D, 20 ml. E and 20 ml. F and making up to 1 litre with distilled water. For cloning a suitable stock medium (*e.g.* 109, ten times strength) is combined with serum and made up to volume with this buffered salt solution. The medium will maintain pH 7·4 in equilibrium with air at 37° C. and supports clonal growth of many cell strains with high plating efficiency. It is necessary to enclose the Petri dishes in a sealed vessel to maintain humidity. Polystyrene boxes with tight lids, sealed with adhesive tape (sellotape) have proved satisfactory. The cultures can be incubated in an ordinary incubator or hot room.

The techniques described above are perfectly adequate for quantitative procedures where it is desired to determine the efficiency of plating. However, they are obviously unreliable if it is desired to know with certainty that a strain has grown from a single cell since the colony may have grown from a group of cells inadvertently included in the suspension. To be certain of isolating single cells a micropipetting procedure has been developed. Although this appears difficult at first sight it is, in fact, extraordinarily simple. The method described is derived from that originally described by Lwoff, Dulbecco, Vogt and Lwoff, with modifications introduced by other workers (Wildy and Stoker).

Cloning cells by the isolation technique

MATERIALS AND APPARATUS REQUIRED

1. A supply of sterile 60 mm. Petri dishes.
2. Pasteur pipettes.
3. A CO_2 incubator.
4. A supply of medium (20 per cent. human or calf serum in one of the synthetic media).
5. BSS.
6. A low-power microscope ($\times 100$ magnification). A three-dimensional dissecting microscope is best, but an ordinary microscope with $\frac{2}{3}''$ objective will do.
7. Liquid paraffin saturated with medium. (To about 200 ml. of paraffinum liquidum B.P., in a sterile bottle, add 20 ml. of medium and shake. Leave in a 37° incubator for several days to permit the paraffin to clear. The paraffin need not be sterilised.)
8. Micropipettes. To prepare these, first make a microburner by connecting a piece of tubing to a hypodermic needle. Then take a piece of glass tubing and draw it out to form a fine Pasteur pipette on an ordinary Bunsen burner. Finally, place the fine capillary area of this pipette in the flame of the microburner. When the glass has thoroughly softened (but not enough to seal the lumen) take it quickly out of the flame and pull sharply to form a capillary point with bore of around 50 μ (see illustration). Coat this with

16

silicone by sucking in a little Repelcote and expelling it again.
(This can be omitted if desired.) Wash with BSS before use. (It
may require about an hour's practice to make suitable pipettes.)

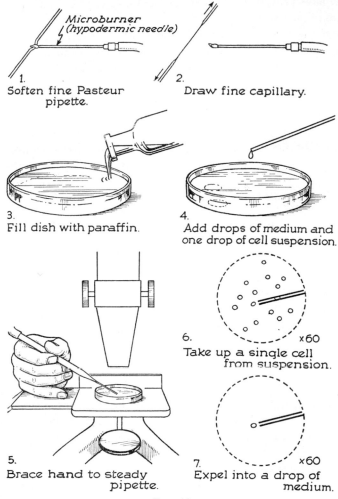

1. Soften fine Pasteur pipette.

2. Draw fine capillary.

3. Fill dish with paraffin.

4. Add drops of medium and one drop of cell suspension.

5. Brace hand to steady pipette.

6. Take up a single cell from suspension. ×60

7. Expel into a drop of medium. ×60

Fig. 44

Production of colonies from single cells by the isolation procedure.

Technique

1. Take a glass Petri dish and rinse out the bottom half with clean
ether. When this has evaporated flame quickly on the bottom side

to ensure that all the ether has gone. Alternatively use a polystyrene Petri dish of a type suitable for cell culture. Fill up the Petri dish (to a depth of 10-12 mm.) with medium-saturated paraffin.

2. Place about ten drops of medium round the dish about 1 cm. from the edge. The drops will fall through the paraffin and spread out on the glass. A suitable size of drop is about 10 μl. of medium, which will spread out to about 5 mm. Finally, in the centre of the dish place a few drops of the cell suspension.

3. Take one of the prepared micropipettes and attach a mouth tube to it. Take a little medium into the capillary section. Now, bracing the edge of the hand against the microscope stage, insert the tip of the pipette into the pool of suspended cells, watching it through the microscope. Select an isolated cell, place the tip of the pipette near it and by gentle suction draw the cell into the lumen. Remove the pipette, move one of the drops of medium into the field, insert the pipette into this and expel the cell.

4. When all ten drops have received cells, replace the lid on the Petri dish and place it in a CO_2 incubator. The drops may be examined in a day or two.

This technique is much easier than one might think and it can easily be mastered after a few hours' practice. It is not necessary to carry it out exactly as described and, for instance, the cells may be transferred from one vessel to another if required. To transfer the colony it is only necessary to carry out trypsinisation within the drop under the paraffin.

The efficiency of cloning depends on a number of factors, some of which have already been mentioned. The serum used in the medium is very important and a good source should be sought. Healthy, rapidly growing cells give the best results. Some cells grow colonies from single cells much more easily than others. It has been claimed by Neumann and McCoy that a very much higher cloning efficiency can be obtained with some cells of fibroblastic type by adding a keto-acid (pyruvic acid, oxaloacetic acid or α-ketoglutaric acid) to the medium.

Characterisation of cell strains

Since it has become apparent that contamination of one cell strain by another may occur quite readily and that this may, in fact, account for many cases of so-called 'transformation' attempts have been made to evolve methods for the positive identification of cell strains. At the present time four general kinds of criteria have proved useful in this respect.

1. **Chromosomal morphology.**—Although the numbers of chromosomes may vary very greatly in cultured cells and chromosomes of bizarre morphology may make their appearance it is now firmly established that many of the chromosomes of the original tissue retain their morphology even after years of subculture. Hence a competent cytologist may be able to identify the animal from which a cell strain originated.

2. **Viral susceptibility.**—In general terms many cell strains have typical patterns of susceptibility to certain viruses and may be identified by this means.

3. **Enzymic constitution.**—Species-specific electrophoretic patterns for certain enzymes persist *in vitro* and the cellular content of certain constitutive enzymes is typical. By application of enzymatic analyses the species of origin of a cell-strain may be identified with certainty and the cell-strain itself may sometimes be provisionally identified.

4. **Immunological properties.**—Species-specific antigens are preserved in culture; hence immunological methods have proved particularly valuable for characterising cell strains. The tests most commonly employed are Coombs' mixed agglutination test, Stulberg's fluorescent antibody reaction and the haemagglutinin test introduced by Brand and Syverton. Other tests are based on the reduction of plating efficiency by specific antibodies and on the entry of trypan blue to cells damaged by antibody.

It may be added that although morphology is an unreliable guide it can sometimes also aid in making a provisional diagnosis as to the cell-type. In particular fibroblastic, epithelial and lymphoid cells can be distinguished by a practised observer. No absolutely reliable method of identifying an unknown cell-strain has yet been evolved but a reasonably accurate identification can be made on the basis of the above methods.

In addition to the general criteria which have been mentioned a few special criteria may exist for special cases, *e.g.* mutants which preferentially use pentoses as carbon sources.

TABLE XXI

SOME STANDARD PERMANENT CELL STRAINS

Origin		Designation of strain	Reference
Species	Tissue		
Hamster, Chinese	Peritoneal cells	B14FAF28-G3 (CCL 14)	Yerganian, G. & Leonard, M. (1961)
	Lung, diploid	Don (CCL 16)	Hsu, T. C. (no publication)
	Lung	C	Ford, D. K. & Yerganian, G. (1959)
	Lung	P	Ford, D. K. & Yerganian, G. (1959)
	Lung	V	Ford, D. K. & Yerganian, G. (1959)
Hamster, Syrian	Kidney	HaK (CCL 15)	Spense, I. M. (1959) Unpublished
	Kidney	BHK 21	Macpherson, I. & Stoker, M. G. (1962)
Human	Amnion	FL	Fogh, J. & Lund, R. O. (1957)
	Amnion	Amnion strain— Fernandes	Fernandes, M. V. (1958)
	Amnion	WISH (CCL 25)	Hayflick, L. (1961)
	Amnion	AV_3 (CCL 21)	Robbins, F. C. & Lepow, M. I. (No publication)
	Appendix	Chang appendix	Chang, R. S. (1954)
	Blood, non-leukaemic	Detroit-B16	Berman, L., Stulberg, C. S & Ruddle, F. H. (1957)
	Blood, non-leukaemic	Detroit-B17	Berman, L., Stulberg, C. S & Ruddle, F. H. (1957)
	Blood, non-leukaemic	Detroit-173B	Berman, L., Stulberg, C. S & Ruddle, F. H. (1957)
	Blood (subacute monocytic leukaemia)	Oregon J96	Osgood, E. E. & Brooke, J. H. (1955)

TABLE XXI (*contd.*)

SOME STANDARD PERMANENT CELL STRAINS

Origin		Designation of strain	Reference
Species	Tissue		
Human (*contd.*)	Blood (monocytic leukaemia)	J-111 (CCL 24)	Osgood, E. E. & Brooke, J. H. (1955)
	Cervix (carcinoma)	HEP 1	Toolan, H. W. (1954); Fjelde, A. (1955)
	Cervix (carcinoma)	HeLa (CCL 2)	Gey, G. O., Coffman, W. D. & Kubiceck, M. T. (1952)
	Conjunctiva	Chang conjunctiv	Chang, R. S. (1954)
	Heart (right atrial appendage)	Girardi heart	Girardi, A. J., Warren, J., Goldman, C. & Jeffries, B. (1958)
	Intestine, embryonic	Intestine 407 (CCL 6)	Henle. G. & Deinhardt (1957)
	Kidney	Chang kidney	Chang, R. S. (1954)
	Larynx (carcinoma)	HEP 2 (CCL 23)	Toolan, H. W. (1954); Fjelde, A. (1955)
	Liver	Chang liver (CCL 13)	Chang, R. S. (1954)
	Liver, foetal	HLM	Leslie, I., Fulton, W. C. & Sinclair, R. (1956)
	Lung, embryonic	L-132 (CCL 5)	Davis, E. V. (1960)
	Lymph node (containing meta static epidermoid cancer, Grade III, primary in the buccal mucosa)	HEP 3	Moore. A. E., Sabachewsky, L. & Toolan, H. W. (1955)
	Marrow (bone) (leukaemic)	MCN	McCulloch, E. Z. (1955)
	Marrow (sternal) from lung carcinoma	Detroit-6 (CCL 3)	Berman, L., Stulberg. C. S. & Ruddle, F. H. (1957)
	Marrow (sternal)	Detroit 6 (clone 12) (CCL 3·1)	Stulberg (1959) (unpublished)

TABLE XXI (*contd.*)

SOME STANDARD PERMANENT CELL STRAINS

Origin		Designation of strain	Reference
Species	*Tissue*		
Human (*contd.*)	Marrow (sternal) from carcinomatosis	Detroit-32	Berman, L., Stulberg, C. S. & Ruddle, F. H. (1957)
	Marrow (sternal) from metastatic carcinoma of bone	Detroit-34	Berman, L., Stulberg, C. S. & Ruddle, F. H. (1957)
	Marrow (sternal)	Detroit-52	Berman, L. & Stulberg, C. S. (1956)
	Marrow (sternal)	Detroit-98 (CCL 18)	Berman, L. & Stulberg, C. S. (1956)
	Marrow (bone)	Detroit-143	Berman, L., Stulberg, C. S. & Ruddle, F. H. (1957)
	Mouth, epidermoid carcinoma	KB (CCL 17)	Eagle, H. (1955)
	Esophagus (epithelium)	Minnesota-EE (CCL 4)	Syverton, J. T. & McLaren, L. C. (1957)
	Pituitary (foetus)	Wistar 6	Defendi, V. & Colter, J. S. (1957)
	Pituitary (foetus)	Wistar 12	Defendi, V. & Colter, J. S. (1957)
	Pleural fluid (metastatic adenocarcinoma)	Maben	Frisch, A. W., Jentoft, B. S., Barger, R. & Losli, E. J. (1955)
	Pleural fluid (lymphosarcoma)	Detroit-116P	Berman, L., Stulberg, C. S. & Ruddle, F. H. (1957)
	Skin (urticaria pigmentosa) (same as 196 Ep-1)	Detroit-196-Fb-L	Stulberg, C. S., Page, R. H. & Berman, L. (1958)
	Skin (urticaria pigmentosa)	Detroit-196 Ep.-1.	Stulberg, C. S., Page, R. H. & Berman, L. (1958)
	Skin (foreskin)	D-189	Leighton, J., Kline, I. & Orr, H. C. (1956)

TABLE **XXI** (*contd.*)

SOME STANDARD PERMANENT CELL STRAINS

Origin		Designation of strain	Reference
Species	Tissue		
Human (*contd.*)	Uterus	U12-705	Swim, H. E. & Parker, R. F. (1957)
Monkey	Kidney (Rhesus)	LLC-MK$_2$ Derivative (CLL 7·1)	Hull, R. N., Cherry, W. R. & Johnson, I. S. (1956)
	Kidney (Rhesus)	MK1	Westwood, J. C. N., Macpherson, I. A. & Titmus, D. H. J. (1957)
	Kidney (Rhesus)	MK2	Westwood, J. C. N., Macpherson, I. A. & Titmus, D. H. J. (1957)
Mouse	Connective tissue	NCTC Strain L clone 929 (CCL 1)	Sanford, K. K., Earle, W. R. & Likely, G. D. (1948)
	Connective tissue	L-M (CCL 1·2)	Kuchler, R. J. & Merchant, D. J. (1956 & 1958)
	Connective tissue, high-tumour-producing line	NCTC clone 2472 (CCL 11)	Sanford, K. K., *et al.* (1959)
	Connective tissue, low-tumour-producing line	NCTC clone 2555 (CCL 12)	Sanford, K. K., *et al.* (1959)
	Liver (C3H)	NCTC clone 1469	Hobbs, G .L., Sanford, K. K., Evans, V. J. & Earle, W. R. (1957)
	Lymphocytic neo-plasm (ascitic) DBA/2 mouse	L5178	Fischer, G. A. & Welch, A. D. (1957)
	Lymphosarcoma	T86157 (MB)	DeBruyn, W. M., Korteweg, R. & van Waveren, E. K. (1949)
	Sarcoma 180 (CFW mouse)	S-180	Foley, G. E. & Drolet, B. P. (1956)
Rat	Areolar tissue (subcutaneous)	14p	Gey, G. O., Bang, F. O. & Gey, M. K. (1954)

TABLE **XXI** (*contd.*)

SOME STANDARD PERMANENT CELL STRAINS

| Origin | | Designation of strain | Reference |
Species	Tissue		
Rat (*contd.*)	Areolar tissue (subcutaneous)	ANSAT-21 or AN-21	Gey, G. O. (1954)
	Novikoff hepatoma (Wistar strain)	Novikoff cells	Hotchin, J. E. (1957)
	Jensen sarcoma (Holtman)	JA-1	McCoy, T. A., Maxwell, M., Irvine, E. & Sartorelli, A. C. (1959)
	Jensen sarcoma (Holtman)	JA-2	McCoy, T. A., Maxwell, M., Irvine, E. & Sartorelli, A. C. (1959)
	Walker carcinoma	WRC-256	McCoy, T. A. & Neuman, R. E. (1956)

CELL-STRAIN NOMENCLATURE

In view of the rapid increase in the number of cell strains being isolated, it is obviously desirable to reach some general agreement on nomenclature. As a result of discussions held at the International Tissue Culture Meeting at Glasgow in 1957, a committee was set up and recommendations were made as a basis for subsequent development of a system. More recently a committee of the Tissue Culture Association considered the matter and added further recommendations to the earlier proposals. It was recommended that cells cultivated in vitro for the first time be called *primary cultures*. In addition a *primary cell line* or a *primary cell strain* should refer to a population of cells derived by direct isolation from the intact organism, and capable of serial proliferation for variable periods *in vitro* but not indefinitely. Cells of such populations usually exhibit a normal diploid karyotype through this interval and may retain a number of characters corresponding to the cell type of origin. They may grow for a few or many transfers but eventually decline and die out unless replaced by a permanent cell strain or permanent cell line. A *permanent cell strain* or *permanent cell line* should refer to a population of cells which can apparently be maintained indefinitely *in vitro* by serial transfer. Cells of such populations are usually aberrant in chromosome pattern and often exhibit morphological characteristics unlike those of any recognisable normal cell type within the intact organism.

An individual *cell strain* or *cell line*, be it primary or permanent, should be named as proposed at the 1957 International Tissue Culture Meeting, which recommended that authors should give the following information when first mentioning a cell line or cell strain in the course of publication:

1. Whether the tissue of origin was normal or neoplastic and, if neoplastic, whether benign or malignant.

2. Whether the tissue was adult or embryonic.

3. Animal species of origin.

4. Organ of origin.

5. The cell-type (if known).

6. The designation of the strain.

7. Whether the strain has been cloned and, if so, the clone number.

8. The reference to the original article in which the strain was described.

It was further suggested that the designation of the strain should consist of a series of not more than four letters indicating the laboratory of origin, followed by a series of numbers indicating the strain, *e.g.* NCL 123. Thus, a strain might be described: Normal adult rat heart fibroblast, strain NBG 111, clone 29 (Lobachovsky, Z. (1922). *J. Metaphys. Cytol.* **99**, 77). Subsequently, in the same communication it would suffice to refer to the strain by its strain designation.

Because it is often not possible to identify specialised functions, of the type customarily attributed to the organ of origin, in cell populations in culture the Tissue Culture Association committee recommended that a strain or line should be described as follows (taking the above example): permanent cell line or permanent cell strain derived from normal rat heart, strain NBG 111 etc.

General availability of cell strains

In the United States an American Type Culture Collection Cell Repository (12301 Parklawn Drive, Rockville Md.) has been established. All the cell strains in the above table which carry, in addition to their main designation, a designation in parentheses commencing with the letters CCL, are maintained by the Cell Culture Repository. These lines are of certified purity and are free of PPLO. Several commercial firms, notably Microbiological Associates, also carry and supply many cell strains. In Great Britain the British Tissue Culture Association publishes, in its Membership List, a list of the cell strains readily available and the names of the members from whom they may be obtained.

BIBLIOGRAPHY

BARSKI, G. (1961). Clones cellulaires 'hybrides' isolés à partir de cultures cellulaires mixtes. *C.R. Acad. Sci. (Paris)* **253**, 1186.

BARSKI, G., SORIEUL, S. & CORNEFERT, FR. (1961). Hybrid type cells in combined cultures of two different mammalian cell strains. *J. nat. Cancer Inst.* **26**, 1269.

BERMAN, I. & STULBERG, C. S. (1956). Eight culture strains (Detroit) or human epithelial-like cells. *Proc. Soc. Exp. Biol. (N.Y.)* **92**, 730.

BERMAN, L. & STULBERG, C. S. (1958). The Detroit strains of human epithelial-like cells from nonleukemic peripheral blood. *Blood* **13**, 1149.

BERMAN, L., STULBERG, C. S. & RUDDLE, F. H. (1956). Epithelium-like cells derived from tissue cultures of human bone marrow and ascitic fluid. *J. Mich. med. Soc.* **55**, 269.

BERMAN, L., STULBERG, C. S. & RUDDLE, F. H. (1957). Human cell culture. Morphology of the Detroit strains. *Cancer Res.* **17**, 668.

BRAND, K. G. (1962). Persistence and stability of species-specific haemagglutinogens in cultivated mammalian cells. *Nature (Lond.)* **194**, 752.

BRAND, K. G. (1963). Species-specific haemagglutinogens in cultivated mammalian cells. I. The nature of species-specific erythrocyte receptors. *Exp. Cell Res.* **32**, 36.

BRAND, K. G. (1963). Species-specific haemagglutinogens in cultivated mammalian cells. II. The intracellular location of haemagglutinogens. *Exp. Cell Res.* **32**, 43.

BRAND, K. G. & SYVERTON, J. T. (1959). Hemagglutination test for species specificity of cultivated mammalian cells. *Proc. Amer. Ass. Cancer Res.* **3**, 8.

BRAND, K. G. & SYVERTON, J. T. (1960). Immunology of cultivated mammalian cells. I. Species specificity determined by hemagglutination. *J. nat. Cancer Inst.* **24**, 1007.

BRAND, K. G. & SYVERTON, J. T. (1962). Results of species-specific haemagglutination tests on 'transformed', nontransformed, and primary cell cultures. *J. nat. Cancer Inst.* **128**, 147.

DEBRUYN, WILLEMINA M., KORTEWEG, R. & VAN WAVEREN, E. K. (1949). Transplantable mouse lymphosarcoma T 86157 (MB) studied *in vivo*, *in vitro*, and at autopsy. *Cancer Res.* **9**, 282.

BUONASSISI, V., SATO, G. & COHEN, A. I. (1962). Hormone-producing cultures of adrenal and pituitary tumor origin. *Proc. nat. Acad. Sci. (Wash.)* **48**, 1184.

CHANG, R. S. (1954). Continuous subcultivation of epithelial-like cells from normal human tissues. *Proc. Soc. Exp. Biol. (N.Y.)* **87**, 440.

CHANG, R. S. (1957). Isolation of Nutritional Variants from Conjunctival and HeLa Cells. *Proc. Soc. exp. Biol. (N.Y.)* **96**, 818-820.

CHU, E. H. Y. (1962) Chromosomal stabilization of cell strains. *Nat. Cancer Inst. Monograph* No. **7**, 55.

CHU, E. H. Y. & GILES, N. H. (1958). Comparative chromosomal studies on mammalian cells in culture. I. The HeLa strain and its mutant clonal derivatives. *J. nat. Cancer Inst.* **20**, 383.

CLAUSEN, J. J. & SYVERTON, J. T. (1962). Comparative chromosomal study of thirty-one cultured mammalian cell lines. *J. nat. Cancer Inst.* **28**, 117.

COOMBS, R. R. A. (1961). The mixed agglutination reaction in the study of normal and malignant cells. *Cancer Res.* **21**, 1198.

COOMBS, R. R. A. (1962). Identification and characterization of cells by immunologic analysis, with special reference to mixed agglutination. *Nat. Cancer Inst. Monograph No.* **7**, 91.

COOMBS, R. R. A., DANIEL, M. R., GURNER, B. W. & KELLUS, A. (1961). Species-characterizing antigens of "L" and "ERK" cells. *Nature (Lond)* **189**, 503.

COOMBS, R. R. A., DANIEL, M. R., GURNER, B. W. & KELLUS, A. (1961). Recognition of the species of origin of cells in culture by mixed agglutination. I. Use of antisera to red cells. *Immunology* **4**, 55.

COOMBS, R. R. A., DANIEL, M. R., GURNER, B. W. & KELLUS, A. (1961). Recognition of the species of origin of cells in culture by mixed agglutination. II. Use of heterophile (anti-Forssman) sera. *Int. Arch. Allergy* **19**, 210.

COOMBS, R. R. A., GURNER, B. W., BEALE, A. J., CHRISTOFINIS, G. & PAGE, Z. (1961). The identity of three strains of cells derived from pig or rabbit kidney tissue, checked by means of the mixed agglutination reaction. *Exp. Cell Res.* **24**, 604.

DARNELL, J. E., Jr. & SAWYER, T. K. (1959). Variation in plaque-forming ability among parental and clonal strains of HeLa cells. *Virology* **8**, 223-229.

DAVIS, E. V. & BOLIN, V. S. (1960). Continuous cultivation of isogenous cell lines from the human embryo. *Fed. Proc.* **19**, 386.

DEFENDI, V., BILLINGHAM, R. E., SILVERS, W. K. & MOORHEAD. P. (1960). Immunological and karyological criteria for identification of cell lines. *J. nat. Cancer Inst.* **25**, 359.

DEFENDI, V. & COLTER, J. S. (1959). Immunological studies with nucleoproteins from tissue culture cells. II. Nucleoproteins from HeLa and H.Ep. No. 1 cells. *J. nat. Cancer Inst.* **23**, 411.

EAGLE, H. (1955). Propagation in a fluid medium of a human epidermoid carcinoma, Strain KB (21811). *Proc. Soc. exp. Biol. (N.Y.)* **89**, 362.

EAGLE, H., BARBAN, S., LEVY, M. & SCHULZE, H. O. (1958). Metabolic differences between parenchymal cells and a cultured cell line derived from liver. *Science* **125**, 1290.

EARLE, W. R. (1943). Production of malignancy *in vitro*. IV. The mouse fibroblast cultures and changes seen in the living cells. *J. nat. Cancer Inst.* **4**, 165.

EARLE, W. R., BRYANT, J. C. & SCHILLING, E. L. (1954). Certain factors limiting the size of the tissue culture and the development of massive cultures. *Ann. N.Y. Acad. Sci.* **58**, 1000.

EARLE, W. R. & HIGHHOUSE, F. (1954). Culture flasks for use with plane surface substrate tissue cultures. *J. nat. Cancer Inst.* **14**, 841.

EARLE, W. R., SANFORD, KATHERINE K., EVANS, VIRGINIA J., WALTZ, HELEN K. & SHANNON, J. E. (1951). The influence of inoculum size on proliferation in tissue cultures. *J. nat. Cancer Inst.* **12**, 133.

EBELING, A. H. (1922). A ten year old strain of fibroblasts. *J. exp. Med.* **35**, 755.

EDWARDS, G. A. & FOGH, J. (1959). Micromorphologic changes in human amnion cells during trypsinization. *Cancer Res.* **19**, 608.

EVANS, VIRGINIA J. (1951). Preparation in handling of replicate tissue cultures for quantitative studies. In *Methods in Medical Research.* Visscher, M. B., ed. Chicago: Year Book Publishers.

EVANS, V. J., EARLE, W. R., SANFORD, KATHERINE K., SHANNON, J. E. & WALTZ, H. K. (1951). The preparation and handling of replicate tissue cultures for quantitative studies. *J. nat. Cancer Inst.* **11**, 907.

EVANS, V. J., LAROCK, J. F., YOSIDA, T. H. & POTTER, M. (1963). A new tissue culture isolation and explantation of the P388 lymphocytic neoplasm in a chemically characterized medium. *Exp. Cell Res.* **32**, 212.

FEDOROFF, S. (1962). Method for distinguishing between human and mouse cells in tissue cultures. *Nature (Lond.)* **196**, 394.

FERNANDES, M. V. (1958). The development of a human amnion strain of cells. *Tex. Rep. Biol. Med.* **16**, 48

FJELDE, AUDREY (1955). Human tumor cells in tissue culture. *Cancer* **8**, 845.

FIROR, W. M. & GEY, G. O. (1945). Observations on the conversion of normal into malignant cells. *Ann. Surg.* **121**, 700.

FISCHER, A. (1922). A three months old strain of epithelium. *J. exp. Med.* **35**, 367.

FISCHER, A. (1922). A pure strain of cartilage cells *in vitro. J. exp. Med.* **36**, 399.

FISCHER, G. A. (1958). Studies of the culture of leukemic cells *in vitro. Ann. N.Y. Acad. Sci.* **78**, 673.

FISCHER, G. A. & WELCH, A. D. (1957). Effect of citrovorum factor and peptones on mouse leukemia cells L-5178 in tissue culture. *Science* **126**, 1018.

FOGH, J. & LUND, R. O. (1957). Continuous cultivation of epithelial cell strain (FL) from human amniotic membrane. *Proc. Soc. exp. Biol. (N.Y.)* **94**, 532.

FOLEY, G. E., HANDLER, A. H., ADAMS, R. A. & CRAIG, J. M. (1962). Assessment of potential malignancy of cultured cells: further observations on the differentiation of ' normal ' and ' neoplastic ' cells maintained *in vitro* by heterotransplantation in Syrian hamsters. *Nat. Cancer Inst. Monograph No.* **7**, 173.

FOLEY, J. F., KENNEDY, B. J. & ROSS, J. D. (1963). A factor from HeLa cells promoting clonal growth of human fibroblast-like cells in culture. *Cancer Res.* **23**, 368.

FORD, D. K. (1959). Chromosomal changes occurring in Chinese hamster cells during prolonged culture *in vitro.* In *Third Canadian Cancer Conference.* Ed. Begg, R. W. New York: Academic Press.

FORD, D. K., BOGUSZEWSKI, C. & AUERSPERG, N. (1961). Chinese hamster cell strains *in vitro.* Spontaneous chromosome changes and latent polyoma-virus infection. *J. nat. Cancer Inst.* **26**, 691.

FORD, D. K. & YERGANIAN, G. (1958). Observations on the chromosomes of Chinese hamster cells in tissue culture. *J. nat. Cancer Inst.* **21**, 393.

FRANKS, D., COOMBS, R. R. A., BESWICK, T. S. L. & WINTER, M. M. (1963). Recognition of the species of origin of cells in culture by mixed agglutination. III. Identification of the cells of different primates. *Immunology* **6**, 64.

FRISCH, A. W., JENTOFT, V., BARGER, R. & LOSLI, E. J. (1955). A human epithelium-like cell (Maben) derived from an adenocarcinoma of lung. *Amer. J. clin. Path.* **25**, 1107.

GEY, G. O. (1933). An improved technique for massive tissue culture. *Amer. J. Cancer* **17**, 752.

GEY, G. O. (1954). Some aspects of the constitution and behavior of normal and malignant cells maintained in continuous culture. *Harvey Lect.* **50**, 154.

GEY, G. O., BANG, F. B. & GEY, M. K. (1954). An evaluation of some comparative studies on cultured cell strains of normal and malignant cells of animals and man. *Tex. Rep. Biol. Med.* **12**, 805.

GIRARDI, A. J., WARREN, J., GOLDMAN, C. & JEFFRIES, B. (1958). Growth and CF antigenicity of measles virus in cells deriving from human heart. *Proc. Soc. exp. Biol. (N.Y.)* **98**, 18.

GRACE, T. D. C. (1962). Establishment of four strains of cells from insect tissues grown *in vitro*. *Nature (Lond.)* **195**, 788.

GEY, G. O., COFFMAN, W. O. & KUBICEK, M. T. (1952). Tissue culture studies of the proliferative capacity of cervical carcinoma and normal epithelium. *Cancer Res.* **12**, 264.

HAFF, R. F. & SWIM, H. E. (1957). Isolation of a nutritional variant from a culture of rabbit fibroblasts. *Science* **125**, 1294.

HAYFLICK, L. (1961). The establishment of a line (WISH) of human amnion cells in continuous cultivation. *Exp. Cell Res.* **23**, 14.

HAYFLICK, L. & MOORHEAD, P. S. (1961). The serial cultivation of human diploid cell strains. *Exp. Cell Res.* **25**, 585.

HAYFLICK, L., PERKINS, F. T. & STEVENSON, R. E. (1963). Characterization and uses of human diploid cell strains. *Nature (Lond.)* **200**, 1161.

HENLE, G. & DEINHARDT, F. (1957). The establishment of strains of human cells in tissue culture. *J. Immunol.* **79**, 54.

HIRAMOTO, R., JURANDOWSKI, J., BERNECKY, J. & PRESSMAN, D. (1961). Immunohistochemical identification of tissue culture cells. *Proc. Soc. exp. Biol. (N.Y.)* **108**, 347.

HOBBS, G. L., SANFORD, K. K., EVANS, V. J. & EARLE, W. R. (1957). Establishment of a clone of mouse liver cells from a single isolated cell. *J. nat. Cancer Inst.* **18**, 701.

HOTCHIN, J. E. (1957). The cultivation of Novikoff rat hepatoma cells *in vitro*. *Cancer Res.* **17**, 682.

HULL, R. N. (1953). Establishing long-term cultures of mammalian normal solid tumor, and ascites tumor cells on glass. *Science* **117**, 223.

HULL, R. N., CHERRY, W. R. & JOHNSON, I. S. (1956). Proc. Amer. Assoc. Anat. *Anat. Rec.* **124**, 490.

HULL, R. N. & TRITCH, O. J. (1962). Characterization of cell strains by viral susceptibility. *Nat. Cancer Inst. Monograph No.* **7**, 161.

JORDAN, W. S. JR. (1956). Human nasal cells in continuous cultures. I. Establishment of two lines of epithelial-like cells. *Proc. Soc. Exp. Biol. (N.Y.)* **92**, 867.

KAHN, R. H., CONKLIN, J. L. & DEWEY, M. M. (1962). Cytological and cytochemical characterization of cells grown *in vitro*. *Nat. Cancer Inst. Monograph No.* **7**, 123.

KAPLAN, A. S. (1955). Comparison of susceptible and resistant cells to infection with poliomyelitis virus. *Ann. N.Y. Acad. Sci.* **61**, 830.

KELUS, A., GURNER, B. W. & COOMBS, R. R. A. (1959). Blood group antigens on HeLa cells shown by mixed agglutination. *Immunology* **2**, 262.

LEIGHTON, J. (1958). Economic maintenance of continuous lines of human cells with bead-in-tube cultures. *Lab. Invest.* **7**, 513.

LEIGHTON, J., KLINE, I. & ORR, H. C. (1956). Transformation of normal human fibroblasts into histologically malignant tissue *in vitro*. *Science* **123**, 502.

LESLIE, I., FULTON, W. C. & SINCLAIR, R. (1956). Biochemical tests for malignancy applied to a new strain of human cells. *Nature (Lond.)* **178,** 1179.

LEVAN, A. & HAUSCHKA, T. S. (1952). Chromosome numbers of three mouse ascites tumours. *Hereditas* **38,** 251.

LIKELY, GWENDOLYN D., SANFORD, KATHERINE K. & EARLE, W. R. (1952). Further studies on the proliferation *in vitro* of single isolated tissue cells. *J. nat. Cancer Inst.* **13,** 177.

LWOFF, A., DULBECCO, R., VOGT, MARGUERITE & LWOFF, MARGUERITE (1955). Kinetics of the release of poliomyelitis virus from single cells. *Virology* **1,** 128.

McALLISTER, R. M. & CORIELL, L. L. (1959). Tumorigenicity of tissue culture cells. *Cancer Res.* **19,** 1040.

McCOY, T. A. & NEUMAN, R. E. (1956). The cultivation of Walker carcinosarcoma 256 *in vitro* from cell suspensions. *J. nat. Cancer Inst.* **16,** 1221.

McCOY, T. A., MAXWELL, M., IRVINE, E. & SARTORELLI, A. C. (1959). Two nutritional variants of cultured Jensen sarcoma cells. *Proc. Soc. exp. Biol. (N.Y.)* **100,** 862.

McCULLOCH, E. A., PARKER, R. C. & WIGHTMAN, K. J. R. (1956). Continuous cultivation of cells derived from hemic cells of man and pure strain mice. *Proc. Amer. Ass. Cancer Res.* **2,** 132.

MARCUS, P. I., CIECIURA, S. J. & PUCK, T. T. (1956). Clonal growth *in vitro* of epithelial cells from normal human tissues. *J. exp. Med.* **104,** 615.

MOEN, J. K. (1935). The development of pure cultures of fibroblasts from single mononuclear cells. *J. exp. Med.* **61,** 247.

MOORE, A. E., SABECHEWSKY, L. & TOOLAN, H. W. (1955). Culture characteristics of four permanent lines of human cancer cells. *Cancer Res.* **15,** 598.

MOORE, A. E., SOUTHAM, C. M. & STERNBERG, S. S. (1956). Neoplastic changes developing in epithelial cell lines derived from normal persons. *Science* **124,** 127.

MOORE, G. E. & KOIKE, A. (1964). Growth of human tumor cells *in vitro* and *in vivo*. *Cancer* **17,** 11.

MUIR, W. H., HILDEBRANDT, A. C. & RIKER, A. J. (1954). Plant tissue cultures produced from single isolated cells. *Science* **119,** 877.

NEUMANN, R. E. & McCOY, T. A. (1958). Growth-promoting properties of pyruvate, oxalacetate and α-ketoglutarate for isolated Walker carcinosarcoma 256 cells. *Proc. Soc. exp. Biol. (N.Y.)* **98,** 303.

OSGOOD, E. E. & BROOKE, J. H. (1955). Continuous tissue culture of leukocytes from human leukemic bloods by application of 'gradient' principles. *Blood* **10,** 1010.

OSGOOD, E. E. & KRIPPAEHNE, M. L. (1955). The gradient tissue culture method. *Exp. Cell Res.* **9,** 116.

PERRY, V. P., EVANS, VIRGINIA J., EARLE, W. R., HYATT, G. W. & BEDELL, W. C. (1956). Long-term tissue culture of human skin. *Amer. J. Hyg.* **63,** 52.

PERRY, V. P., SANFORD, K. K., EVANS, V. J., HYATT, G. W. & EARLE, W. R. (1957). Establishment of clones of epithelial cells from human skin. *J. nat. Cancer Inst.* **18,** 709.

PETURSSON, G., COUGHLIN, J. I. & MEYLAN, C. (1964). Long-term cultivation of diploid rat cells. *Exp. Cell Res.* **33,** 60.

PIGOT, H. C. & POTTER, V. R. (1960). An enzymatic study of the cellular origin of the Dunning and Novikoff hepatomas in the rat. *Biochim. Biophys. Acta* **40,** 537.

POSTLETHWAITE, R. & MACPHERSON, I. A. (1963). *In vitro* growth of the Landschütz ascites tumour with retention of high mouse virulence. *Brit. J. Cancer* **17**, 487.

PUCK, T. T. (1958). Quantitative colonial growth of single mammalian cells. *J. exp. Med.* **103**, 653.

PUCK, T. T., CIECIURA, S. J. & ROBINSON, A. (1958). Genetics of somatic mammalian cells. III. Long-term cultivation of euploid cells from human and animal subjects. *J. exp. Med.* **108**, 945.

PUCK, T. T. & FISCHER, H. W. (1956). Genetics of somatic mammalian cells. I. Demonstration of the existence of mutants with different growth requirements in a human cancer cell strain (HeLa). *J. exp. Med.* **104**, 427.

PUCK, T. T. & MARCUS, P. I. (1955). A rapid method for viable cell titration and clone production with HeLa cells in tissue culture. The use of X-irradiated cells to supply conditioning factors. *Proc. nat. Acad. Sci. (Wash.)* **41**, 432.

PUCK, T. T. & MARCUS, P. I. (1956). Action of X-rays on mammalian cells. *J. exp. Med.* **103**, 653.

PUCK, T. T., MARCUS, P. I. & CIECIURA, S. J. (1956). Clonal growth of mammalian cells *in vitro*. *J. exp. Med.* **103**, 273.

PUMPER, R. W. (1958). Adaptation of tissue culture cells to a serum-free medium. *Science* **128**, 363.

ROSENAU, W. & MOON, H. D. (1961). Organ and species specificity of tissue culture cells. *Lab. Invest.* **10**, 1209.

ROTHFELS, K. H., AXELRAD, A. A., SIMINOVITCH, L., McCULLOCH, E. A. & PARKER, R. C. (1959). The origin of altered cell lines from mouse, monkey and man, as indicated by chromosome and transplantation studies. *Proc. Third Canadian Cancer Conference.* Ed. Begg, R. W. New York: Academic Press.

ROUS, P. & JONES, F. S. (1916). A method for obtaining suspensions of living cells from the fixed tissues, and for plating out of individual cells. *J. exp. Med.* **23**, 549.

RUECKERT, R. R. & MUELLER, G. C. (1960). Studies on unbalanced growth in tissue culture. I. Induction and consequences of thymidine deficiency. *Cancer Res.* **20**, 1584.

SANFORD, K. K., COVALESKY, A. B., DUPREE, L. T. & EARLE, W. R. (1961). Cloning of mammalian cells by a simplified capillary technique. *Exp. Cell Res.* **23**, 361.

SANFORD, KATHERINE K., EARLE, W. R. & LIKELY, GWENDOLYN, D. (1948). The growth *in vitro* of single isolated tissue cells. *J. nat. Cancer Inst.* **9**, 229.

SANFORD, KATHERINE K., LIKELY, GWENDOLYN D. & EARLE, W. R. (1954). The development of variations in transplantability and morphology within a clone of mouse fibroblasts transformed to sarcoma-producing cells *in vitro*. *J. nat. Cancer Inst.* **15**, 215.

SANFORD, K. K., WESTFALL, B. B., WOODS, M. W. & EARLE, W. R. (1959). Metabolic variations within a clone of mouse fibroblasts transformed to neoplastic cells *in vitro*. *Acta Un. int. Cancr.* **15**, 675.

SAX, H. J. & PASSANO, K. N. (1961). Spontaneous chromosome aberrations in human tissue culture cells. *Amer. Naturalist* **95**, 97.

SCHENCK, DOROTHY M. & MOSKOWITZ, M. (1958). Method for isolating single cells and preparation of clones from human bone marrow cultures. *Proc. Soc. exp. Biol. (N.Y.).* **99**, 30.

SCOTT, D. B. M., PAKOSKEY, A. M. & SANFORD, K. K. (1960). Analysis of enzymatic activities of clones derived from variant cell lines transformed to malignant cells in tissue culture. *J. nat. Cancer Inst.* **25**, 1365.

SHANNON, J. E. Jr. & EARLE, W. R. (1951). Qualitative comparison of the growth of chick-heart and strain L fibroblasts planted as suspensions on pyrex glass and perforated cellophane substrates. *J. nat. Cancer Inst.* **12**, 155.

SIMPSON, W. F. & STULBERG, C. S. (1963). Species identification of animal cell strains by immunofluorescence. *Nature (Lond.)* **199**, 616.

STULBERG, C. S., PAGE, R. H. & BERMAN, L. (1958). Comparative behavior of 16 ECHO virus type fibroblast-like and epithelial-like human cell strains. *Proc. Soc. exp. Biol. (N.Y.)* **97**, 355.

STULBERG, C. S., SIMPSON, W. F., PETERSON, W. D. & BERMAN, L. (1961). Determination of species antigens of cultured cells by immunofluorescence. *Fed. Proc.* **20**, 150.

SWIM, H. E. & PARKER, R. F. (1957). Culture characteristics of human fibroblasts propagated serially. *Amer. J. Hyg.* **66**, 235.

SYVERTON, J. T. & MCLAREN, L. C. (1957). Human cells in continuous culture. I. Derivative of cell strains from oesophagus, palate, liver and lung. *Cancer Res.* **17**, 923.

SYVERTON, J. T., SCHERER, W. F. & ELWOOD, P. M. (1954). Studies on the propagation *in vitro* of poliomyelitis viruses. V. The application of strain HeLa human epithelial cells for isolation and typing. *J. Lab. clin. Med.* **43**, 286.

TJIO, J. H. & PUCK, T. T. (1958). Genetics of somatic mammalian cells. II. Chromosome constitution of cells in tissue culture. *J. exp. Med.* **108**, 259.

TOOLAN, HELENE W. (1954). Transplantable human neoplasms maintained in cortisone-treated laboratory animals: H. S. 1; H. Ep. 1; H. Ep. 2; H. Ep. 3; and H. Emb. Rh. 1. *Cancer Res.* **14**, 600.

VOGT, M. (1958). A genetic change in a tissue culture line of neoplastic cells. *J. cell. comp. Physiol.* **52**, 271-285.

WALLACE, R. E. & HANKS, J. H. (1958). Agar substrates for study of microepidemiology and physiology in cells *in vitro*. *Science* **128**, 658.

WESTFALL, B. B. (1962). Characterization of cells in tissue culture. *Nat. Cancer Inst. Monograph No.* **7**, 147.

WESTFALL, B. B., EVANS, V. J., PEPPERS, E. V., HAWKINS, N. M., BRYANT, J. C., SCHILLING, E. L. & EARLE, W. R. (1958). Observations on the metabolic behavior of a clone of mouse liver cells grown in agitated fluid suspension. *Cancer Res.* **18**, 947.

WESTFALL, B. B., EVANS, VIRGINIA J., SHANNON, J. E., JR. & EARLE, W. R. (1953). The glycogen content of cell suspensions prepared from massive tissue culture: comparison of cells derived from mouse connective tissue and mouse liver. *J. nat. Cancer Inst.* **14**, 655.

WESTFALL, B. B., PEPPERS, E. V., EVANS, V. J., SANFORD, K. K., HAWKINS, N. M., FIORAMONTI, M. C., KERR, H. A., HOBBS, G. L. & EARLE, W. R. (1958). The arginase and rhodanese activities of certain cell strains after long cultivation *in vitro*. *J. Biophys. Biochem. Cytol.* **4**, 567.

WESTWOOD, J. C., MACPHERSON, I. A. & TITMUSS, D. H. J. (1957). Transformation of normal cells in tissue culture: its significance relative to malignancy and virus vaccine production. *Brit. J. exp. Path.* **38**, 138.

WESTWOOD, J. C. N. & TITMUSS, D. H. J. (1957). Transformation in tissue culture cell lines. The possible genetic mechanism. *Brit. J. exp. Path.* **38**, 587.

17

WILDY, P. & STOKER, M. (1958).   Multiplication of solitary HeLa cells. *Nature (Lond.)* **181**, 1407.

YAMANE, I. & MATSUYA, Y. (1963).   Culture of single mammalian cells. *Nature (Lond.)* **199**, 296.

YERGANIAN, G. & LEONARD, M. J. (1961).   Maintenance of normal *in situ* chromosomal features in long-term tissue culture. *Science* **133**, 1600.

ZITCER, ELSA M. & DUNNEBACKE, THELMA H. (1957).   Transformation of cells from the normal human amnion into established strains. *Cancer Res.* **17**, 1047.

CHAPTER XVI

SUSPENSION CULTURES AND LARGE-SCALE METHODS

FOR a great many purposes the ideal way to grow cells is in suspension. This produces much more uniform conditions of cell culture and provides a situation analogous to that encountered in the growth of micro-organisms. It permits much more accurate sampling and therefore provides the ideal system for biochemical and kinetic studies. A system of this sort would also be expected to be more efficient in terms of cell population per unit volume of medium if a rich enough supply of nutrients were available. Hence for the production of large numbers of cells it is most likely to be the best system.

Owens, Gey and Gey were the first to grow cells in suspension, using a ' tumble-tube ' arrangement. This consisted of culture tubes arranged radially on a roller-drum. The cells used by these workers tended to grow in suspension spontaneously. The first attempts to evolve a general method for growing cells in suspension were made by Earle's group at the National Cancer Institute in the United States. They first showed that if the rate of rotation of the drum was increased, strain L cells would leave the walls of roller tubes and continue to proliferate in the medium. At 300 r.p.h. some of the cells remained adherent to the walls of the test-tube but at 2,400 r.p.h. they were all in suspension. Addition of 0·1 per cent. methylcellulose helped to keep the cells in suspension. Under these conditions the cells suffered no damage and continued to proliferate freely. Later, the same group developed much larger cultures of different cell-types in shaker flasks and other workers have produced other modifications of the system.

It was noticed at an early stage that some cells would remain in suspension much more easily than others. Thus a strain of monkey kidney cells in Parker's laboratory underwent a transformation as a result of which they grew spontaneously in suspension in stationary flasks. This strain was successfully grown in suspension in roller tubes by Graham and Siminovitch and reached a population density of 10^7 cells per ml., at which point it was still growing logarithmically. Another cell, the MB III cell of de Bruyn has already been referred to. It was found by Owens, Gey and Gey to remain in suspension in a simple, 'tumble-tube' arrangement. Other workers have maintained this cell in suspension in relatively slowly moving roller drums. Deliberate attempts have been made to select out variants from cell-strains, which will behave in this way. In our laboratory the LS strain, which grows spontaneously in suspension, was obtained by persistent selection from strain L, clone 929. Japanese workers have obtained a similar variant of HeLa in the same way. These strains are ideal for suspension culture work but at present they must be considered rather unusual.

From these latter observations it is clear that cells may adapt to being grown in suspension culture and, indeed, this feature has been emphasised time and again by most workers who have had extensive experience in this field. Hence it is common experience that, when cells are first put into suspension culture, there is a lag phase of some days before rapid proliferation occurs. Also it may take considerably longer before a suspension culture behaves in a stable fashion.

Media for suspension cultures

Cells have been grown successfully in suspension in media ranging from horse serum/embryo extract/BSS to rigorously defined, protein-free media. In earlier studies 10-20 per cent. serum was often used in the medium and this commonly gave rise to trouble owing to the precipitation of material on the side of the culture vessel at the surface of the medium, in which cells became enmeshed. It was found empirically that the addition of certain substances, such as methylcellulose or polyglycoll (Pluronic F68) prevented this. Since then many successful attempts have been made to grow cells in defined media without macromolecular supplements. The most striking of these is the cultivation of a subline of strain L cells in serum-free Eagle's medium by Merchant and his colleagues. It is generally agreed, however, that the addition of a small amount of serum enhances growth and that better survival is obtained when methylcellulose or carboxymethylcellulose (15-20 cps) is added to the medium at a concentration of 0·1 per cent.

Sodium carboxymethylcellulose ('Edifas B', I.C.I.) is preferable to methylcellulose since it dissolves readily and can be made up conveniently as a 3 per cent. stock solution in BSS. Methylcellulose (Methocel) has the unusual property of being less soluble at high temperatures than at low temperatures. Hence, it has to be made up first as a slurry. After sterilisation by autoclaving it forms an insoluble curd which, however, goes back into solution if it is cooled in the refrigerator. It can also be used as a 3 per cent. stock solution. Pluronic F68 (Wyandotte Chemical Co., Michigan) is readily soluble and presents no difficulties. It is also used at a final concentration of 0·1 per cent.

Despite the use of these devices some cells tend to aggregate at the meniscus, even in the absence of serum. Sinclair and his colleagues have found that this can be prevented by adding trypsin to the medium (serum-free modified Waymouth's MB 752/1) at a concentration of 50µg./litre. L cells grew well in this medium. Most commonly cells in suspension culture are grown in a synthetic medium (such as Eagle's or 109) supplemented with 5-10 per cent. serum and 0·1 per cent. methylcellulose or carboxymethylcellulose.

Gas phase

Oxygen at different tensions has been used to gas suspension culture. There is general agreement that high oxygen tensions are not beneficial and probably harmful. Most workers have had satisfactory results with atmospheric air and, indeed, Cooper reported that he obtained rather better results with slightly lower oxygen tension.

Most workers have gassed the cultures with 5 per cent. CO_2 but it is questionable whether this is necessary, presumably because the cell population is dense enough to ensure some CO_2 in solution, especially in large cultures. McLimans and Eagle have used strong phosphate buffers and made no attempt to control CO_2 in the gas phase. We ourselves have routinely used tris/citrate buffer in cultures exposed to the atmosphere and have found it entirely satisfactory.

General methods

Most of these methods have developed from the work of Earle and his colleagues using a rotary shaker of the Brunswick type which produces a swirling movement of the medium in the flasks

The cells are suspended in medium in ordinary Erlenmeyer or round-bottom flasks, with an arrangement for producing a flow of gas over the surface of the culture while it is shaken in the incubator at a speed of about 13,000 r.p.h. The medium used has been of the usual type, either a completely natural medium (serum, embryo extract and BSS) or serum plus one of the synthetic media. Populations of HeLa cells as high as 5.9×10^9 in 400 ml. of medium in a 1·5 litre flask have been obtained by this means.

Other workers have employed simple stirring devices to maintain the cells in suspension. Danes used a spiral glass stirrer in a rather long (20 cm.), narrow (44 mm.) vessel. A mean generation time of about 30 hours was obtained and logarithmic growth could be maintained by renewing 25 per cent. of the medium every 12 hours.

Other stirrer vessels have been described by Cherry and Hull and by McLimans and his colleagues. The latter group have developed the use of large capacity commercially available fermenter vessels for this purpose. They obtained rapid growth with a mean generation time, in the case of the L cell, varying between 24 and 60 hours.

Currently, the most commonly used method employs a magnetic stirrer. A silicone-enclosed magnet with a thin ring of silicone rubber round the middle (so that it will spin clear of the bottom of the flask) is the simplest device and it can be used in any kind of vessel, from small conical flasks to large aspirator bottles. A range of spinner culture vessels has been specially developed by Bellco Glass Inc. Many variations of the prototype illustrated in Plate 11 have been developed; the design proposed by Smith and Burrows is particularly reliable. In many laboratories banks of culture vessels of this type with magnets driven by a common motor are set up either in a warm box or a water-bath. For a detailed description of equipment of this type the reader may refer to papers by Smith and Burrows and Gordy, Moore and Sieber.

General management of suspension cultures

Nobody has yet reported the successful culture in suspension of normal cells taken directly from an animal. Some tumours can be removed from the animal and grown in suspension but cells which have already been established as permanent strains are generally used. To initiate a suspension culture, cells are first obtained in suspension from a monolayer, either by mild trypsinisation or by scraping and pipetting. They are then inoculated into the culture vessel (some kind of spinner vessel is most useful) at an inoculum of between 10^5 and 5×10^5 cells per ml. of medium. The depth of medium should be sufficient to ensure that frothing does not occur. The stirring speed should be the minimum necessary to maintain the cells in suspension; this is usually about 250 to 500 r.p.m. The culture should be examined daily and a sample taken for total and viability counts (Chapter XX). For the first few days (perhaps as long as ten days) the cell population may not increase; it may even fall for a day or two. Eventually, however, the population begins to increase. The medium is then supplemented with new medium so as to keep the cell density at about $5\text{-}7 \times 10^5$ cells per ml. in most cases. This figure actually varies from strain to strain and is also dependent on the medium used. Some strains may reach densities about ten times higher but this is unusual.

It is in the early stages of establishment of a suspension culture that most difficulties arise. One of the major problems is the tendency of cells to aggregate in a ring round the culture vessel at the surface of the medium. As already mentioned this can often be minimised by the use of Pluronic F68. This behaviour is sometimes particularly marked in cultures which have been obtained in suspension by trypsinisation and it may be worthwhile suspending the cells by another method if it is encountered. Certain sera seem to give rise to this trouble more than others and calf serum seems to be more satisfactory than horse serum. The presence of dead cells in the suspension also seems to aggravate the situation and the inoculum should always consist of healthy cells from a rapidly-growing culture with a viability of 95 per cent. or better. When cells have eventually become established in suspension this difficulty is almost never encountered and stationary cultures which originated from suspension cultures can usually be returned to suspension without trouble. Merchant has found that the dispersing agent, Darvan 2 (R. T. Vanderbilt Co., New York) is non-toxic at 0·05 per cent. and is effective in preventing clumping of cells.

The other problem in the early stages of suspension cultures concerns the renewal of medium when the lag phase is prolonged. If no increase in cell number has occurred within four to five days the action to be taken depends on the viability count. If this is very low, under 20 per cent., it is probably futile to continue the attempt. If it is higher than this, however, the cells may be centrifuged down and resuspended in medium sufficient to give a count of viable cells of the order of 5×10^5 per ml. It may help to use up to 50 per cent. of old medium combined with new medium but this is questionable. If no increase in the viable population occurs within a further four or five days it is doubtful whether the attempt will be successful.

Batch cultures

Two main principles have to be kept in mind in handling batch cultures. First, most cells do not grow satisfactorily in suspension if the cell density falls too low (*e.g.* below 5×10^4-10^5 cells per ml.). Secondly, cells in suspension tend to die rapidly as soon as the population becomes stationary. (These statements are generalisations and may not apply to some strains.) It follows that a population increase of more than five- to tenfold cannot normally be expected from a single inoculum without medium change. The normal practice, therefore, is to start with a small volume of medium and increase it by adding fresh medium (at a rate determined by cell growth) every two to three days until the required amount of cells is obtained. Hence, in setting up a 20-litre batch culture in a fermenter (of the kind used for growing bacteria) the procedure (as, for instance, used by McLimans) is as follows: First, a spinner culture is set up with a volume of 250-500 ml. When this is established it is used as the inoculum for a 3-litre culture in a 5-litre fermenter. This, in turn, is used as the inoculum for the large fermenter.

Continuous medium replacement

Clearly, when a suspension culture is established, it is unnecessary to start each batch with a fresh seed culture. For instance, the 20-litre batch culture referred to above can be kept going for long periods by removing most of the suspension at intervals of a few days and replacing it with fresh medium, the residual suspensions providing the inoculum. Naturally, this has led to the development of methods for automatic medium replacement. Several systems have been developed which have given satisfactory results for short runs but most have encountered troubles when attempts have been made to make them operate indefinitely.

In Graff and McCarty's ' cytogenerator' the cells are grown in a U-tube with vertical walls of sintered glass, enclosed within

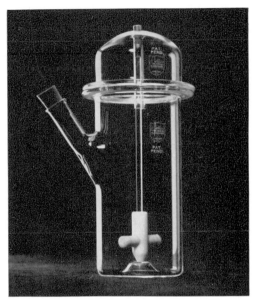

PLATE 11

A vessel for growing cells in suspension. The plastic-enclosed magnet is rotated by means of a magnetic stirrer outside the vessel. (Bellco Glass Inc.)

facing p. 264

glass jackets. Medium enters at one side and leaves at the other. The cells are maintained in suspension by causing the medium to oscillate from one side of the U-tube to the other by alternating the gas pressure. Very high cell densities have been obtained with this machine but its operation is troublesome.

Merchant, Kuchler and Munyon, and Cohen and Eagle used systems similar to the original device developed for micro-organisms by Novik and Szilard, in which medium is allowed to enter the growth vessel at a steady rate from a reservoir while the excess cell suspension is drained off by an overflow. The behaviour of animal cells in culture has proved too erratic so far to permit the establishment of a steady state for long with apparatus of this kind.

Some other workers have developed machines in which the cell density is continually monitored by an electronic device and medium is automatically added as required. In the most successful apparatus of this kind, developed by Cooper and his colleagues, cell density was determined turbidimetrically (Fig. 45). The photo-cell actuated a pump which introduced fresh medium as required; excess cell suspension was allowed to escape to a collecting vessel by an overflow. ERK cells were maintained continuously in this apparatus for four months.

There is still room for considerable advance in this field; most of the development work is aimed at applying experience from the fermentation industry to the culture of animal cells.

Other massive culture methods

Some cell types are refractory to growth as suspensions and seem to have a requirement for a solid substrate. Methods have also been devised for growing these in large numbers. McCoy and his colleagues employ glass columns packed with glass helices as culture chambers. Cells are inoculated on to these and the column is then continuously perfused with medium at a rate which increases as the cell number increases. Eventually, when the maximum population has been reached the cells are harvested by passing trypsin through the column. Several grams of cells are grown at a time in this apparatus (Fig. 46).

Very large roller bottles have also been used for culturing cells which require a solid substrate. Two-litre Winchester bottles

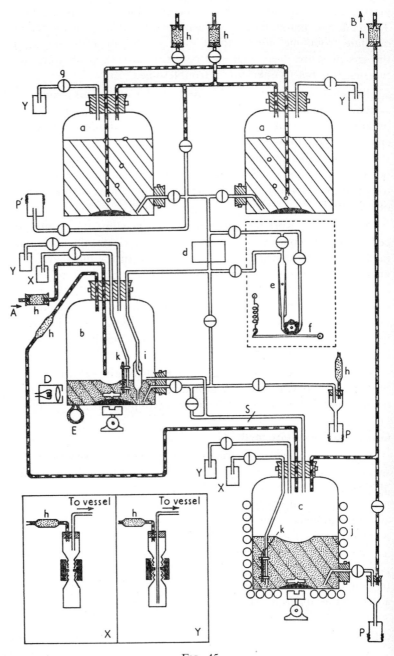

FIG. 45
(See legend opposite.)

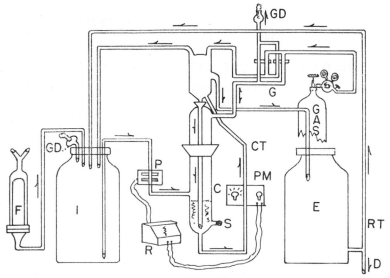

FIG. 46

Schematic diagram of McCoy's solid matrix perfusion circulating system.

C—Cell chamber.	I—Influent vessel.
CT—Circulating tube.	P—Perfusion Pump.
D—Drain.	PM—Photometric monitor.
E—Effluent vessel.	R—Recorder.
F—Filter.	RT—Recycle Tube.
G—Graff-McCarty Pulsator.	S—Sample Orifice.
GD—Gas discharge.	

The cell chamber is packed with glass helices. The rate of addition of fresh medium from the influent vessel is regulated by the perfusion pump, which is controlled by the output from the photometric monitor which, in turn, monitors the change in colour of phenol red in the medium. The Graff-McCarty Pulsator ensures agitation of the medium.

FIG. 45

Diagram of apparatus designed by Cooper, Wilson and Burt for the continuous cultivation of cells in suspension.

Key to lettering.—The lines carrying air or gas are stippled: a, medium reservoirs; b, culture vessel; c, receiver; d, solenoid valve closure; e, rotameter; f, pump; g, screw clips; h, cotton-wool filters; i, antisplash medium inlet; j, rubber tubing of cooling jacket; k, thermometers; A, gas inlet; B, gas outlet; D, light source; E, photocell; P, harvesting and P′ replenishing ports. X and Y are sampling and inoculating ports respectively, shown in detail in the inset; samples are withdrawn via X or added via Y by sucking or blowing through the cotton wool filters. The bar across the medium line at S indicates the position of a sterile connection made during assembly.

The rate of influx of medium is controlled by the peristaltic pump (f) or by intermittent opening of the solenoid valve (d). This in turn is controlled by the output from the photocell (E) which monitors the turbidity of the suspension in the culture vessel (b). The level of medium in (b) is kept constant by permitting it to overflow into the receiver (c).

are commonly used. Each takes 200 ml. of medium and the bottles
are rotated by placing them on their sides on rotating rubber rollers
driven by an electric motor.

GROWTH OF PLANT CELLS IN SUSPENSION

Plant cells can be grown in suspension, using much the same
general principles as apply to animal cells; representatives of almost

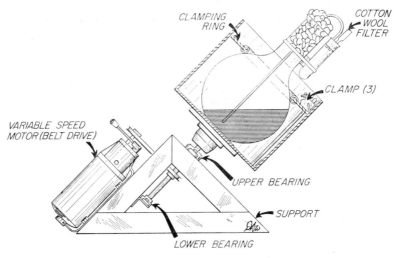

Fig. 47
Apparatus used by Lamport for large-scale suspension culture of plant cells.

every kind of plant tissue have been cultured successfully. A
primary culture is first established from the plant and grown up
into a callus. Rapidly-growing friable calluses are most suitable
for subsequent growth in suspension. The callus is broken up by
shaking vigorously in liquid medium in a reciprocal shaker. The
suspension of fragments obtained in this way continues to grow.
It may be transferred to a roller bottle, a shaking apparatus or a
vessel fitted with a stirrer. Modifications of the roller-bottle technique are generally favoured. The simple apparatus used by
Lamport to grow several litres of sycamore cell suspension at a
time is illustrated in Figure 47.

Modifications of White's medium have been found suitable as
a basis for growth of many plant tissues in suspension; the addition
of coconut water is virtually essential. Some tissues have been

grown in this with a mean generation time of two days to give a
final yield of 17 mg. tissue (dry weight) per ml. of medium. Other
inexpensive supplements have also proved useful and, for instance,
Nickell and his colleagues have obtained excellent yields of rose
tissues in a medium containing 0·1 per cent. yeast extract, 0·1 per
cent. malt extract and 6 ppm. 2, 4-dichlorophenoxyacetic acid.

BIBLIOGRAPHY

BERGMANN, L. (1959). Über die Kultur von Zellsuspensionen von Daucus
    carota. *Naturwiss* **46**, 20.
BJÖRKLUND, B., BJÖRKLUND, V. & PAULSSON, J. E. (1961). The cytostat, an
    apparatus for automatically controlled continuous propagation of sus-
    pended cells. *Proc. Soc. exp. Biol. (N.Y.)* **108**, 385.
BRYANT, J. C., SCHILLING, E. L. & EARLE, W. R. (1958). Massive fluid-
    suspension cultures of certain mammalian tissue cells. I. General
    characteristics of growth and trends of population. *J. nat. Cancer
    Inst.* **21**, 331.
CHERRY, W. R. & HULL, R. N. (1960). Studies and observations on the
    growth of mammalian cells in agitated fluid medium. *J. biochem.
    microbiol. Technol. Engng.* **2**, No. 3, 267.
COHEN, E. P. & EAGLE, H. (1961). A simplified chemostat for the growth
    of mammalian cells: characteristics of cell growth in continuous
    culture. *J. exp. Med.* **113**, 467.
COOPER, P. D., BURT, A. M. & WILSON, J. N. (1958). Critical effect of
    oxygen tension on rate of growth of animal cells in continuous sus-
    pended culture. *Nature (Lond.)* **182**, 1508.
COOPER, P. D., WILSON, J. N. & BURT, A. M. (1959). The bulk growth of
    animal cells in continuous suspension culture. *J. gen. Microbiol.* **21**, 702.
DANES, BETTY S. (1957). Suspension cultures of Strain L mouse fibro-
    blasts. *Exp. Cell Res.* **12**, 169.
DAVIS, E. V., GLOVER, F. & McLIMANS, W. F. (1958). Proliferation of
    human amnion cells (FL strain) in submerged culture. *Proc. Soc.
    Exp. Biol. (N.Y.)* **97**, 454.
EARLE, W. R. (1958). Long-term cultivation of animal tissue cells in large
    cultures. *Fed. Proc.* **17**, 967.
EARLE, W. R., SCHILLING, E. L. & BRYANT, J. C. (1954). Influence of tube
    rotation velocity on proliferation of strain L cells in surface substrate
    roller-tube cultures. *J. nat. Cancer Inst.* **14**, 853.
EARLE, W. R., SCHILLING, E. L., BRYANT, J. C. & EVANS, VIRGINIA J. (1954).
    The growth of pure strain L cells in fluid suspension cultures. *J. nat.
    Cancer Inst.* **14**, 1159.
EARLE, W. R., BRYANT, J. C., SCHILLING, E. L. & EVANS, VIRGINIA J. (1956).
    Growth of cell suspension in tissue culture. *Ann. N.Y. Acad. Sci.*
    63, 666.
GEY, G. O. (1933). An improved technique for massive tissue culture.
    Amer. J. Cancer **17**, 752.
GEY, G. O. & GEY, M. K. (1936). The maintenance of human normal cells
    and tumor cells in continuous culture. I. Preliminary report: Cultivation
    of mesoblastic tumors and normal tissue and notes on methods of
    cultivation. *Amer. J. Cancer* **27**, 45.

GIARDINELLO, F. E., MCLIMANS, W. F. & RAKE, G. W. (1958). The apparent toxicity of metallic materials of construction and antifoam agents for mammalian cell lines. *Appl. Microbiol.* **6**, 30.

GORDY, E., MOORE, G. E. & SIEBER, G. (1962). Air-thermostated chamber with proportional temperature control for tissue culture application. *J. appl. Physiol.* **17**, 356.

GRAFF, S. & MCCARTY, K. S. (1957). Sustained cell culture. *Exp. Cell Res.* **13**, 348.

GRAHAM, A. F. & SIMINOVITCH, L. (1955). Proliferation of monkey kidney cells in rotating cultures. *Proc. Soc. Exp. Biol. (N.Y.)* **89**, 326.

GWATKIN, R. B. L., TILL, J. E., WHITMORE, G. F., SIMINOVITCH, L. & GRAHAM, A. F. (1957). Multiplication of animal cells in suspension measured by colony counts. *Proc. nat. Acad. Sci. (Wash.)* **43**, 451.

KUCHLER, R. J. & MERCHANT, D. J. (1956). Propagation of strain L (Earle) cells in agitated fluid suspension cultures. *Proc. Soc. Exp. Biol. (N.Y.)* **92**, 803.

KRUSE, P. F., JR., MYHR, B. C., JOHNSON, J. E. & WHITE, P. B. (1963). Perfusion system for replicate mammalian cell cultures in T-60 flasks. *J. nat. Cancer Inst.* **31**, 109.

LAMPORT, D. T. A. (1964). Cell suspension cultures of higher plants: isolation and growth energetics. *Exp. Cell Res.* **33**, 195.

LIEBERMAN, I. & OVE, P. (1958). Catalase requirement for mammalian cells in culture. *J. exp. Med.* **108**, 631.

MCCOY, T. A., WHITTLE, W. & CONWAY, E. (1962). A glass helix perfusion chamber for massive growth of cells *in vitro. Proc. Soc. exp. Biol. (N.Y.)* **109**, 235.

MCLIMANS, W. F., GIARDINELLO, F. E., DAVIS, E. V., KUCERA, C. J. & RAKE, G. W. (1957) Submerged culture of mammalian cells: the five liter fermentor. *J. Bact.* **74**, 768.

MERCHANT, D. J., KUCHLER, R. J. & MUNYON, W. H. (1960). Population dynamics in suspension cultures of an animal cell strain. *J. biochem. microbiol. Technol. Engng.* **2**, No. 3, 253.

MOORE, G. E., MOUNT, D., TARA, G. & SCHWARTZ, N. (1963). Growth of human tumor cells in suspension cultures. *Cancer Res.* **23**, 1735.

NICKELL, L. G. (1956). The continuous submerged cultivation of plant tissue as single cells. *Proc. nat. Acad. Sci. (Wash.)* **42**, 848.

NICKELL, L. G. & TULECKE, W. (1960). Submerged growth of cells of higher plants. *J. biochem. microbiol. Technol. Engng.* **2**, No. 3, 287.

OWENS, O. VON H., GEY, M. K. & GEY, G. O. (1953). A new method for the cultivation of mammalian cells suspended in agitated fluid medium. *Proc. Amer. Assoc. Cancer Res.* **1**, 41.

RIGHTSEL, W. A., MCCALPIN, H. & MCLEAN, I. W. (1960). Studies on large-scale methods for propagation of animal cells. *J. biochem. microbiol. Technol. Engng.* **2**, No. 3, 313.

SIMINOVITCH, L., GRAHAM, A. F., LESLEY, S. M. & NEVILL, A. (1957). Propagation of L-strain mouse cells in suspension. *Exp. Cell Res.* **12**, 299.

SINCLAIR, R., REID, R. A. & MITCHELL, P. (1963). Culture of strain L cells in suspension: replacement of polymer by traces of trypsin in a defined medium. *Nature (Lond.)* **197**, 982.

SMITH, H. M. & BURROWS, T. M. (1963). Laboratory apparatus for the suspended culture of tissue cells. *Lab. Practice,* May 1963.

SWIM, H. E. & PARKER, R. F. (1960). Effect of Pluronic F68 on growth of fibroblasts in suspension on rotary shaker. *Proc. Soc. Exp. Biol. (N.Y.)* **103**, 252.

THOMAS, W. J., ZIEGLER, D. W., SCHEPARTZ, S. A. & McLIMANS, W. F. (1958). Use of arginine to eliminate medium changes in tissue culture systems. *Science* **127,** 591.

THOMPSON, K. W., PRICE, T. T. & LEWIN, S. Z. (1962). Control of ambient conditions in cell suspension cultures. *Cancer Chemother. Rep.* **20,** 45.

TULECKE, W. & NICKELL, L. G. (1959). Production of large amounts of plant tissue by submerged culture. *Science* **130,** 863.

UBERTINI, B., NARDELLI, L., SANTERO, G. & PANINA, G. (1960). Process report: large-scale production of foot-and-mouth disease virus. *J. biochem. microbiol. Technol. Engng.* **2,** No. 3, 327.

ZIEGLER, D. W., DAVIS, E. V., THOMAS, W. J. & McLIMANS, W. F. (1958). The propagation of mammalian cells in a 20-litre stainless steel fermentor. *Appl. Microbiol.* **6,** 305.

CHAPTER XVII

CULTIVATION OF CELLS IN VIVO— TRANSPLANTATION

ON the assumption that the best environment for a cell is the one it encounters in its normal situation in the body, it has been a guiding principle of tissue culture to try to reproduce this as closely as possible. Transplantation methods assume that the next best alternative to a tissue's normal environment is a similar environment in another host.

In plants, grafting is a well-established procedure and it is well-known that sometimes the grafts grow even better in another host, a principle which has been used in improving yields from fruit trees. Transplantation in animals has turned out to be much more complicated. The earliest successful attempts were performed in invertebrates and amphibian embryos, and Joest managed to obtain a permanent union between different worms while a little later Born, Harrison and Morgan were able to transplant tissues in tadpoles. These observations were the precursors of the classical studies on amphibian embryos which form a large part of the literature of experimental embryology. When experiments of this kind were extended to adult animals, particularly of the higher vertebrates, it was found that almost invariably the host rejected the grafted tissue after a few days in a manner which suggested an immune type of reaction. The development of immunity to foreign tissue has proved the main barrier to transplantation in animals.

The relationships involved in the rejection of grafts in higher animals are now clearly recognised. It is well-known that tissues can be grafted from one part to another of an individual and, provided the requisite level of technical skill is employed, these autografts will survive. Successful grafting can be extended to genetically identical individuals—uniovular twins and inbred animal strains. Grafts of this kind are called isografts. However, when grafts are exchanged between two genetically dissimilar individuals the grafts are rejected after a period of some days (even when the grafts are between two closely related individuals, *e.g.*, binovular twins). Grafts between two individuals of the same species who are not genetically identical are called homografts and the rejection of homografts is called the homograft reaction or transplantation immunity. Grafts between different species are called heterografts. Transplantation immunity reactions apply to them also and in much the same way as homograft reactions, provided the tissue can be made to 'take' at all in the first instance.

A characteristic course of events occurs in the rejection of foreign tissue. At first the graft may take and give every appearance of becoming permanently established in the host. After about seven or eight days, however, it becomes invaded by mononuclear cells. The blood and lymphatic supplies stop and the graft begins to deteriorate. Three or four days later the graft is completely destroyed. This reaction has been found to occur in mammals, birds, amphibia and fish. It does not occur in the embryo of these species, however, and the intolerance of foreign tissue seems to develop at about the time of birth or hatching—earlier or later depending on species.

It has been shown that the immunological mechanism of the homograft reaction is quite different from the ordinary antibody-antigen type of reaction. In some way the reticulo-endothelial system is involved, especially the lymphocytes. These cells seem to possess the ability to recognise foreign tissue when they come in contact with it and to carry this information back to the lymph-nodes where antibodies may be produced. Thus, if lymphocytes are unable to reach foreign tissues the homograft reaction is not initiated.

A remarkable feature of this process is that animals may be made tolerant to foreign tissue provided they are inoculated with it before birth (or before the immune mechanism has developed). A naturally occurring example of this is the bovine 'freemartin' in which binovular twins can be shown to be chimeras (individuals having two genetically distinct species of cells) because of the exchange of some cells *via* a common placental circulation in utero. Experimentally, mice can be rendered tolerant to foreign tissue by inoculation with it at birth. Subsequently they will not reject tissue from the same donor.

18

The immunological mechanism is sensitive to certain forms of treatment. In particular irradiation or treatment with radiomimetic substances, such as nitrogen mustards, can completely suppress it. Treatment with cortisone, which is known to have a depressant action on the reticulo-endothelial system, can also suppress the homograft reaction. Other substances can produce similar results but no others approach cortisone or x-irradiation in effectiveness.

The above remarks have been concerned with the rejection of normal tissue by hosts of the same species. For some reason which is not understood, certain neoplastic cells and tissues do not seem to stimulate the response to the same degree and thus there are some transplantable animal tumours which can be transferred to a variety of hosts. However, transplantable tumours are often carried in the host for a period rather shorter than that required for development of immunity (*e.g.*, ascites tumours) and in other cases transmission of the tumour may be due to a virus (*e.g.*, the Rous sarcoma).

From the foregoing it can be understood that in order to grow animal tissues in a foreign host the immunological mechanism involved in the homograft reaction must either be circumvented or eliminated. This has been done in the following ways.

1. Transplantation into embryos or very young animals.
2. Transplantation into animals rendered tolerant by treatment with donor cells before the stage of development of transplantation immunity.
3. Transplantation into genetically identical hosts (inbred strains).
4. Transplantation into areas without direct blood supply or lymphatic drainage (anterior chamber of the eye, cornea, brain).
5. Transplantation into artificial chambers from which blood and lymphatic cells are mechanically excluded (by millipore membranes).
6. Suppression of the host's ability to react (by treatment with cortisone and X-rays).
7. Transfer of implanted tissues to a new host before immunity develops (many ascites tumours).

Some cells cultured *in vitro* can be grown in the animal or passaged through the animal by means of these techniques.

BIBLIOGRAPHY

ALBRINK, W. S. & GREENE, H. S. N. (1953). The transplantation of tissues between zoological classes. *Cancer Res.* **13**, 64.

BILLINGHAM, R. E. (1959). Reactions of grafts against their hosts. *Science* **130**, 947.

BILLINGHAM, R. E. (1956). Acquired tolerance of foreign cells. In *Cellular Mechanisms in Differentiation and Growth*, p. 221. Ed. Rudnick, D. Princeton: Princeton University Press.

BILLINGHAM, R. E. & BRENT, L. (1957). A simple method of inducing tolerance of skin homografts in mice. *Transpl. Bull.* **4**, 67.

BRENT, L. (1958). Tissue transplantation immunity. *Progr. Allergy* **5**, 271.

FOLEY, G. E., HANDLER, A. H., McCARTHY, R. E. & ADAMS, R. A. (1961). Heterograft and homograft responses elicited by mammalian cells following *in vitro* cultivation. *Quart. Rev. Pediat.* **16**, 14.

GORER, P. A. (1955). The antibody response to skin homografts in mice. *Ann. N.Y. Acad. Sci.* **59**, 365.

GREENE, H. S. N. (1941). Heterologous transplantation of mammalian tumors. I. The transfer of rabbit tumors to alien species. *J. exp. Med.* **73**, 461.

GREENE, H. S. N. (1951). A conception of tumor anatomy based on transplantation studies: A review. *Cancer Res.* **11**, 899.

GREENE, H. S. N. (1952). The significance of heterologous transplantability of human cancer. *Cancer* **5**, 24.

GREENE, H. S. N. (1955). Compatibility and non-compatibility in tissue transplantation. In *Biological Specificity and Growth*, p. 177. Ed. Butler, E. G. Princeton: Princeton University Press.

HANDLER, A. H., DAVIS, SALLY & SOMMERS, S. C. (1956). Heterotransplantation experiments with human cancers. *Cancer Res.* **16**, 32.

HOTCHKIN, J. E. (1957). The cultivation of Novikoff rat hepatoma cells in vitro. *Cancer Res.* **17**, 682.

McCARTHY, R. E., FOLEY, G. E. & FILLER, D. A. (1959). Homograft response elicited by mammalian cells following *in vitro* cultivation. (Abstract.) *Fed. Proc.* **18**, 492.

MEDAWAR, P. B. (1958). The homograft reaction. *Proc. roy. Soc.* **B148**, 145.

MEDAWAR, P. B. (1958). The immunology of transplantation. In *The Harvey Lectures, 1956-57.* New York: Academic Press.

MOORE, ALICE E. (1958). Tumorigenic activity of cultures. *Ann. N.Y. Acad. Sci.* **76**, 497.

MURPHY, J. B. (1912). Transplantability of malignant tumors to the embryos of a foreign species. *J. Amer. med. Ass.* **59**, 874.

MURPHY, J. B. (1913). Transplantability of tissues to the embryo of foreign species. Its bearing on questions of tissue specificity and tumor immunity. *J. exp. Med.* **17**, 482.

SIMONSEN, M. (1957). The impact on the developing embryo and newborn animal of adult homologous cells. *Acta path. microbiol. scand.* **40**, 480.

SNELL, G. D. (1957). The homograft reaction. *Ann. Rev. Microbiol.* **II**, 439.

Transplantation into embryos

The experimental embryologist has performed transplantation experiments between embryos for many years and we know that the success of these depended on the fact that in the embryo the homograft reaction does not develop until a late stage. The techniques do not have a place in this account since they are of a highly specialised nature. However, these successful experiments

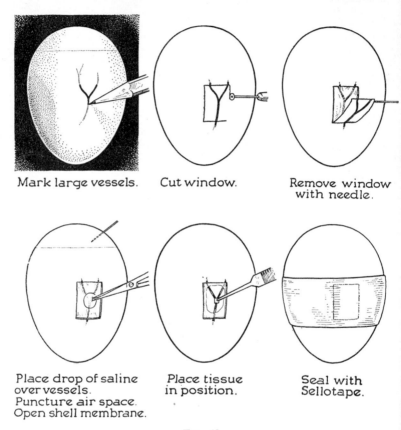

Mark large vessels.   Cut window.   Remove window with needle.

Place drop of saline over vessels. Puncture air space. Open shell membrane.   Place tissue in position.   Seal with Sellotape.

FIG. 48

Cultivation of tissue on the chorio-allantoic membrane of the fertile egg.

suggested that embryos might provide a general kind of substrate to which animal tissues might be grafted and eventually Murphy, in 1912, was able to demonstrate convincingly the survival of heterologous tumour tissue in the chorio-allantoic membrane of the chick embryo. Since then the fertile hen's egg has been used for the cultivation of both tumour and normal tissue from a variety of adult animals, including man.

Many techniques have been employed. In general, a window is made in the egg shell and the tissue to be planted is placed in the selected site. The yolk sac and the chorio-allantoic membrane have been most frequently used. The preferred technique is implantation on the chorio-allantoic membrane at an area where several large blood vessels join.

Many refinements have been introduced and the following account is based on the method used by Harris (1958).

PROCEDURE (Fig. 48)

1. Candle some fertile hen's eggs which have been incubated for nine days at 38° C. Eggs should be selected which show large healthy blood vessels. The area with the major blood vessels should be marked with pencil.

2. Prepare the tissue to be implanted. Cut fragments about 1-3 mm. in size and place in BSS or a tissue culture medium until required.

3. Wipe the eggshell with 70 per cent. alcohol and allow to dry.

4. Using a dentist's or similar drill with an abrasive disc, grind grooves in the shell for the window (about 1 cm. square), taking care not to penetrate to the membrane. With an egg-punch or a needle make a small hole over the airspace of the egg. Remove the shell over the window with a needle or a sharp pair of forceps.

5. The opaque shell membrane is now exposed. Place a small drop of BSS on this and rupture it with a sharp needle to permit the BSS to pass between it and the chorio-allantoic membrane. If the chorio-allantoic membrane does not separate spontaneously from the shell membrane as a result of this manoeuvre, apply a little suction to the hole over the airspace (by means of a rubber bulb). Remove the shell membrane, leaving the chorio-allantoic membrane exposed.

6. Place a piece of tissue over the junction of two large blood vessels and seal the window with transparent adhesive tape. Seal the air-hole similarly.

7. Incubate the eggs at 38° with the window uppermost.

After a period of 3-4 days the implanted tissue can be examined by removing the tape over the window. If it is desired to observe the implant continuously good visualisation can be obtained by sealing a small coverslip to the eggshell with molten beeswax. Water vapour usually condenses on this and it is necessary to clear it by applying a warm object to the glass prior to examination. An auroscope is useful for this purpose.

Murphy was able to demonstrate growth in the chick chorio-allantoic membrane of the Jensen rat sarcoma, the Ehrlich carcinoma, a chondroma of the mouse, a mammary carcinoma of the mouse, the Flexner-Jobling rat adenocarcinoma and a human sarcoma as well as embryonic tissue of chicken, mouse and rat. Many other workers since then have demonstrated the growth of a variety of human tumours, normal human tissue, such as skin (Goodpasture *et al.*) and lines of tumour cells, some of which have also been cultured *in vitro* (Dagg *et al.*).

BIBLIOGRAPHY

DAGG, C. P., KARNOFSKY, D. A. & RODDY, JACQUELINE (1956). Growth of transplantable human tumors in the chick embryo and hatched chick. *Cancer Res.* **16,** 589.

GOODPASTURE, E. W., DOUGLAS, B. & ANDERSON, KATHERINE (1938). A study of human skin grafted upon the chorio-allantois of chick embryos. *J. exp. Med.* **68,** 891.

HARRIS, J. J. (1958). The human tumor grown in the egg. *Ann. N.Y. Acad. Sci.* **76,** 764.

MURPHY, J. B. (1912). Transplantability of malignant tumors to the embryos of a foreign species. *J. Amer. med. Ass.* **59,** 874.

WOLFF, E. (1961). Utilisation de la membrane vitelline de l'oeuf de poule en culture organotypique. I. Technique et possibilités. *Develop. Biol.* **3,** 767.

Transplantation into tolerant chimeras

At the present time this technique has been used only in studies to investigate the nature of the homograft reaction.

Transplantation into genetically similar hosts

Many experimental tumours are maintained by serial transfer (of solid implants or by injection of tissue minces) in inbred animals of the strain from which the tumour originally arose. The techniques are simple. Implants are introduced either by a trocar and cannula or through a small incision into a suitable site. Minces are prepared by a Latapie mincer or similar instrument and injected through a wide-bore needle directly, usually subcutaneously or intramuscularly. No special methods are required in most cases.

Transplantation into non-vascular areas

The sites most commonly employed for this purpose are the anterior chamber of the eye and the brain. Attempts to transfer heterologous tissue to the anterior chamber of the eye were made as early as 1884 and at regular intervals thereafter, but at first they were almost uniformly unsuccessful. Hegner and Keysser independently reported successful heterotransplantation experiments in 1913 and very many workers have been successful since. Current techniques have been developed mainly by Greene.

Procedure for anterior eye chamber implantation (Fig. 49)

1. Prepare the tissue to be transplanted. Suitable implants are about 1 mm. in size.

2. Anaesthetise the animal. For large animals, such as rabbits, Greene uses a local anaesthetic, such as cocaine, applied to the cornea. A general anaesthetic may be used instead. It is essential for small animals, which can be placed in a jar containing some swabs soaked in ether. Nembutal injected intramuscularly, is generally used for larger animals.

3. With the left finger and thumb hold the eyelids open and, by gentle pressure, cause the eye to protrude. Using a double-edged corneal knife open the anterior chamber near the superior border of the corneoscleral junction with a quick jab directing the knife blade slightly forward to avoid cutting the iris. (Single-edged knives are unsatisfactory.)

FIG. 49
Introduction of tissue into the anterior chamber of the eye.

4. Introduce the tissue through a small cannula (fitted with a stylet or plunger to permit extrusion of the fragment).

5 After withdrawing it, use the side of the cannula to gently massage the tissue down until it is wedged in the inferior angle of the iris.

Certain soft tissues, such as brain, are liable to escape through the corneal incision, particularly in small animals. In cases of this sort Greene recommends that the initial incision should intentionally be carried back through the iris. The cannula should then be inserted into the posterior part of the anterior chamber (behind the iris) and brought forward through the pupil into the lower part of the anterior part of the chamber. On withdrawing the cannula the fragment is then retained at the border of the pupil.

Procedure for brain implantation

1 Prepare the implants as before.

2. Anaesthetise the animal. Shave and wash the skin over the upper anterior portion of the parietal bone. Make a small incision and retract the skin to expose the skull.

3. Drill a small hole through the skull, just large enough to take the inoculating cannula (for large animals 1·5 mm. bore; for small animals an adapted hypodermic needle, 20 bore). In mice the hole can be drilled by rotating a scalpel blade. For larger animals a drill is necessary and an ordinary metal drilling bit can be used. As soon as the skull has been penetrated the drill must be withdrawn to prevent damage to the brain. This point can be recognised by the sensation of yielding transmitted to the hand.

4. Insert the implant through the cannula, making sure it is expelled into the brain and retained there.

5. Approximate the edges of the skin incision and seal with a drop of collodion or a clip.

This technique has been used successfully for rabbits, guinea-pigs, rats and mice.

BIBLIOGRAPHY

GREENE, H. S. N. (1941). Heterologous transplantation of mammalian tumors. II. The transfer of human tumors to alien species. *J. exp. Med.* **73**, 475.

GREENE, H. S. N. (1946). The heterologous transplantation of mouse tumors induced *in vitro*. *Cancer Res.* **6**, 396.

GREENE, H. S. N. (1947). The use of the mouse eye in transplantation experiments. *Cancer Res.* **7**, 491.

GREENE, H. S. N. (1951). The transplantation of tumors to the brains of heterologous species. *Cancer Res.* **11**, 529.

GREENE, H. S. N. (1953). The transplantation of human brain tumors to the brains of laboratory animals. *Cancer Res.* **13**, 422.

MORRIS, D. S., McDONALD, J. R. & MANN, F. C. (1950). Intra-ocular transplantation of heterologous tissues. *Cancer Res.* **10**, 36.

SHRIGLEY, E. W., GREENE, H. S. N. & DURAN-REYNALS, F. (1947). Growth of avian tumors other than the Rous sarcoma in the anterior chamber of the guinea pig eye. *Cancer Res.* **7**, 15.

Diffusion chambers

Rezzesi and also Bisceglie in the early 1930s developed methods for the short-term cultivation of tissues in collodion bags within the peritoneal cavity of small laboratory animals. Algire and his associates developed the use of millipore membrane chambers for the same purpose. Type HA or Type AA millipore filters can be used. The AA filter excludes particles larger than 0·8 μ and is quite satisfactory.

A diffusion chamber (Fig. 50) for intraperitoneal implantation is prepared from two rings of perspex and two discs of millipore

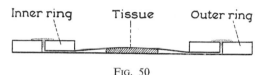

FIG. 50

Cross-section of an Algire diffusion chamber.

membrane as follows. The two perspex rings are cut from 5 mm. sheet. One is made with an outside diameter of 17·5 mm. and an inside diameter of 14 mm., the other with an outside diameter of 13·9 mm. and an inside diameter of 10 mm. A disc 17·5 mm. in diameter and another, 14 mm. in diameter, are cut from a small piece of millipore membrane. The larger disc is stuck to the larger ring with a 1 per cent. solution of perspex in acetone. The smaller disc is similarly stuck to the smaller ring.

The tissue is cut to form a small explant about 0·5 mm. in size. The surface of the membrane in the larger part of the chamber is moistened with a drop of tissue culture medium and the tissue is placed in it. The inner ring is then placed in position and the junction between outer and inner rings is sealed with the minimum amount of perspex solution.

On removal of the chamber from the animal it can be placed in fixative and stained intact. After dehydration and clearing with xylol the chamber can be taken apart.

Algire also developed an observation chamber on the same principle. In this chamber one side consisted of a glass coverslip and the other of a millipore membrane. The chamber was inserted into a fold of skin on the back of the animal so that continuous observation, by means of a microscope if desired, could be carried out.

BIBLIOGRAPHY

ALGIRE, G. H., WEAVER, J. M. & PREHN, R. T. (1954). Growth of cells *in vivo* in diffusion chambers. I. Survival of homografts in immunised mice. *J. nat. Cancer Inst.* **15**, 493.

PREHN, R. T., WEAVER, J. M. & ALGIRE, G. H. (1954). The diffusion chamber technique applied to a study of the nature of homograft resistance. *J. nat. Cancer Inst.* **15**, 509.

WEAVER, J. M., ALGIRE, G. H. & PREHN, R. T. (1955). The growth of cells *in vivo* in diffusion chambers. II. The role of cells in the destruction of homografts in mice. *J. nat. Cancer Inst.* **15**, 1737.

Transplantation to irradiated and cortisone-treated animals

It has already been mentioned that the host's immune response can be suppressed in a number of ways and that the best have proved to be irradiation with X-rays and treatment with cortisone, either separately or combined. The development of these techniques has been due mainly to the recent work of Toolan although Murphy demonstrated as long ago as 1914 that irradiation with X-rays permitted heterotransplantation.

Several kinds of animals have been used as hosts for transplanted tumour tissue. The mouse and rat usually require combined treatment with irradiation and cortisone, but the hamster gives satisfactory results when treated with cortisone alone.

CONDITIONED RATS. Young (4-week-old) rats are recommended. 1-4 days before inoculation they are subjected to about 150 r of x-irradiation. The inoculum, consisting of 0·5 - 1 ml. of a mince or suspension containing 0·25 - 0·5 g. tissue, is injected into the flank. At the same time 3 mg. cortisone acetate is administered subcutaneously. This is repeated on alternate days for a total of four injections. The tumours are usually ready for harvesting between the 9th and 12th day.

CONDITIONED MICE. The technique is essentially similar. The animals are given 50-150 r (usually 100 r) total body irradiation 1 - 4 days before inoculation. An inoculum of about 0·5 ml. of tissue suspension is made either subcutaneously into the flank or, preferably, intramuscularly into the thigh. 1·5 mg. cortisone acetate is injected at the same time and 1 mg. on alternate days for a total of four injections. The tumour may be harvested in 7 - 12 days.

CONDITIONED HAMSTERS. The Syrian hamster can be adequately conditioned with cortisone alone. Animals weighing 50 - 60 g. receive 3 mg. cortisone acetate at the time of inoculation with the tumour and the same dose twice in the following week. They can be inoculated in the same way as rats and mice. However, in the hamster the cheek-pouch offers a particularly suitable site and a special technique has therefore been developed.

FIG. 51
Introduction of tissue into the hamster cheek-pouch.

The hamster is first anaesthetised with nembutal, administered intraperitoneally. The cheek-pouch membrane is everted and pinned down to a piece of perspex. It is then washed with a mild antiseptic (acraflavine, zephiran) and dried thoroughly with a sterile gauze swab. A small puncture is made through the cheek-pouch membrane and tissue fragments are inoculated by means of a small cannula. Alternatively, a cell or tissue mince or suspension may be injected. The cheek-pouch is returned into the mouth.

Besides human tumours, embryonic tissues of a number of species and some strains of cultured cells have been grown by this technique.

BIBLIOGRAPHY

BILLINGHAM, R. E., FERRIGAN, L. W. & SILVERS, W. K. (1960). Cheek pouch of the Syrian hamster and tissue transplantation immunity. *Science* **132,** 1488.

FOLEY, G. E. & HANDLER, A. H. (1957). Differentiation of 'normal' and neoplastic cells maintained in tissue culture by implantation into normal hamsters. *Proc. Soc. exp. Biol. (N.Y.)* **94,** 661.

GALLILY, RUTH & WOOLLEY, G. W. (1958). The human tumor in the mouse. *Ann. N.Y. Acad. Sci.* **76,** 791.

HANDLER, A. H. (1958). Chemotherapy studies on transplantable human and animal tumors in Syrian hamster. *Ann. N.Y. Acad. Sci.* **76,** 775.

IVERSEN, H. G. (1956). Human tumor in cortisone-treated mice. *Brit. J. Cancer* **10,** 472.

LUTZ, B. R., FULTON, G. P., PATT, D. I., HANDLER, A. H. & STEVENS, D. F. (1951). The cheek pouch of the hamsters as a site for the transplantation of a methylcholanthrene-induced sarcoma. *Cancer Res.* **11,** 64.

MERKER, P. C. & WOOLLEY, G. W. (1959). A study of human epidermoid carcinoma (H.Ep.3) growing in conditioned Swiss mice. I. Applicability to chemotherapy studies. *Cancer Res.* **19,** 664.

PALM, JOY E., TELLER, M. N. MERKER, P. C. & WOOLLEY, G. W. (1958). Host conditioning in experimental chemotherapy. *Ann. N.Y. Acad. Sci.* **76**, 812.

PATTERSON, W. B., CHUTE, ROSANNA N. & SOMMERS, S. C. (1954). Transplantation of human tumors into cortisone-treated hamsters. *Cancer Res.* **14**, 656.

TAKAYAMA, S. & WOOLLEY, G. W. (1958). Successful intramuscular growth of human tumor in conditioned mice. *Ann. N.Y. Acad. Sci.* **76**, 797.

TELLER, M. N., MERKER, P. C., PALM, JOY E. & WOOLLEY, G. W. (1958). The human tumor in cancer chemotherapy in the conditioned rat. *Ann. N.Y. Acad. Sci.* **76**, 742.

TOOLAN, HELENE W. (1953). Conditioning of the host. *J. nat. Cancer Inst.* **14**, 745.

TOOLAN, H. W. (1953). Growth of human tumors in cortisone-treated laboratory animals; possibility of obtaining permanently transplantable human tumors. *Cancer Res.* **13**, 389.

TOOLAN, H. W. (1954). Transplantable human neoplasms maintained in cortisone-treated laboratory animals: H.S. 1; H.Ep. 1; H.Ep. 2; H.Ep. 3; and H.Emb,Rh. 1. *Cancer Res.* **14**, 600.

TOOLAN, H. W. (1955). The possible role of cortisone in overcoming resistance to the growth of human tissues in heterologous hosts. *Ann. N.Y. Acad. Sci.* **59**, 394.

Ascites tumours

The term ascites tumour is applied to certain transplantable tumours of animals which have been made to grow as suspensions of free cells in an exudate within the peritoneal cavity. They are of special interest since they behave in very many ways exactly like explanted cell cultures and some of them can be cultured *in vitro*. This permits cells to be alternated between *in vitro* and *in vivo* conditions with great ease.

Hesse, in 1927, demonstrated first that the Flexner-Jobling rat carcinoma could be transmitted by the injection of ascitic fluid which had developed during the growth of the tumour in the peritoneal cavity. Koch repeated and confirmed Hesse's observation the following year. However, the use of ascites tumours in experimental work did not become established until Loewenthal and Jahn, collaborators of Koch's, found in 1932 that after repeated trials they were able to produce an ascites tumour using the Ehrlich carcinoma. Thereafter this tumour became widely used and attempts were made to produce ascites tumours from other material. Since the original work a very large number of these have been developed, mainly in mice and rats. Some are able to grow in many strains while others will grow only in the strain of origin. In Table XXII some characteristics of a few commonly used ascites tumour strains are shown.

TABLE XXII

ASCITES TUMOURS

Designation	Type	Year of Origin	Derivation	Host
6C3HED	Ind. lymphosarcoma	1941	Thymus	C3H mice
DBA lymphoma (Dalton)	Sp. Ca.	1947	Thymus	DBA mice
L5178				DBA2 mice
Ehrlich	Sp. Ca.	1896 ?	Mammary gland	All mice
15091a	Sp. Ca.	1928	Mammary gland	A mice
Krebs 2	Sp. Ca. ?	1933	——	All mice
TA3	Sp. Ad. Ca.	1948	Mammary gland	A mice
MC1A	Ind. Rabdomyosarcoma	1945	Muscle	C3H mice
MC1M	Ind. sarcoma	1946	Muscle	C3H mice
Lymphoma EL4	Ind. lymphoma	1945	——	C57BL mice
Yoshida	Ind. sarcoma	1943	Scrotum	Rats
MTR sarcoma II	Ind. sarcoma	1951		Wistar Rats
Takeda sarcoma	Sp. sarcoma	1952		Rats
Watanabe	Ind. Hepatoma	1954		Rats

Sp.—spontaneous; Ind.—induced; Ca.—carcinoma; Ad. Ca.—Adeno-carcinoma.

Although attempts were made from the beginning to grow these tumours in tissue culture, it proved surprisingly difficult to keep them alive and only recently has any real success been achieved.

MAINTENANCE OF ASCITES TUMOURS. Most ascites tumours are extremely easy to maintain provided a suitable strain of mice or rats is bred for the purpose. Normally, mice with a mature tumour are killed a week after inoculation. The tumour (in suspension in ascites fluid) is removed from the abdominal cavity of infected animals by means of a syringe and needle and reinoculated into new hosts. Details of the procedure as used for the Ehrlich ascites tumour are as follows. Mice containing a mature tumour are put into an ether jar to be anaesthetised. They are then removed one by one and killed by decapitation or dislocation of the neck. The skin of the abdomen is liberally swabbed with alcohol and a syringe with a No. 18 gauge needle is used to extract the cell suspension. Sometimes, difficulty is found in withdrawing the fluid due to the gut being drawn against the end of the needle. Occasionally it is easier, therefore, to open up the abdomen and remove the ascites fluid by means of a Pasteur pipette. Alternatively, the skin can be reflected to reveal the thin muscular abdominal wall. In mice this is quite transparent and the aspirating needle can be directly observed. The tip of the needle can be used to hold up a small cone of abdominal wall and from this viscera-free area the tumour suspension can be aspirated. On withdrawal of the ascites fluid it is transferred to a test-tube. When all the donor mice have been handled in this way, the mice to be inoculated are then placed in the anaesthetising jar and lightly anaesthetised. They are removed one by one, the abdominal skin is swabbed with alcohol and the tumour suspension is inoculated direct into the abdomen by means of a syringe and needle. As a general rule, the amount of inoculum varies from 0·1 to 0·25 ml. depending on the rate of growth of the tumour.

REMOVAL OF CELLS FOR CULTURE IN VITRO. In the above procedure it is desirable to maintain relatively aseptic conditions but strict asepsis is not essential because the mouse peritoneal cavity has a high resistance to infection. However, if the cells are to be cultured *in vitro*, it is necessary to take somewhat greater care. It is recommended that the skin of the mouse should be everted in the manner described on page 211. This exposes a sterile area of abdominal wall through which a needle can be inserted to withdraw some of the cell suspension.

Ascites tumour cells occur in ascites fluid in concentrations varying from about 25 million to more than 100 million per ml. of fluid. It is therefore usually necessary to dilute them very considerably before trying to culture them in the usual media. Otherwise it is exhausted very quickly and the cells die before they have an opportunity to grow. It should be noted that at least 10 per cent. of the cells in the exudate are likely to be cells derived from the peritoneal lining or phagocytes which have entered the peritoneal cavity from the blood. This factor must therefore be allowed for in experiments. Alternatively, special measures may be taken to remove them. Most ascites tumours tend to grow in suspension *in vitro* and do not settle down on the glass of culture vessels. It is possible therefore, to remove unwanted cells simply by permitting them to stick to the glass of a culture vessel. The supernatant containing the suspended ascites cells can then be pipetted off. This can be done within a matter of hours of removal from the animal.

BIBLIOGRAPHY

AHLSTRÖM, C. G. & STORMBY, N. (1958). Ehrlich mouse ascites carcinoma in hydrocortisone-treated hamsters. *Acta path. microbiol. scand.* **42**, 15.

D'ACUNZO, L. (1956). Heterotransplantability of Ehrlich ascites carcinoma in the peritoneum of rats treated with cortisone. *Riv. Anat. pat.* **10**, 1046.

FISCHER, G. A. (1958). Studies of the culture of leukemic cells *in vitro. Ann. N.Y. Acad. Sci.* **78**, 673.

KATSUTA, H., TAKAOKA, T., HORI, M., OKUMURA, H., YASUKAWA, M., SAITO, S. & SUZUKI, S. (1957). Cultivation of rat ascites hepatoma cells in the simplified replicate tissue culture. *Jap. J. exp. Med.* **27**, 443.

KATSUTA, H., TAKAOKA, T., MITAMURA, K., SOMEYA, Y. & KAWADA, I. (1959). Cultivation of Yoshida sarcoma cells in the simplified replicate tissue culture. *Jap. J. exp. Med.* **29**, 143.

KLEIN, G. & KLEIN, EVA (1951). The transformation of a solid transplantable mouse carcinoma into an ' Ascites Tumour '. *Cancer Res.* **11**, 466.

KLEIN, EVA & KLEIN, G. (1954). Differential survival of solid tumor cells after inoculation into established ascites tumors. *Cancer Res.* **14**, 139.

KLEIN, EVA (1954). Gradual transformation of solid into ascites tumors. Permanent difference between the original and the transformed sublines. *Cancer Res.* **14**, 482.

PATT, H. M. (1958). Parameters of ascites tumor growth. *Ann. N.Y. Acad. Sci.* **76**, 572.

SCHLEICH, ANNELIES (1954). Behaviour of solid and ascites sublines of two tumors in tissue culture. *Cancer Res.* **14**, 486.

TAKAOKA, T. & KATSUTA, H. (1958). Establishment of cell strains of rat ascites hepatoma cells in tissue culture. *Jap. J. exp. Med.* **28**, 115.

CHAPTER XVIII

PRESERVATION, STORAGE AND TRANSPORTATION OF LIVING TISSUES AND CELLS

NOW that very many cell-strains have been isolated, one of the major problems confronting some laboratories is the maintenance of the large number of cultures necessary to carry several strains simultaneously. A further difficulty is the tendency for cell-types to change after they have been kept in a state of rapid proliferation for some years. Similar problems have been encountered in the handling of micro-organisms and the answers which have been suggested for the maintenance and storage of cells are very similar to those which have been adopted by bacteriologists. All the methods depend on the maintenance of the cells at reduced temperatures but there are some differences in technique depending on the temperature used.

Cells can be maintained at slightly reduced temperatures, refrigerator temperatures or very low temperatures ($-70°$ to $-190°C$.). Room temperature and refrigerator storage are sometimes used for short-term maintenance but for long-term storage very low temperatures are necessary. In the deep-frozen state metabolism is, of course, suspended completely.

Maintenance at slightly reduced temperatures

Most mammalian cells and tissue fragments will survive indefinitely at $30°$ C. provided the medium is renewed when required. By this means the frequency of feeding can be greatly reduced. Thus, compared with $37°$ C. the intervals between feeding can be about three times as long.

The temperature can be still further reduced and many cells will survive unharmed at about $20°$. At this temperature very infrequent renewal of medium is required, although the cells rarely continue to behave quite normally if their normal incubation temperature is of the order of $37°$. They tend to round up and may leave the glass and sometimes they become packed with fat droplets. However, if the medium is renewed and the temperature raised to normal once more the cells very rapidly return to normal after a short lag period.

Maintenance at refrigerator temperature

Some reports have appeared concerning the storage of tissue in the refrigerator (2 - 6°). It would appear that sheets of cells and single cells do not survive well for more than a few days in these conditions but that tissue fragments will survive for several weeks in a nutrient medium. This may be due to the high oxygen tension which can develop in the medium. The main practical use of this method is in the preservation of surviving tissue before explantation, usually only for a few days. The tissue should be cut into pieces of a few cubic millimetres and stored in a nutrient medium.

Preservation by freezing

In several fields advantage has been taken of the observation that deep-frozen tissue may remain viable. This principle was applied to the storage of viruses and bacteria but when it was applied to animal cells they did not survive. At first this was thought to be due to laceration of the cell membranes by ice crystals but more recent evidence suggests that the cause may be osmotic changes which give rise to irreversible changes in lipoprotein complexes resulting in splitting of membranes within the cell. In any event the answer to the preservation of living animal cells proved to be the addition of a substance such as glycerol or ethylene glycol to the medium and slow freezing. The technique was worked out in some detail by Smith who demonstrated the survival of ovarian granulosa cells after deep freezing. Scherer and Hoogasian demonstrated its effectiveness with some stock lines of cultured cells and since then it has been widely applied.

The following principles summarise generally accepted current practice.

1. The cells should be in a healthy state before freezing.
2. They should be suspended in growth medium containing glycerol or dimethyl sulphoxide (5-15 per cent.) shortly before freezing, and sealed in a gas-tight ampoule.

19

3. Freezing to $-70°$ should be controlled over a period of about an hour or preferably longer. A cooling rate of one degree a minute is recommended.

4. Storage temperature should be maintained at $-70°$ or lower.

5. Thawing should be rapid (2 - 3 minutes).

Details of the technique are given below.

Equipment

1. *Refrigerator.*—Cells may be stored in a low-temperature deep-freeze cabinet operating at a temperature in the region of $-70°$ C. (*e.g.* Revco deep-freeze) or in a dry-ice chest at about the same temperature. However, viability tends to be lost over a period of months at these temperatures. At temperatures of less than $-90°$ no progressive loss of viability can be detected over very long periods and these very low temperatures are therefore recommended. Liquid nitrogen is usually used as the refrigerant. It has a temperature of $-196°$ C. and the overlying vapour in a well-insulated vessel gives temperatures within the range of $-150°$ to $-180°$. Suitable containers (often called liquid nitrogen refrigerators) are manufactured by several companies. The Linde division of the Union Carbide Company (New York, N.Y.) manufactures a range of suitable vessels, including a small one with a capacity of 972 ampoules, which is suitable for a relatively small laboratory.

2. *Devices for recovery of cells.*—Cells are usually stored in 1 ml. ampoules in liquid nitrogen refrigerators. Most methods for marking ampoules are unsatisfactory. Hence, it is important that records be kept meticulously and that ampoules be stored systematically. The liquid nitrogen refrigerator amounts to a Dewar flask, similar to a large Thermos flask. The contents are distributed to a series of containers, usually deep cans, like pipette canisters, which can be recovered individually by some device or another. Within these containers the ampoules are held either in tubes or clipped to 'canes'. A cane is a metal rod bearing a number of clips to which individual ampoules can be attached. Each cane or tube carries a reference number.

3. *Cooling devices.* In order to ensure a steady slow rate of cooling several devices have been developed. The simplest can be made from a block of expanded polystyrene insulating material about four inches thick. This is sliced down the middle to give a top

and bottom half and matching cavities are then made in each half with a large cork borer to hold ampoules. Ampoules are placed in the cavities, the two halves held together with an elastic band, and the whole device placed in a Revco deep-freeze cabinet for two hours. The cells are transferred direct to the liquid nitrogen refrigerator.

A similar device, invented by Greaves and his colleagues, consists of a modified stopper for a liquid nitrogen refrigerator and operates on exactly the same principle. It is available from the Linde company.

For meticulous large-scale work programmed cooling devices have been developed but these are not necessary for the ordinary laboratory. Simpler methods than the ones mentioned above are also available. For instance, reasonably good results can be obtained by packing the ampoules in cotton-wool in an ice-cream carton and putting them first in the 4° refrigerator for one hour, then in the −20° freezer for one hour before transferring them to the coldest temperature available. Results are not so good by this method but in a laboratory not equipped to handle cell-freezing routinely it provides a satisfactory makeshift.

4. *Other equipment.*—A large Dewar flask will be required to store or transport liquid nitrogen if a liquid nitrogen refrigerator is used. (It may be remarked that it is best to have a well-established routine of topping-up every week, although the reservoir of liquid nitrogen may be sufficient for many weeks.)

General Procedure

The procedure for preparing twelve ampoules of a cell strain is described.

1. Harvest 1-2×10^8 cells, which must be growing exponentially) by a standard method, such as trypsinisation. Resuspend in 21·5 ml. of fresh growth medium. Open ampoules.

2. Add 2·5 ml. dimethyl sulphoxide (to give a final concentration of 10 per cent.). Mix quickly and dispense approximately 2 ml. rapidly to each ampoule. Store ampoules on ice.

3. Seal ampoules (practice may be required). Return to ice.

(3A. Test ampoules by submerging in a solution of crystal violet in methyl alcohol. If the ampoules are leaky some dye will be sucked in. This step is unnecessary if the operator is proficient.)

4. Place ampoules in cooling device and leave 1-2 hours to cool to below $-30°$.

5. Rapidly transfer ampoules to liquid nitrogen refrigerator. (Thawing at this stage will kill the cells).

6. Complete records.

7. Within the next few days remove two ampoules, thaw as described below, and test for viability by dye exclusion or plating efficiency. If viability is good confirm the record. If it is bad prepare a new batch of cells to replace the bad batch.

8. To recover cells from the deep-freeze proceed as follows. Prepare a beaker by filling it with water at $37°$ C. and provide it with a cover. Put on protective goggles. (Occasionally a defective ampoule may fill with liquid nitrogen and explode on thawing.) Remove an ampoule with forceps and slip it under the cover into the beaker. When it has thawed open the ampoule and transfer the contents to a suitable vessel. Adding medium slowly at first, make the volume up to at least 25 ml. Transfer to culture vessels and incubate.

In the procedure described above dimethyl sulphoxide was recommended as the protecting agent. In our experience better results are obtained with it than with glycerol and this is probably the general experience. The reason may be that it can diffuse in and out of cells more readily with the result that there is less osmotic damage when it is added to medium or diluted out.

Transportation of cells

It is now common practice to transport samples of cell strains over long distances. The availability of air freight and reliable mail services reduces the problem to the relatively simple one of maintaining the cells alive for, at the most, two days in transit.

It has to be accepted that the culture vessel will be agitated during handling so that there is no point in attempting to maintain the cells as a monolayer on the wall of a vessel partially filled with medium which may slop about. If it is desirable to despatch them as a monolayer practically all the medium should be removed from the vessel or else it should be completely filled. Alternatively the cells may be transported as a suspension.

The main hazard in transporting cells is exposure to extremes of temperature. Thus, in winter if cells are sent by ordinary mail it is possible that they will be frozen. If they are sent by air freight at any time of the year the same may happen due to low temperatures in the uninsulated freight compartment of a high-flying aircraft. In summer in many parts of the world the air temperature alone may rise to levels lethal to cells, while they may be killed rapidly even in temperate climates if the sun shines directly on the package containing them. However, awareness of these factors is usually all that is necessary to ensure that adequate steps are taken to deal with them.

At most times of the year in Great Britain it has been found adequate to send the cells, either as a suspension or as a monolayer with about 2 ml. of medium in the bottle, by Express letter post. An ordinary prescription bottle or a large test-tube is used. It is protected with some wadding and wrapped up securely in a parcel which is despatched in the late afternoon. From most parts of the country this ensures delivery first thing the following morning. In cold or hot weather, it is necessary to insulate the package much more thoroughly. If it is to be sent over a distance in the winter it is advisable to send it by passenger train with an arrangement to have it collected at the other end.

If cells have to be carried over a longer distance, it is best to send them by air. In making arrangements for international shipments it is advisable to consult a government organisation to avoid unnecessary customs delay. Transatlantic shipments to Great Britain from the United States have been arranged by the United Kingdom Treasury and Supply Delegation by arrangement with the Medical Research Council. It should be emphasised to those responsible that the package must not be exposed to extremes of temperature.

In countries, such as the United States, in which extremes of temperature are encountered, it is necessary to send cells in insulated packages most of the year. Foam plastics, powdered cork and cotton are effective insulators.

If for any reason cells have to be transported over a long distance by slower methods this can be achieved satisfactorily by filling the culture vessel completely with fresh medium immediately before transportation and then keeping them at a temperature of about $20°$ C. By this means cells have been known to survive in a suitcase for a period of at least three weeks. Where possible the other methods described are to be preferred.

BIBLIOGRAPHY

ALLGÖWER, M. & BLOCKER, T. G., JR. (1952). Viability of skin in relation to various methods of storage. *Tex. Rep. Biol. Med.* **10,** 3.

ASHWOOD-SMITH, M. J. (1961). Viability of mouse bone marrow frozen to −79° C. in the presence of dimethyl sulphoxide. *J. Physiol.* **155,** 26.

BILLINGHAM, R. E. & MEDAWAR, P. B. (1951). The viability of mammalian skin after freezing, thawing and freeze-drying. In *Freezing and Drying.* Ed. R. J. C. Harris. London: Institute of Biology.

BREEDIS, C. (1942). The action of extreme cold on leukemic cells. *J. exp. Med.* **76,** 221.

CRAVEN, C. (1960). The survival of stocks of HeLa cells maintained at −70° C. *Exp. Cell Res.* **19,** 164.

FERGUSON, J. (1960). Long term storage of tissue culture cells. *Aust. J. exp. Biol. med. Sci.* **38,** 389.

FISCHER, A. (1926). The growth of tissue cells from warmblooded animals at lower temperature. *Arch. exp. Z.* **2,** 303.

GREAVES, R. I. N., NAGINGTON, J. & KELLAWAY, T. D. (1963). Preservation of living cells by freezing and by drying. *Fed. Proc.* **22,** 90.

HANKS, J. (1948). The longevity of chick tissue cultures without renewal of medium. *J. cell. comp. Physiol.* **31,** 235.

HANKS, J. & WALLACE, ROSLYN (1949). Relation of oxygen and temperature in the preservation of tissues by refrigeration. *Proc. Soc. exp. Biol.* (*N.Y.*) **71,** 196.

HAUSCHKA, T. S., MITCHELL, J. T. & NIEDERPRUEM, D. J. (1959). A reliable frozen tissue bank: viability and stability of 82 neoplastic and normal cell types after prolonged storage at −78° C. *Cancer Res.* **19,** 643.

KITE, J. H. & DOEBBLER, G. F. (1961). Effects of cooling rates and additives on survival of frozen tissue culture cells. *Fed. Proc.* **20,** 149.

LIPTON, M. M. & STEIGMAN, A. J. (1955). Practicability of shipping HeLa cell suspensions for use in color test for poliomyelitis antibodies. *Proc. Soc. exp. Biol.* (*N.Y.*) **90,** 367.

LOVELOCK, J. E. & BISHOP, M. W. H. (1959). Prevention of freezing damage to living cells by dimethyl sulphoxide. *Nature* (*Lond.*) **183,** 1394.

McPHERSON, S. D., DRAHEIM, J. W., EVANS, VIRGINIA J. & EARLE, W. R. (1956). The viability of fresh and frozen corneas. *Amer. J. Ophthal.* **41,** 513.

MELNICK, J. L., RAPPAPORT, C., BANKER, D. D. & BHATT, P. N. (1955). Stabilized suspensions of monkey kidney cells suitable for intercontinental shipment. *Proc. Soc. exp. Biol.* (*N.Y.*) **88,** 676.

MERRYMAN, H. T., ed. *Freezing and Drying of Biological Materials. Ann. N.Y. Acad. Sci.* **85,** 501.

MERRYMAN, H. T. (1960). General principles of freezing and freezing injury in cellular materials. *Ann. N.Y. Acad. Sci.* **85,** 503.

MERRYMAN, H. T. (1962). Freezing of living cells: Biophysical considerations. *Nat. Can. Inst. Monograph* **7,** 7-15.

MERRYMAN, H. T. (1963). Preservation of living cells. *Fed. Proc.* **22,** 81.

MORGAN, J. F., GUERIN, L. F. & MORTON, HELEN J. (1956). The effect of low temperature and storage on the viability and mouse strain specificity of ascitic tumor cells. *Cancer Res.* **16,** 907.

NAGINGTON, J. & GREAVES, R. I. N. (1962). Preservation of tissue culture cells with liquid nitrogen. *Nature* (*Lond.*) **194,** 993.

PEIRCE, E. C. I., GROSS, R. E., BILL, A. H. JR. & MERRILL, K. JR. (1949). Tissue culture evaluation of the viability of blood-vessels stored by refrigeration. *Ann. Surg.* **129**, 333.

PHAN THE TRAN & BENDER, M. A. (1960). Survival of mouse bone-marrow cells frozen and thawed in solutions of amino acids. *Exp. Cell Res.* **20**, 651.

PHAN THE TRAN & BENDER, M. A. (1960). Protection of mouse bone marrow by inorganic compounds during freezing and thawing. *Proc. Soc. exp. Biol. (N.Y.)* **104**, 388.

PORTERFIELD, J. S. & ASHWOOD-SMITH, M. J. (1962). Preservation of cells in tissue culture by glycerol and dimethyl sulphoxide. *Nature (Lond.)* **193**, 548.

RINFERT, A. P. (1960). Factors affecting the erythrocyte during rapid freezing and thawing. *Ann. N.Y. Acad. Sci.* **85**, 576.

SCHERER, W. F. (1960). Effects of freezing speed and glycerol diluent on 4-5 year survival of HeLa and L cells. *Exp. Cell Res.* **19**, 175.

SCHERER, W. F. & BROWN, R. W. (1956). Transportation of human cells cultured *in vitro*. *Proc. Soc. exp. Biol. (N.Y.)* **92**, 82.

SCHERER, W. F. & HOOGASIAN, ALICIA C. (1954). Preservation at subzero temperatures of mouse fibroblasts (Strain L) and human epithelial cells (Strain HeLa). *Proc. Soc. exp. Biol. (N.Y.)* **87**, 480.

SLOVITER, H. A. (1962). Mechanism of haemolysis caused by freezing and its prevention. *Nature (Lond.)* **193**, 884.

SMITH, A. U. (1952). Cultivation of ovarian granulosa cells after cooling to very low temperatures. *Exp. Cell Res.* **3**, 574.

SMITH, A. U. (1954). Effects of low temperature on living cells and tissues. *Biological Applications of Freezing and Drying.* Inst. of Cancer Research, The Royal Cancer Hospital, London.

STULBERG, C. S., PETERSON, W. D., JR., & BERMAN, L. (1962). Quantitative and qualitative preservation of cell-strain characteristics. *Nat. Cancer Inst. Monograph No.* **7**, 17.

STULBERG, C. S., RIGHTSEL, W. A., PAGE, R. H. & BERMAN, L. (1959). Virologic use of monkey kidney cells preserved by freezing. *Proc. Soc. exp. Biol. (N.Y.)* **101**, 415.

STULBERG, C. S., SOULE, H. D. & BERMAN, L. (1958) Preservation of human epithelial-like and fibroblast-like cell strains at low temperatures. *Proc. Soc. exp. Biol. (N.Y.)* **98**, 428.

SWIM, H. E., HAFF, R. F. & PARKER, R. F. (1958). Some practical aspects of storing mammalian cells in the dry-ice chest. *Cancer Res.* **18**, 711.

SWIM, H. E. & PARKER, R. F. (1955). Preservation of cell cultures at 4° C. *Proc. Soc. exp. Biol. (N.Y.)* **89**, 549.

TAKAMO, K., YAMADA, M. & HIROKAWA, Y. (1961). Long term frozen storage of mammalian cell lines. *Jap. J. med. Sci. Biol.* **14**, 27.

WEISS, L. & ARMSTRONG, J. A. (1960). Structural changes in mammalian cells associated with cooling to −79° C. *J. biophys. biochem. Cytol.* **7**, 673.

PART IV

SPECIAL APPLICATIONS

CHAPTER XIX

MORPHOLOGICAL STUDIES

TISSUE cultures have been used very widely in a variety of morphological studies. In some respects the results have been disappointing since one of the most striking features of cultured cells is their tendency to lose their typical morphology. This generalisation requires immediate qualification since a few cells, such as neurones, do maintain their typical morphology *in vitro*. Also, very many other cells which apparently lose their typical appearance nevertheless retain certain characteristics. The criteria of identification have to be different from those usually adopted, however, since the cell is essentially rendered two-dimensional by growing on a surface. Thus the general shape of the cultured cell provides little information since the cell margins tend to be actively changing and the same cell can change from a spindle cell to a squamous cell and then to a round cell, depending on the conditions imposed. On the other hand, even after years of subcultivation, the HeLa cell can easily be distinguished from the L cell by a practised observer. Only a few workers have undertaken the task of identifying the morphological characteristics of cells in tissue culture in this way. However, without necessarily identifying the cell-types there is a great deal of information to be obtained from observation of the morphological behaviour of cells in response to different stimuli and for this purpose the cells may either be fixed and stained or they may be examined while they are living.

At the outset it should be mentioned here that these remarks do not, in general, apply to organ cultures. In organ cultures typical morphology is retained and a great deal of information can be obtained by fixing, sectioning and staining the cultures in the manner usually employed for whole tissues.

297

There are a few special practical points about the fixation and staining of tissue cultures. It is, of course, desirable to grow the cells or tissues on a coverslip since this immediately gives us the material in a form which is convenient to handle and subsequently to mount for microscopical examination. Thus, simple coverslip cultures, either on depression slides or on flying coverslips in test-tubes, are ideal for this purpose, particularly with primary explants.

When it is desired to grow cells of a strain on coverslips for morphological examination a suitable method is to place the coverslips in the bottom of 50 mm. Petri dishes and add a cell suspension. The dishes may then be placed in a CO_2 incubator or a sealed vessel into which 5 per cent. CO_2 in air has been passed. After 24 hours' incubation there is a layer of cells on the coverslip which is excellent for morphological study. In some cases it may be adequate simply to prepare a smear of cells on a slide in the manner commonly adopted for blood films.

The nature of the material determines subsequent handling. A culture consisting of a monolayer of cells grown direct on glass requires very brief fixation and staining. The ordinary procedures for staining blood films and smears are directly applicable to preparations of this kind.

On the other hand, cultures embedded in thick plasma clots require very different handling. First of all, it is necessary to wash them very thoroughly with a balanced salt solution to remove as much of the proteinaceous medium as possible before staining. Thereafter, fixation must be rather prolonged to ensure that the fixatives penetrate the culture thoroughly. Subsequently most of the stains require to be applied for rather longer times than would be the case with a microtome section.

A very large number of staining procedures have been applied to tissue cultures. However, for most purposes a relatively small number of techniques suffice.

As a general purpose stain the Jenner-Giemsa stain is excellent. This is a simple methylene blue-eosin stain of the type used for blood films and the modification described was originally employed by Jacobson. If better nuclear detail is required a very simple and effective stain is Harris's haematoxylin. In addition to these general purpose stains there is frequently a desire to have specific stains for chemical constituents of the cell. Hence a few common histochemical techniques will be described in addition to these two routine stains. The best known of the histochemical stains is the Feulgen stain for deoxyribonucleic acid. It has to be only slightly modified for tissue cultures. A rather similar technique is the PAS (periodic acid-Schiff) reaction which specifically stains carbohydrates. In addition to these two stains, it is worthwhile having a stain for lipids and the one to be described employs Sudan black.

COMMON FIXATION AND STAINING TECHNIQUES FOR TISSUE CULTURE MATERIAL

For successful treatment of whole mounts, the cultures must have been washed and fed at least once before fixation. All cultures must be rinsed in several changes of warm balanced salt solution for 15 - 30 minutes immediately before fixation. It is best to keep a flask of balanced salt solution in the incubator, also the jars in which the cultures are rinsed.

I. Commonly used fixatives

A. BOUIN'S FLUID

  1. Formula

Formalin	250 ml.
Sat. aq. sol. picric acid	750 ml.
(approximately 10 grams picric acid will saturate 750 ml. dist. water)	
Acetic acid, glacial	5 ml.

  2. For fixation of cultures in plasma clots
  Half hour in Bouin.
  Several changes in 80 per cent. alcohol until yellow colour has disappeared.
  Store in 80 per cent. alcohol until ready to stain.

B. ZENKER'S FLUID

  1. Formula of stock solution

Potassium dichromate	25 g.
Mercuric chloride	50 g.
Distilled water...	1,000 ml.

  Dissolve the mercuric chloride and the potassium dichromate in the water with the aid of heat.

2. *For fixation of cultures in plasma clots*
　　When ready to use, pipette 0·2 ml. of glacial acetic acid into
　　a 10 ml. Coplin jar and fill jar with Zenker stock solution.
　　Fixation time is ½ hour or less.
　　Rinse in gently running tap water overnight.
　　Store in 80 per cent. alcohol.

C. HELLY'S FLUID
　　1. *Formula.*—Stock solution same as Zenker.
　　2. *For fixation of cultures in plasma clots*
　　　　Add 0·5 ml. of formalin to 10 ml. Zenker stock solution in
　　　　Coplin jar just before using.
　　　　Fixation time is ½ - 1 hour.
　　　　Rinse quickly in gently running tap water.
　　　　Store in 80 per cent. alcohol.

D. FORMALIN
　　1. *Formula.*—10 per cent. formalin in balanced salt solution
　　　　(neutralised with $NaHCO_3$).
　　2. *For fixation of cultures in plasma clots*
　　　　Fixation time is 1 - 5 hours.
　　3. *For fixation of cell monolayers on glass*
　　　　Fixation time is 30 minutes.
　　Cultures exposed to any fixative containing mercuric chloride
must, at some time before staining, be treated with Gram's iodine
solution for 5 minutes, rinsed with distilled water, and placed for
a few minutes in a 5 per cent. sodium hyposulphite solution. The
culture is then rinsed several times in distilled water over a period
of about twenty minutes and returned for storage in 80 per cent.
alcohol.

II. Routine stains

A. HARRIS HAEMATOXYLIN.—This is a basic dye in cake form,
primarily a nuclear stain, but will also stain cytoplasm to varying
degrees. Will not stain intercellular fibres.

　　1. *Preparation*
　　　　(*a*) Haematoxylin—1 g. dissolved in 6 ml. of 95 per cent.
　　　　　　alcohol. (Prepare a few days in advance.)
　　　　(*b*) Add saturated solution of ammonium alum—100 ml.
　　　　　　(2 g. per 100 ml. of distilled water.)

(c) Add mercuric oxide—0·5 g. per 100 ml.

(d) Boil and cool rapidly.

(e) Add glycerin—25 ml.

methyl alcohol—25 ml.

(f) Filter.

(g) Haematoxylin may be used the next day.

2. *Suitable fixatives in order of preference*

(a) Helly.

(b) Zenker.

(c) Bouin.

3. *Methods of staining* (plasma clot cultures or monolayers)

(a) From 80 per cent. storage alcohol rinse in distilled water for a few minutes.

(b) Add 2 - 3 drops Harris haematoxylin to a 10 ml. Coplin jar which has been filled with distilled water.

(c) Put cultures into this and leave overnight. It should not be necessary to differentiate.

(d) Rinse in running tap water for 15 - 30 minutes.

(e) Counterstain, if desired, in 0·5 per cent. aqueous eosin Y for 0·5 to 1 minute.

(f) Rinse once in water.

(g) Dehydrate in 95 per cent. alcohol, absolute alcohol.

(h) Clear in creosote.

(i) Several changes of toluol.

(j) Mount in balsam.

4. *Results.*—Nuclei blue, cytoplasm fainter blue, or, if counterstained, red.

B. JENNER-GIEMSA STAIN

1. Rinse 15 - 20 minutes in warm balanced salt solution.

2. Fix cultures 5 minutes in absolute methyl alcohol. It is important that the alcohol be water-free.

3. Stain 5 minutes in May-Grünwald's stain (or Jenner's or Wright's).

4. Stain 10 minutes in dilute Giemsa (1 : 10 in glass distilled water).

5. Rinse quickly in glass distilled water 15 seconds to 15 minutes. Check under microscope.

6. Rapidly dehydrate in two changes of acetone and acetone-xylol (equal parts).
7. Clear in xylol and mount in DPX or Canada balsam.

III. Special histochemical stains

A. FEULGEN STAIN

1. Preparation of Feulgen reagent (Coleman, 1938).

Dissolve 1 g. basis fuchsin in 200 ml. boiling water ; filter, cool, and add 2 g. potassium metabisulphite ($K_2S_2O_5$) and 10 ml. 1 N hydrochloric acid. Let bleach for 24 hours, and then add 0·5 g. activated carbon (Norit), shake for about 1 minute and filter through coarse paper. The filtrate should be colourless.

Sulphurous acid bleach—Add 30 ml. 1 M sodium hydro-sulphite solution to 600 ml. distilled water.

2. Fixation.—1 - 3 hours in 10 per cent. neutral formalin.

3. Method of staining (for tissue cultures)

(*a*) Rinse fixative out overnight in running tap water.

(*b*) Rinse 15 minutes in 70 per cent. ethanol.

(*c*) Leave 12 minutes in 1 N HCl at 60° C.

(*d*) 1 hour in Feulgen reagent.

(*e*) 3 rinses of 5 minutes each in sodium hydrosulphite.

(*f*) Wash in distilled water, take through alcohol and xylol. Mount.

B. PERIODIC ACID SCHIFF (PAS)

Reagents

1. Periodic acid, 0·5 per cent. aqueous (of its double hydrate) in double-distilled water. Make up fresh. May be kept in refrigerator a limited time.
2. Schiff's reagent (Feulgen reagent). (See Feulgen's reagent.)
3. Sulphurous acid bleach. (See Feulgen's reagent.)

Method

1. Wash in balanced salt solution 15 minutes at 37° C.
2. Fix in methanol. Rinse in distilled water.
3. 0·5 per cent. periodic acid, 5 minutes (not longer).
4. Rinse carefully in distilled water ; several changes.
5. Schiff's reagent, 10 - 15 minutes.
6. Rinse in two changes of sulphurous acid bleach, each 3 minutes.

7. Rinse in running water, 5 minutes.
8. Counterstain with Harris haematoxylin, 20 - 30 seconds.
9. Wash in running water, 5 minutes.
10. Dehydrate and mount.

C. SUDAN BLACK B STAIN

Reagents

1. Sudan Black B, saturated solution in ethylene glycol.

Method

1. Fix in methyl alcohol.
2. Stain $\frac{1}{2}$ hour in Sudan black B (in a stoppered jar).
3. Rinse in water.
4. Rinse thoroughly in 70 per cent. ethanol.
5. Dry and mount in glycerol.

Chromosome spreading technique

The chromosomes of cultured cells are particularly easy to study and methods of preparing specimens for this purpose are of importance. Hughes and later Hsu and Pomerat, found that, if treated with hypotonic saline prior to fixation, cells which are in mitosis swell, causing the chromosomes to be separated from each other. All the chromosome spreading techniques are based on this principle. When a cell has simply been treated in this way, the chromosomes are separated in three dimensions and consequently they are found at different depths of focus when examined with a high power objective. Modifications have therefore been introduced to bring the chromosomes into the same plane of focus. In one common modification the cells are flattened after fixation and staining by applying firm pressure to the coverslip. The right amount of pressure is difficult to judge and either a machine has to be used or a considerable amount of practice has to be obtained in applying the correct amount of pressure with the thumb. The other common modification is based on the observation that if preparations are allowed to dry in air after fixation the cells collapse, presenting the chromosomes in one plane. The method of Rothfels and Siminovitch, as detailed below, is recommended.
1. The cells are grown on slides or coverslips. If it is desired to accumulate metaphases colchicine is added 6-8 hours before harvesting, to give a final concentration of 1/40,000 (w/v).

2. The slides or coverslips are transferred to warm hypotonic saline solution. (The optimum time and concentration must be determined for each cell strain. Rothfels and Siminovitch suggested 1/4 Tyrode's solution for 30 minutes. Most other authors have used 1 part Hanks' BSS plus 9 parts distilled water for periods varying from 5 to 45 minutes. Chu suggests a relatively short time, about 15 minutes, for fibroblastic cells and about 45 minutes for epithelial cells.)

3. The slides are fixed by transferring to acetic-alcohol (1 part glacial acetic acid: 3 parts ethanol) for 10 minutes.

4. They are then placed horizontal and left to dry completely at room temperature.

5. The chromosomes may be examined unstained by phase contrast microscopy or they may be stained by the Feulgen method or with aceto-orcein. The latter is the commonest method for chromosome studies.

Aceto-orcein stain.—The stain is prepared by dissolving 2 g. *natural* orcein (G. T. Gurr, London) in 100 ml. 50 per cent. glacial acetic acid. To stain the preparation a drop of stain is added to the coverslip and it is immediately mounted on a slide. It is ready for examination in a few minutes and may be preserved for some time by ranging with petroleum jelly or rubber solution to prevent evaporation. The slides may be made permanent by the method of Conger and Fairchild.

Cells in suspension may be treated similarly. First they are sedimented by centrifugation. They are then resuspended in hypotonic saline, spun again and fixed as a pellet. The pellet is dispersed in acetic-alcohol and a drop of suspension allowed to dry on a slide as in 4.

Determining the mitotic coefficient

The mitotic coefficient is the proportion of dividing cells in a population. In general it provides an index of the rate of growth of the cells, provided there is no inhibition of cell division. The latter point has to be kept in mind in interpreting results because, as is well known, colchicine arrests cell division at metaphase and consequently the mitotic index determined in cultures of this type is likely to be high although cell division has been stopped.

Fixed cultures, stained with Harris haematoxylin or Feulgen stain, or chromosome preparations prepared as above, are used.

The procedure is relatively simple. A micrometer disc is placed in a ×10 eyepiece in a microscope fitted with a mechanical stage. An area of the culture is viewed with the 8 mm. objective, the total number of cells in the field is counted and then the total number of mitoses is noted. When this has been done on a number of fields (to give about 1,000 cells), the index can be computed by dividing the number of cells in division by the total number of cells. It is often stated as a percentage value.

In studies of the effect of mitotic inhibitors on cell cultures the procedure is carried out in rather more detail, each individual phase of mitosis being noted separately. This, of course, requires considerably more skill and practice, not to mention patience.

Planimetry

In a number of studies involving the use of primary explants, the rate of migration is a useful and surprisingly reliable index of the state of health of the explants. The rate of migration can readily be determined by measuring the area covered by the culture. This is easily achieved by projecting an image of the culture on to a piece of paper and drawing it roughly. The area can then be determined by using a planimeter. Alternatively, provided the same paper is always used, relative areas can be compared by cutting them out and weighing them. Actually, in many cases where this technique is appropriate, migration is uniform in all directions from the explant and it is then adequate to measure the diameter of the explant by means of a micrometer eye piece or by means of a ruler and camera lucida.

Examination of living cells

The power of the tissue culture method lies in the opportunities it gives us to study the morphology and metabolism of living cells. The morphology of living cells can be studied either by vital staining methods or by special optical techniques.

The value of vital staining methods is very limited and the techniques are not often used now. The commonest stain employed is neutral red. The cells are exposed to a 1:10,000 solution of neutral red in BSS. This technique has some use in helping to visualise small colonies of cells during cloning. The other stains

20

occasionally employed are Janus green B which, in favourable conditions, reveals mitochondria and lithium carmine.

Supravital stains have been replaced almost entirely by the development of phase contrast microscopy and its variants. Actually, there are three special methods of microscopical examination of living cells which are commonly employed. The oldest and in some ways the best of these is dark ground observation. It has two disadvantages: it requires almost perfect material and it requires a very intense light source for photography. With the development of cell strains which grow direct on glass the ideal material is now available and with the development of the electronic flash it is no longer necessary to use an intense arc lamp to obtain photographs.

Many systems of phase contrast microscopy are available on the market and it is necessary for the individual operator to decide on the system he prefers. In tissue culture work it should be remembered that it is an advantage to have long working distances for condensers and objectives.

There are one or two practical points about the preparation of tissue cultures for examination by phase contrast microscopy. In the first place, it is essential that the preparation should be optically uniform. For this reason phase contrast microscopy cannot be used satisfactorily with a preparation mounted in the usual depression slide, in which the concave depression acts as a lens distorting the optical system. Special depression slides can be used instead, in which the well has a flat bottom. Alternatively, chambers may be made by mounting coverslips on either side of a perforated plate or by mounting the preparation on a glass, bakelite or metal ring on a plain glass slide (see Chapter I). The essential point is that all the surfaces must be parallel to each other and the space between the slide and the coverslip should be filled with fluid to render the preparation as optically homogeneous as possible.

One of the main disadvantages of phase contrast microscopy is that intracellular detail may be obscured by the formation of an intense halo round the margin of particularly dense cells. Since the halo is due to a large difference in the refractive indices of the cytoplasm and the surrounding medium it can be reduced by increasing the refractive index of the medium. This is done by adding albumen to the medium until the refractive index of cell and medium are virtually identical. The halo being absent, it is then easy to observe intracellular detail. The large albumen molecule makes little difference to the osmotic pressure of the medium. Armour's bovine albumen is suitable for this purpose.

The interference microscope is also used for qualitative studies of living cells. It is capable of giving most beautiful coloured images but this is the least important aspect of its use. Its main virtue is that it is a quantitative instrument, by means of which the mass of objects can be determined by optical methods. Thus the weight of a cell can be determined and the weights of a number of different cells can be compared. The disadvantage of even the best interference systems is that resolution is not so high as with good phase contrast optics, particularly at the highest magnifications. There are a number of interference systems available, the two best known being the Dyson system and the Baker system. The Dyson system is entirely for use as a quantitative instrument. It may be the more accurate and sensitive instrument but requires skilled handling and is difficult to use with thick preparations, such as tissue cultures in perfusion chambers. There are two modifications of the Baker system, called the shearing system and the double-focus system. Both of these are capable of giving useful quantitative information and both can be used for general morphological studies. In the shearing system the reference beam is focused in the same plane as the object but passes through a different part of the field. Thus it is particularly good for isolated single objects although it can be used effectively to study the edge of an outgrowth if attention is paid to orientation of the specimen on the microscope. It is probably more accurate than the double-focus system when these conditions are satisfied but is quite unsatisfactory otherwise. In the double-focus system the reference beam is focused in a different plane from the object so that it is less susceptible to interference by other objects in the field. As in the case of phase contrast optics, it is essential to mount the specimen in such a way that the optical pathway is uniform, and for this special slides are necessary.

Photography

The photography of living cells presents no special problems and so far as single photographs are concerned any good photomicrographic apparatus can be used in the usual way. Living cells are susceptible to infra-red and ultra-violet radiations but in taking a single exposure it is unlikely that dangerous levels of irradiation will be approached. However, if a very intense light source is used for a long time while focusing or examining the specimen these facts must be kept in mind and a green light is usually recommended as being least harmful.

Special problems of this sort become more acute when repeated photographs have to be taken over a long period of time, as in time-lapse cinemicrography. This is a particularly powerful tool in the study of cell behaviour. As its name implies, it consists of taking a cinematographic record of the behaviour of the cells at a very slow speed (usually about eight frames per minute). By projecting the film subsequently at sixteen frames per second, movements are accelerated so that their patterns become obvious. It is then possible to analyse these patterns frame by frame and express them quantitatively. Many research workers have built their own time-lapse cinemicrographic apparatus but there are a number of machines available on the market now, notably those manufactured by Zeiss-Winkel and Emdeco. The essential parts of such a machine are a timing unit which periodically operates a drive mechanism attached to the camera, a source of illumination and a warm box within which the microscope is placed. It is important to use a camera which is suitable for the purpose and the Cine-Kodak Special is particularly to be recommended. For reasonably sharp results it is essential to eliminate vibration so that a sturdily built apparatus situated on a strong foundation is desirable. For the majority of purposes it is desirable to be able to operate the microscope con-trols from outside the warm box. The author has found that the easiest way to do this is to cut holes in the sides or front of the incub-ator box and to cover these with two overlapping flaps of rubber sheet so that the hand can be inserted without opening the box. This latter consideration is important since rapid temperature fluctuations affect the behaviour of the cells. As a light source, a ribbon filament low voltage high wattage lamp with a condenser and iris diaphragm is adequate for most purposes. It is convenient to control the current flowing to this by means of a rheostat. In this way the correct illumination can be achieved rapidly. If very intense illumination is required the zirconium arc lamp promises to be useful.

PERFUSION CHAMBERS

Morphological studies of living cells can be greatly facilitated by the use of a perfusion chamber, which enables the environment to be changed at any time without opening the culture vessel or even removing it from the incubator. Essentially, a perfusion chamber consists of a special slide designed to permit fluid to flow over the culture from a reservoir outside the culture chamber itself.

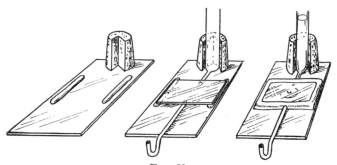

FIG. 52
Construction of a simple perfusion chamber.

A very simple perfusion chamber can be made from an ordinary $3'' \times 1''$ microscope slide. A mixture of beeswax and soft paraffin is melted in a double boiler and with a paint-brush a platform of this mixture is built up near either edge of the slide. This strip of wax should be a few millimetres wide, rather longer than the length of the coverslip to be used and about 1 millimetre deep. A fine capillary tube, with a kink in one end, is then affixed to the slide to act as an outlet tube. The reservoir is made from a piece of 3/16th" glass tubing drawn out into a capillary and turned at a right angle. This is affixed at the opposite end of the slide to the outlet tube and is supported in position by a cork with a channel cut out along one side. The culture is then placed over the trough on its coverslip and the whole chamber is sealed by means of the wax mixture. Medium may then be added to the reservoir and will pass through the culture chamber and out of the outflow tube. The finished chamber is illustrated in Figure 52.

It is quite possible to make a perfectly adequate chamber in the way described but it requires skill, experience and time to get good results and therefore if perfusion chambers are being used regularly it is advisable to use a specially made apparatus. The simplest of these is the Pomerat chamber, which is an improved version of the one described.

All chambers which rely on wax to seal them tend to be unreliable since the wax seal is liable to break at a crucial point in an experiment. A number of specially designed perfusion chambers have therefore been developed. The Rose and Richter chambers consist of a sandwich of rubber between two steel plates, with an aperture in the centre to form the culture chamber. The Rose chamber is probably the most widely used general purpose perfusion chamber. Its construction is shown in Figure 54. In use a coverslip is sandwiched between the rubber and one steel plate on one side of the chamber and another coverslip, bearing the culture, is sandwiched between the rubber and the steel plate on the other side. In this way a cavity is formed and fluid can be introduced or withdrawn by inserting hypodermic needles through the rubber into the chamber.

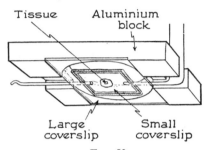

Tissue   Aluminium block

Large coverslip   Small coverslip

FIG. 53

Pomerat's perfusion chamber (from below).

A disadvantage of this type of chamber is that it is rather deep and therefore some difficulty is experienced with some optical systems. Also, insertion of the needles often results in distortion or breaking of the coverslip. The chamber designed by the author is a compromise and adopts principles employed in a number of others. As the illustration shows, it uses the system of rubber gaskets employed in the Rose chamber but it also introduces a plastic centre section. This section carries two reservoirs which are connected to the culture chamber by means of two channels running underneath it. When the chamber is assembled, these channels act as ducts. One reservoir is used for adding medium to the culture chamber and the other for removing it.

A number of more elegant chambers have been used and, in particular, the chamber designed by Buchsbaum permits carefully controlled variation in the environment from moment to moment.

Time-lapse cinemicrography

The most useful application of perfusion chambers is in time-lapse cinemicrography. Experiments are usually designed to

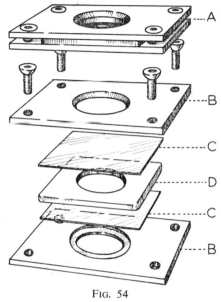

FIG. 54

The Rose chamber. The assembled chamber is shown at the top and an 'exploded' diagram underneath. A—complete chamber. B—stainless steel plates. C—glass coverslips. D—rubber gasket.

demonstrate the immediate effects of a change of environment on the morphological behaviour of the cell. Experiments must be designed with care and adequate records kept. The usual design of a perfusion experiment is as follows. First the culture is photographed for a period in a control medium to give the 'baseline'. Then, at zero time, test medium is perfused through the chamber, replacing the control medium. Subsequently, after a test period of observation, it is usually desirable to replace test medium with control medium once more and take a further record. It is necessary to emphasise the importance of the following points in carrying out such an investigation. The test medium and control medium should be identical in all respects but the substance under test. When the control medium is replaced with test medium no change of temperature must be permitted. Therefore, the medium must be heated up to the temperature of the culture beforehand (by keeping it in the incubator box) and the transfer must be carried out entirely within the incubator box. The film record must be marked (by a number of blank exposures) at each operation

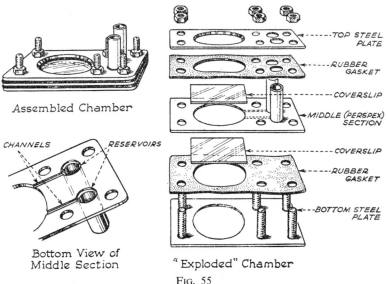

Assembled Chamber

CHANNELS   RESERVOIRS

Bottom View of
Middle Section

------TOP STEEL
        PLATE

-----RUBBER
        GASKET

------COVERSLIP

-MIDDLE (PERSPEX)
       SECTION

----COVERSLIP

----RUBBER
       GASKET

---BOTTOM STEEL
       PLATE

"Exploded" Chamber

FIG. 55
Paul's perfusion chamber.

and a strict record must be kept of each procedure. This can be done conveniently by using a record sheet of a form similar to the one in Table XXIII which is used in the author's laboratory for time-lapse cinemicrographic perfusion studies using an interference microscope.

After the film has been exposed and developed the results should be analysed. Sometimes it is adequate simply to review the happenings as demonstrated when it is projected at normal speed. However, much more information can often be derived by using the technique of frame analysis. For this purpose a film editor is usually employed. An individual frame is projected and a tracing taken of the phenomenon being investigated. The film is then advanced a number of frames, say 20, and another tracing is superimposed on the first. The analysis is continued in this way and some of the phenomena can be transposed into quantitative data by appropriate measurements.

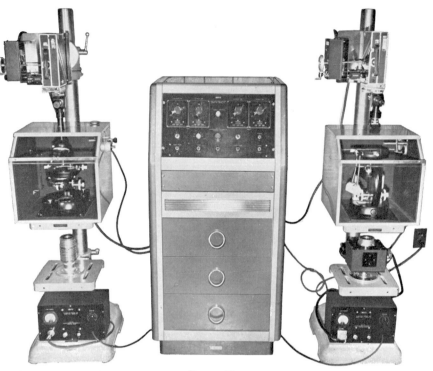

PLATE 12

Equipment for time-lapse cinemicrography (Electro-Mechanical Development Co.)

TABLE **XXIII**

TIME-LAPSE CINEMICROGRAPHY: EXPERIMENTAL RECORD SHEET

Experiment No. ....   Date................................

TISSUE CULTURE MATERIAL.

  Tissue or cell-type:

  How prepared:

  Duration of culture:

MEDIA. Control:

  Test:

OPTICS.

    Illumination: Eyepiece:
    Objective: Goniometer reading:
    Description of colours:
    Exposure meter reading:
    Diaphragm settings:

    Filters:

PHOTOGRAPHY.

    Type of film: No. of reel:
    Exposure meter readings: Frames/minute
    Footage indicator (Beginning):   (End):
    Camera Frame No.   (End):
      (Beginning):

EXPERIMENT.

  Sketch of field:

TABLE **XXIII** (*contd.*)

Time	Frame No. (Drive)	Treatment

COMMENTS ON COMPLETED FILM

File reference:

Emulsion:

Exposure:

Focus:

Illumination:

Faults other than the above:

SUMMARY OF OBSERVATIONS.

QUANTITATIVE OPTICAL METHODS

In recent years a number of methods have been developed which permit estimates of material to be made in single cells. In principle, the simplest method involves staining the cells with a specific stain (such as the Feulgen stain for DNA) and then projecting an image of the cell on to a photosensitive device. By measuring the amount of light absorbed and the area of the stained structure, the total amount of material present can be calculated. In fact, the instrumentation involved is quite complicated.

Similarly, the absorption of ultraviolet light can be measured by using a microscope with quartz lenses or a reflecting system of optics (ordinary glass absorbs ultraviolet light).

Two other techniques, based on common principles, are particularly valuable since they give absolute values for some components of the cell. These are the methods of refractometry, which can be employed with any phase contrast or interferometric microscope, and interferometry, which requires a special optical system. Refractometry simply consists of increasing the refractive index of the medium in which the cells are grown until no phase change can be recognised between the cytoplasm and the medium. The refractive index of medium and cytoplasm are then the same.

Now $n = n_s + \alpha C$ (where n is the refractive index of the solution, n_s is the refractive index of the solvent, C is the concentration of the substance in solution and α is the specific refraction increment, which is characteristic for each substance). For water n_s is 1·334 and for protoplasm a reasonable value for α is considered to be 0·0018.

Thus, if the refractive index of the medium is determined (by any refractometer—one of the pocket type used for sugars is satisfactory), it is possible to substitute the values in the equation and determine C, the result being obtained in grams per 100 ml. of solution.

Now, it is apparent that, knowing the concentration of solids in the cell, we could determine its dry mass if we knew its volume. The area can be readily determined by projection. If we have access to an interference microscope the thickness of the cell can be determined since the phase change (φ) can be established by means of it and the following relationship holds:

$$\varphi = \alpha Ct \text{ (where t is the thickness).}$$

Thus the dry mass of the cell can be determined by purely optical methods. In fact, the above information can be obtained entirely by interferometry (although possibly with somewhat less accuracy than when it is combined with refractometry). Some other calculations can also be made. Thus, if the mean specific volume for the solids of protoplasm is assumed to be the same as for protein (0·75) then the concentration of water is equal to (100−0·75 C) per cent. and the total wet mass is (100+0·25 C) g. per 100 ml. of protoplasm. Hence the density of the protoplasm is 1+C/400 (and this can be determined entirely by refractometry).

Autoradiography

The application of autoradiographic techniques to tissue cultures can provide a great deal of interesting information. The tissue culture material is exposed to a radio-actively labelled compound long enough for the substance to be incorporated. The culture is then fixed and very thoroughly washed to remove any of the original labelled compound remaining in the unbound state. The cells are then covered with a photographic emulsion and placed in the dark for some time. When the emulsion is developed the presence of radioactivity can be detected by tracks in the emulsion. The technique can be applied quantitatively. Two techniques are employed. One requires the application of a liquid emulsion to the specimen. In the other, the 'stripping film' technique, the emulsion is applied as a film on a thin layer of gelatin. The latter technique is simpler except that in order to get the emulsion to strip satisfactorily from the film it is necessary to have controlled conditions of temperature and humidity. All manipulations must be carried out in the dark-room, either in the dark or with a ruby light. The preparation is often protected first with a thin layer of nylon or celloidin (dip in a 0·25 per cent. solution in ether-alcohol). With a razor blade, a piece of stripping film, about $1'' \times 1\frac{1}{2}''$, is cut from a plate of Kodak Autoradiographic Stripping Emulsion, and floated on to a pan of water, emulsion side down. By looking along it at the light, it can be seen that the gelatin takes up water and flattens out. Immediately small drops of moisture appear on the surface (before it sinks) slip the slide bearing the specimen under the film and lift it out of the water. Place the slides aside to drain and when they are dry place them in a light-tight box. After several days' development (depending on the isotope and dosage) the films are developed in the usual way for photographic emulsions. The film may be developed *in situ* (take care it is not washed off) or the film may be restripped from the slide and developed separately. In this case it is essential to have both films and slide marked so that the film can be superimposed once more. This can be done by marking the slide with Indian ink before applying the stripping film. Some of the ink adheres when it is restripped.

Preparation of cultures for electron microscopy

Tissue cultures present certain theoretical advantages for electron microscopic study inasmuch as they present a much greater volume of the cell in one plane. Some of the original studies on animal cells were made by Porter without sectioning the cells. The cultures were grown on Formvar-coated coverslips and were mounted for electron microscopy by raising a flap of this film and slipping under it a gauze disc. The gauze disc could then be lifted out with the culture mounted on top. This technique was adequate for low-power studies but the degree of resolution is greatly limited by the thickness of the section. To improve resolution the cells have to be embedded in plastic and sectioned with the microtome. A particularly simple way of doing this was described by Howatson and Almeida. The cells are fixed with osmium vapour, dehydrated and impregnated with methacrylate. Half of a gelatin capsule of partially polymerised methacrylate is then placed over the culture and polymerisation is completed in an oven at about 50°. The resin, along with the cells, is removed from the coverglass or slide by cooling the latter with solid CO_2. After careful trimming the preparation can be sectioned with a Porter-Blum or similar microtome and photographed in the usual way. This procedure is not invariably successful and the most certain way of preparing cells for electron microscopy is to suspend them and centrifuge to form a pellet which can be fixed and sectioned in the usual way.

BIBLIOGRAPHY

AXELRAD, A. A. & McCULLOCH, E. A. (1958). Obtaining suspensions of animal cells in metaphase from cultures propagated on glass. *Stain Technol.* **33**, 67.

BAKER, R. F. & PEARSON, H. E. (1961). New embedding method for cell suspensions. *J. biophys. biochem. Cytol.* **9**, 217.

BELL, L. G. E. (1962). Microscopical examination of living cells. *Nature (Lond.)* **196**, 291.

BENNETT, A. H., JUPNIK, H., OSTERBERG, H. & RICHARDS, O. W. (1946) Phase microscopy. *Trans. Amer. micr. Soc.* **65**, 99.

BLOOM, W. (1960). Preparation of a selected cell for electron microscopy. *J. biophys. biochem. Cytol.* **7**, 191.

BOTTURA, C. & FERRARI, I. (1960). A simplified method for the study of chromosomes in man. *Nature (Lond.)* **186**, 904.

BUCHSBAUM, R. (1948). Individual cells under phase microscopy before and after fixation. *Anat. Rec.* **102**, 19.

BUCHSBAUM, R. & KUNTZ, J. A. (1954). The effects of certain stimulants and depressants on individual fibroblasts in a perfusion chamber. *Ann. N.Y. Acad. Sci.* **58**, 1303.

BURROWS, M. T. (1912). A method of furnishing a continuous supply of new medium to a tissue culture *in vitro. Anat. Rec.* **6**, 141.

CANTI, R. G. (1928). Cinematograph demonstration of living tissue cells growing *in vitro. Arch. exp. Z.* **6**, 86.

CHAMBERS, R. & FELL, HONOR B. (1931). Micro operations in cells in tissue culture. *Proc. roy. Soc.* **109**, 380.

CHU, E. H. Y., SANFORD, K. K. & EARLE, W. R. (1958). Comparative chromosomal studies on mammalian cells in culture. II. Mouse sarcoma-producing cell strains and their derivatives. *J. nat. Cancer Inst.* **21**, 729.

COMANDON, J., LEVADITI, C. & MUTERMILCH, S. (1913). Étude de la vie et de la croissance des cellules in vitro à l'aide de l'enregistrement cinématographique. *C.R. biol. Soc.* **74**, 464.

CONGER, A. D. & FAIRCHILD, L. M. (1953). A quick-freeze method for making smear slides permanent. *Stain Technol.* **28**, 281.

COONS, A. H. & KAPLAN, M. H. (1950). Localization of antigen in tissue cells. II. Improvements in a method for the detection of antigen by means of fluorescent antibody. *J. exp. Med.* **91**, 1.

COOPER, W. G. (1961). A modified plastic petri dish for cell and tissue cultures. *Proc. Soc. exp. Biol. (N.Y.)* **106**, 801.

DAVIES, H. G., WILKINS, M. H. F., CHAYEN, J. & LA COUR, L. F. (1954). The use of the interference microscope to determine dry mass in living cells and as a quantitative cytological method. *Quart. J. micr. Sci.* **95**, 271.

DAVIES, M. C. & WALLACE, R. (1958). The use of carbon films in the culture of tissue cells for electron microscopy. *J. biophys. biochem. Cytol.* **4**, 231.

DANIELLI, J. F. (1953). *Cytochemistry. A critical approach.* New York: Wiley. London: Chapman & Hall.

DANIELLI, J. F., Ed. (1958). *General cytochemical methods.* Vol. I. New York: Academic Press.

DE FONBRUNE, P. (1949). *Technique de micromanipulation.* Paris: Masson.

DICK, D. A. T. (1955). An easily made tissue culture perfusion chamber. *Quart. J. micr. Sci.* **96**, 363.

DIRSTINE, P. H., MacCALLUM, D. B., ANSON, J. H. & MOHAMMED, A. (1963). A new microscale continuous-flow system for tissue culture. *Exp. cell Res.* **30**, 426.

DONIACH, I. & PELC, S. R. (1950). Autoradiograph technique. *Brit. J. Radiol.* **23**, 184.

FORD, C. E. (1962). Methodology of chromosomal analysis in man. *Nat. Cancer Inst. Monograph No.* **7**, 105.

FORD, C. E. & HAMERTON, J. L. (1956). A cochicine, hypotonic citrate squash sequence for mammalian chromosomes. *Stain Technol.* **31**, 247.

FORD, D. K. & YERGANIAN, G. (1958). Observations on the chromosomes of Chinese hamster cells in tissue culture. *J. nat. Cancer Inst.* **21**, 393.

FREED, J. J. (1963). Cell culture perfusion chamber: adaptation for microscopy of clonal growth. *Science* **140**, 1334.

GLICK, D. (1949). *Techniques of histo- and cyto-chemistry.* New York: Interscience Publishing Co.

GOMORI, G. (1952). *Microscopic Histochemistry, Principles and Practice.* Chicago: University Press.

GORDON, G. B., MILLER, L. R. & BENSCH, K. G. (1963). Fixation of tissue culture cells for ultrastructural cytochemistry. *Exp. cell Res.* **31**, 440.

HALE, A. J. (1958). *The Interference Microscope in Biological Research.* Edinburgh: Livingstone.

HEYNER, S. (1963). *In situ* embedding of cultured cells or tissue, grown on glass, in epoxy resins for electron microscopy. *Stain Technol.* **38**, 335.

HIRUMI, H. (1963). An improved device for cultivating cells *in vitro* and for observations under high power phase magnification. *Contrib. Boyce Thompson Inst.* **22**, 113.

HOWATSON, A. F. & ALMEIDA, J. D. (1958). A method for the study of cultured cells by thin sectioning and electron microscopy. *J. biophys. biochem. Cytol.* **4**, 115.

HSU, T. C. & POMERAT, C. M. (1953). Mammalian chromosomes *in vitro*. II. A method for spreading the chromosomes of cells in tissue culture. *J. Heredity* **44**, 23.

HUGHES, A. (1952). Some effects of abnormal tonicity on dividing cells in chick tissue cultures. *Quart. J. micr. Sci.* **93**, 207.

KEMP, T. (1931). Mitosenzählung in Gewebekulturen als quantitative biologische Messmethode. Prüfung der Methode und ein Beispiel für ihre Anwendung. *Arch. exp. Z.* **11**, 591.

LEACH, K. K., SANDERS, D. C. & LEACH, F. R. (1963). A method for the preparation of permanent slides from cell culture cells grown in plastic vessels. *Exp. cell Res.* **30**, 405.

MACCALLUM, D. B. (1962). Staining and mounting *in situ* of cell monolayers grown in plastic dishes. *Stain Technol.* **37**, 129.

MAKINO, S. & NISHIMURA, I. (1951). Water-pretreatment squash technic. *Stain Technol.* **27**, 1.

MELLORS, R., KUPFER, A. & HOLLENDER, A. (1953). Quantitative cytology and cytopathology. 1. Measurement of the thickness, the volume, the hydrous mass, and the anhydrous mass of living cells by interference microscopy. *Cancer* **6**, 372.

MICOU, J., COLLINS, C. C. & CROCKER, T. T. (1962). Nuclear-cytoplasmic relationships in human cells in tissue culture. V. A method for embedding enucleate cytoplasm for electron microscopy. *J. Cell Biol.* **12**, 195.

MUNRO, T. R. (1963). An improved chamber for micromanipulation work with cell cultures, and a chamber that facilitates comparison of living and stained cells. *Exp. Cell Res.* **32**, 408.

MURRAY, MARGARET R., DE LAM, HELENA H. & CHARGAFF, E. (1951). Specific inhibition by meso-inositol of the colchicine effect on rat fibroblasts. *Exp. Cell Res.* **2**, 165.

Nowell, P. C. (1960). Differentiation of human leukemic leukocytes in tissue culture. *Exp. Cell Res.* **19**, 267.

Ogawa, K. & Okamota, M. (1961). Histochemical demonstration of succinic dehydrogenase system in tissue culture. *Tex. Rep. Biol. Med.* **19**, 134.

Overman, J. R. & Eiring, A. G. (1961). Electron microscope studies of intact epithelial and fibroblast cell cultures. *Proc. Soc. exp. Biol. (N.Y.)* **107**, 812.

Painter, R. B., McAlpine, V. W. R. & Germanis, M. (1961). The relationship of the metabolic state of deoxyribonucleic acid during x-irradiation to HeLa S-3 giant cell formation. *Rad. Res.* **14**, 653.

Paul, J. (1957). A perfusion chamber for cinemicrographic studies. *Quart. J. micr. Sci.* **98**, 279.

Pelc, S. R. & Howard, A. (1952). Techniques of autoradiography and the application of the stripping-film method to problems of nuclear metabolism. *Brit. med. Bull.* **8**, 132.

Pearse, A. G. E. (1954). *Histochemistry, theoretical and applied*. Boston: Little, Graws.

Pomerat, C. M. (1951). *Perfusion chambers. Methods in Medical Research*, Vol. 4, p. 275. Chicago: Year Book Publishers.

Pomerat, C. M., Lefeber, C. G. & Smith, McD. (1954). Quantitative ciné analysis of cell organoid activity. *Ann. N.Y. Acad. Sci.* **58**, 1311.

Porter, K. R. & Thompson, H. P. (1947). Some morphological features of cultured rat sarcoma cells as revealed by the electron microscope. *Cancer Res.* **7**, 431.

Porter, K. R., Claude, A. & Fullam, E. F. (1945). A study of tissue culture cells by electron microscopy. *J. exp. Med.* **81**, 233.

Pulvertaft, R. J. V., Haynes, J. A. & Groves, J. T. (1956). ' Perspex ' slides for roller culture of human cells. *Exp. Cell Res.* **11**, 99.

Richter, K. M. & Woodward, N. W., Jr. (1955). A versatile type of perfusion chamber for long-term maintenance and direct microscopic observation of tissues in culture. *Exp. Cell Res.* **9**, 585.

Roberts, D. C. & Trevan, D. J. (1961). XXX. A versatile microscope chamber for the study of the effects of environmental changes on living cells. *J. R. micr. Soc.* **79**, 361.

Rose, G. (1954). A separable and multi-purpose tissue culture chamber. *Tex. Rep. Biol. Med.* **12**, 1074.

Rose, G. G. (1957). Special uses of the multipurpose tissue culture chamber. *Tex. Rep. Biol. Med.* **15**, 310.

Rothfels, K. H. & Siminovitch, L. (1958). An air drying technique for flattening chromosomes in mammalian cells grown *in vitro*. *Stain Technol.* **33**, 73.

Stanfield, F. J. & Lyman, M. E. (1963). Microscopic examination of cell monolayers grown in plastic bottles. *Nature (Lond.)* **200**, 94.

Tjio, J. H. & Levan, A. (1956). The chromosome number of man. *Hereditas (Lund)* **42**, 1.

Vago, C. (1961). Cellules en matiere plastique pour cultures en gouttes pendantes et en perfusion. *Entomophaga* **6**, 265.

Wagner, B. M., Coriell, L. L., McAllister, R. M. & Shapiro, S. H. (1959). Histological and histochemical observations of tissue culture cell lines *in vivo*. *Lab. Invest.* **8**, 939.

Weathersby, A. B. & Wiseman, O. (1962). A simple and inexpensive mechanism for slow perfusion of tissue culture. *Amer. J. clin. Path.* **37**, 640.

Willmer, E. N. (1933). Studies on the growth of tissues *in vitro*. III. An analysis of the growth of chick heart fibroblasts in flask cultures in a plasma coagulum. *J. exp. Biol.* **10**, 340.

Young, M. R. (1961). Principles and technique of fluorescence microscopy. *Quart. J. micr. Sci.* **102**, 419.

CHAPTER XX

QUANTITATIVE STUDIES

IN the preceding chapter mainly qualitative morphological applications of tissue culture methods were considered. The discussion in this chapter will be concerned mainly with the application of tissue culture to quantitative studies of metabolic processes and related subjects.

The fundamental principles involved in using tissue cultures for quantitative studies are exactly the same as are involved in the use of other materials. These are as follows:

1. The experiment must be so designed that the information obtained is meaningful and unequivocal.

2. Adequate controls must be included.

3. The data obtained should be quantitatively reliable and the methods of analysis should be reproducible and accurate.

4. It should be possible to reproduce the conditions with a high degree of accuracy within the same experiment and from experiment to experiment.

5. All factors in the experiment should be constant except those under investigation.

In fact, it is impossible to achieve these conditions exactly in every experiment and in some cases it is quite difficult to approximate to them. This particularly applies to some kinds of tissue culture materials.

Nonetheless the criteria can be met in large measure by considering carefully the design of the experiment. Experimental design resolves itself into two parts, one being the selection of the proper techniques and the other the planning of the experiment so that it gives an unequivocal answer to the question asked. The first matter, the selection of techniques, can be discussed in a factual manner; there are established rules-of-thumb for most kinds of experiments. It consists mainly of applying these to the preparation of the experimental materials and the analysis of the products. It is less easy to lay down strict rules for the strategy to be employed in experiments. Here, individual flair and the demands of the problem are of major importance. Nevertheless, there are some general principles which apply to many problems and some of these will also be discussed briefly.

PREPARATION OF MATERIALS FOR QUANTITATIVE EXPERIMENTS

Much of the foregoing chapters has, of course, been concerned with this. In undertaking an experimental programme it is essential to obtain reproducibility within individual experiments and highly desirable to obtain reproducibility from one experiment to another. The first aim can usually be achieved by paying meticulous attention to the preparation of culture vessels and media and by employing the replicate culture methods outlined in Chapters XIII, XV and XVI. Nearly all of these methods depend on obtaining cells in suspension and inoculating equal amounts to different vessels. When suspension cultures are used the experiment may be commenced forthwith. When the cells normally grow as monolayers, however, it is usually necessary to give them time to adhere to the surface of the vessel and spread before commencing experimental procedures. Also, if agents, such as trypsin, have been used time may be required for the cells to recover. The time between inoculating replicate cultures and beginning an experiment (the pre-incubation period) varies with circumstances but is usually 24-72 hours, during which time there is always an opportunity for variation among cultures to develop. The degree of this variation should always be determined and the inclusion of conditions which will permit this should be an integral part of the experiment. The easiest way to do this is to analyse a sufficiently large number of samples at the end of the pre-incubation period to permit an estimate of the standard error of the estimates. Clearly it is desirable to keep the pre-incubation time as short as possible and this is determined by the time required for the cells to reach a standard state. The attachment and spreading time of different strains may vary from hours to days and this must be known if it is going to influence the experiment. Also, if metabolism is disturbed by the disaggregation treatment this should, if possible, be determined and the recovery period estimated. In setting up an experiment of this kind it is desirable to make up a very large batch of medium at the beginning so that the same medium can be used for both pre-incubation and exposure to experimental conditions.

The stages in setting up the usual kind of tissue culture experiment can, therefore, be summarised as follows, bearing in mind the qualifications already mentioned and the special requirements of each study.

Phase 1. Grow up stock cells (continuously cultured or freshly disaggregated).

Phase 2. Prepare cell suspensions. Distribute aliquots to culture vessels.

Phase 3. ' Pre-incubation '. Maintain cells in control medium until stabilised.

Phase 4. Start experiment. Take initial samples. Introduce experimental conditions.

Phase 5. Harvest experimental samples. Control and test samples must be taken simultaneously.

Obtaining reproducibility from one experiment to another is very much more difficult. Even with the best procedures it is often difficult to obtain identical results from one tissue culture experiment to another. The commonest causes of variation are, differences in media and differences in cells. To minimise differences in media an attempt should be made to assess requirements at the beginning of an experimental programme and to prepare a large enough batch of medium to last the entire series. The medium will rarely be wasted. If too much is made up (an unusual event) it can always be used for other purposes. There are two problems in adopting this policy. The first is that storage space may be inadequate. Much storage space can be saved by preparing media as powders or preferably concentrated stock solutions. The other snag is that, even if this policy is adopted, changes may take place in media during storage. To minimise this it is desirable to store materials in airtight containers at $-70°$ if the experimental series is to last more than a very few weeks.

Differences in cells present even greater problems. Even with pure cell strains two kinds of differences have to be considered, differences in genetic constitution and differences in physiological state. As has been indicated earlier, cells in culture tend to undergo genetic changes, mainly owing to rearrangement of chromosomes, and the entire character of a cell strain may change during several months of continuous culture. The only way to avoid complications arising from this source is to freeze down a sufficiently large batch

of cells at the beginning of the experiment to provide seed cultures
for renewing the stock at intervals during the experimental programme. (The method of storing cells by freezing is described in
Chapter XVIII.)

Cells in stationary and growing phases behave very differently
and may, for example, exhibit entirely different levels of some
enzymes. Hence, it is important that a cell population in one experiment should be in the same state as a population in another
experiment. In practice, it is only feasible at present to standardise
cells in the logarithmic phase of growth. To achieve this stock cultures should be in the logarithmic phase (as determined by cell
counts) when inocula are removed for setting up experiments. If
pre-incubation is required the conditions should be standardised by
prior experimentation to determine how this may be achieved.

Synchronous and parasynchronous cultures

Many questions would be more readily answered if populations
of cells could be so synchronised that all the cells within it divided
simultaneously. This ideal has not been achieved but many successful attempts have been made to obtain populations in which most
of the cells divide within one or two hours of each other. This is
called parasynchronous replication. None of the methods used is
entirely satisfactory for every application. Newton and Wildy
employed cooling to 4° for a few hours, a method which has been
successfully used for protozoa, and obtained reasonable parasynchrony. Hill and his colleagues found that refeeding a stationary
population induced a wave of parasynchrony. Paul and Hagiwara
found that when the synthesis of DNA was prevented by fluoro-
deoxyuridine and the inhibition was reversed by thymidine a wave
of DNA synthesis occurred; Rueckert and Mueller found that this
gave rise to a wave of parasynchronous division of HeLa cells. A
similar principle was used by Xeros, who found that high concentrations of thymidine prevented cell division (probably by feedback
inhibition of the formation of other deoxyribotides). When the
excess concentration of thymidine was removed a wave of parasynchrony followed. This technique has been employed rather
successfully by Bootsma and his colleagues. A different principle
was introduced by Terasima and Tolmach, who utilised the fact
that cells in metaphase round up and are readily detached from
glass. They found that populations obtained by gently shaking off

the loose cells from exponentially growing cultures subsequently divided nearly synchronously.

QUANTITATIVE CRITERIA

In any quantitative experimental approach the first essential is that methods should be available for measuring suitable parameters with precision. In many experiments the nature of the problem being investigated dictates the parameters to be studied but in cell and tissue culture work generally there are a number of criteria which are very commonly employed. They can be divided into two groups; (1) those which give an estimate of the amount of growth or survival in a cell population, and (2) those which give an assessment of the metabolism of a cell population.

All estimates of growth or survival are based on the measurement of the number of viable cells in a population. In theory the most direct estimate of viable cells is obtained by determining the proportion of individual cells in a population which can give rise to cell colonies, *i.e.* by determining the plating efficiency.

Estimation of plating efficiency

When cells are plated in Petri dishes according to Puck's dilution method of cloning (p. 236) it is rare for all the cells to give rise to individual colonies. However, the proportion that gives rise to colonies may be very constant. The plating efficiency is defined as the ratio:

$$\frac{\text{No. of colonies}}{\text{No. of cells inoculated}}$$

It is usually expressed as a percentage.

In carrying out experiments in which the plating efficiency is to be determined a suspension of cells is usually inoculated into a 50-60 mm. Petri dish. After incubating for 7-10 days to permit colonies of reasonable size to develop they are fixed and stained (*e.g.* with Jenner-Giemsa) and the number of colonies is counted. In initial experiments inocula varying from 100 to about 5,000 cells per dish are used to determine the plating efficiency of the cells in the given conditions. Subsequently, an inoculum is usually used which will yield from 50 to 200 colonies per dish. Any harmful environmental factor will lower the plating efficiency to a reproducible extent.

The great advantages of the estimation of plating efficiency as an experimental criterion are: (1) a direct and unequivocal measure of the proportion of viable cells in the population is obtained; (2) few cells are required so that only small stocks need be carried. The disadvantage is that results are not obtained for several days. Also, the technique described, although it gives highly reproducible results in capable hands, does not give a true measure of the proportion of viable cells in a population, which is usually much higher than the plating efficiency would indicate. Higher plating efficiencies can often be obtained by plating the cells in dishes seeded with irradiated cells (to form a feeder layer); the quality of the medium used and the skill of the operator also greatly affect the results. Hence, the plating efficiency must be regarded as a relative empirical parameter and not as an absolute characteristic of the cell population. Parenthetically, it may be noted that maintenance of a consistently high plating efficiency is probably the best check of quality of media and technical skill in cell culture work.

Feeder layers.—The use of feeder layers was mentioned above; these are sometimes extremely useful for cloning exacting strains. When cells are irradiated with about 2,000 r virtually none of the population will subsequently give rise to colonies although the cells will settle on glass and form giant cells which continue to metabolise. When a dish is seeded with some of these cells before, or at the same time as, it is inoculated with unirradiated cells the irradiated cells act as 'feeders' or 'nurse cells' and facilitate the survival of the unirradiated cells. This technique is based on the observation that the proportion of survivors of certain kinds of cells falls sharply when they are diluted below $1-2 \times 10^4$ cells per ml. of medium. The density of the feeder layer is, therefore, very important. If too dense there is competition for the available glass surface. If not dense enough the feeder effect is not exercised. For a 50 mm. Petri dish containing about 5 ml. of medium $1-3 \times 10^5$ cells is usually suitable.

Very often it is desirable to have a quicker and less cumbersome method for measuring cell growth and viability. Direct cell counts and viability counts based on dye exclusion are then used.

Estimation of the cell number

This can be done directly or indirectly. Direct determination is done by enumeration of the cell number by means of a haemocytometer or electronic counter while indirect determination is done by measurement of the packed cell volume, dry or wet weight or some cellular constituent, such as protein or deoxyribonucleic acid.

Cell counting with a haemocytometer

Many cells can be counted easily and accurately after suspension by trypsinisation, either direct or after staining.

METHOD.—

1. Moisten the supporting ridges of a haemocytometer chamber and apply the coverslip, pressing firmly so that Newton's rings appear.
2. Mix the cells in suspension by pipetting them up and down and then very quickly transfer a drop to the haemocytometer chamber. (Tissue culture cells sediment out very rapidly, giving rise to gross errors.)
3. Using the 16 mm. objective focus on a large square (which should fill the field and consists of 16 smaller squares). Count all the cells in the square omitting those on the top and left-hand lines but including those on the lower and right-hand lines.
4. Count four such squares, take the mean and multiply by 10,000. This gives the number of cells per ml.

For precise results it is necessary to count at least 1,000 cells. All the cells in a clump should be counted but if there are many clumps or if the variation between individual counts is considerable, the counts cannot be regarded as reliable and the whole procedure should be repeated until reliable results are obtained.

Sometimes, especially for the untrained observer, it is difficult to distinguish cells from other material which may be present. If the cells are stained this is made much easier. The staining solution consists of 0·1 per cent. crystal violet in 0·1 M citric acid. An exactly threefold dilution of the cell suspension is made in this staining solution and the count is performed as before, the results being multiplied by 3.

In the author's experience, accurate counts can be obtained by the above methods provided the cells are evenly dispersed and care is taken to prevent sedimentation. Some authorities advocate nuclear counting as being more accurate. This procedure is somewhat more complicated than the above. The medium is first removed from the cells and they are then treated with 0·1 M citric acid for an hour at 37°. The nuclei are separated from the cyto-plasm at the end of this time either by vigorous shaking or by gentle treatment in a Potter homogeniser. They are separated from the supernatant by centrifuging at 1,100 g. for 20 minutes and again suspended in the crystal violet counting fluid described above. The suspension is counted in the same manner.

In all the above procedures the cell suspensions should be diluted to give about 500,000 cells or nuclei per ml. before counting. With experience the operator knows roughly how many cells are likely to be in a culture. Otherwise it is best to use a more concentrated suspension and then to dilute it if the count is found to be too high.

The procedure has been described for the usual blood cell haemocytometer but the Fuchs-Rosenthal chamber is preferable in my opinion. Of course, the calculation has to be modified if it is used.

Electronic cell counters

The recent development of electronic machines for particle counting has greatly facilitated the quantitation of cell culture. Not only do these machines enable counts to be performed much more quickly (about 2 minutes as against twenty minutes for a single count) but their accuracy is very much higher than can be attained by means of a haemocytometer, even in the hands of the most skilful individual. They are rather expensive and are not therefore available in all laboratories but where access to one can be obtained they are invaluable. In the author's opinion the most satisfactory machine of this kind for ordinary cell counting is the Coulter or similar type. In this machine a suspension of cells is sucked through a minute hole in a glass tube. One electrode is placed within the tube and another outside it in the suspension. The passage of a particle through the hole temporarily interrupts the current and the number of interruptions is added up by means of a conventional scaling unit. Before being counted the cells must be obtained in suspension. Cells which already grow in suspension may merely be diluted as required with a suitable diluting solution. One which we have found completely satisfactory consists of 7 g. NaCl, 10·5 g. citric acid and 1 ml. 40 per cent. formalin made up to

1 litre with water. The counting fluid must be filtered through sintered glass to remove all particulate matter. When cells are growing as a monolayer on glass it is essential to remove them completely and to obtain them as a unicellular suspension. We have found that a suitable procedure consists of removing the medium and washing the cells once with calcium and magnesium-free salt solution, followed by digestion with a solution consisting of 0·25 per cent. trypsin in a saline-citrate buffer made up by dissolving 6·0 g. sodium chloride, 3·0 g. sodium citrate and 0·02 g. phenol red in 1 litre of distilled water. The pH should be about 7·6 but if it is very different from this it should be carefully adjusted to this value.

Electronic cell counters do not distinguish between living and dead cells nor, normally, between single cells and clumps. It is therefore essential in using an electronic counter to *examine the cell preparation microscopically before counting*. It is also essential to use scrupulously clean glassware and to ensure that all solutions are free of suspended particles which might give spurious counts. Harris has found that electronic counters give a consistently higher count than is obtained by means of a haemocytometer. An appropriate correction may be made if required and the possibility of such an inconsistency should always be borne in mind.

Packed cell volume

Where large amounts of tissue are being handled it is possible to get a rough idea of the cell number by measuring the volume of packed cells sedimented under standard conditions of centrifugation in a standard haematocrit tube. The technique has been successfully used by Waymouth. It may be noted that a very much cruder estimate of total cell number can be made by a practised observer from the size of the pellet of sedimented cells in the centrifuge tube during ordinary transfer.

Waymouth uses Van Allen haematocrits, pretreated with silicone, and suspends the cells by trypsinisation before transferring them to the tube. This is spun at 2,800 r.p.m. for 30 minutes in an International centrifuge eight-place head before taking the reading on the graduated stem.

Wet weight and dry weight determinations

Except in a few special investigations these methods have little to recommend them, being tedious and insensitive. As a basis for chemical determinations, the most satisfactory criteria are either the deoxyribonucleic acid (DNA) or protein nitrogen (PN) values. There are many ways of determining these, but the methods described are particularly easy and require the minimum of skill. For a more complete analysis of small samples of tissue see the paper by Paul (1958).

Determination of deoxyribonucleic acid (DNA)

The two most convenient methods are the indole and diphenyl-amine methods. The indole method is quicker and more sensitive but the diphenylamine method is, on the whole, more reliable and gives rise to fewer errors.

Determination of DNA by the indole method

REAGENTS.—

1. N perchloric acid.
2. 0·04 per cent. indole (dissolved by warming).
3. Concentrated hydrochloric acid.
4. Chloroform.
5. DNA standard solution, containing about 1 μg DNA phosphorus per ml., dissolved in N perchloric acid by warming.

PROCEDURE.—Obtain the cells in suspension and centrifuge. Discard the medium and add 2 ml. N perchloric acid. Mix the cells in the perchloric acid and place in a water-bath at 70° for 20 minutes. At the end of this time centrifuge and collect the supernatant. Repeat this extraction with warm perchloric acid. Combine the supernatants and, after mixing, transfer 2 ml. to a boiling tube. Add 1 ml. of concentrated hydrochloric acid and 1 ml. indole solution. Place in boiling water bath for 10 minutes. Cool and extract the reaction mixture three times with 4 ml. chloroform each time, discarding the chloroform (heavier) layers. Centrifuge the tube briefly at slow speed to clear any emulsion that may have formed and measure the density of the aqueous layer in a photometer at 490 mμ.

Determination of DNA by the diphenylamine method

REAGENTS.—

1. Diphenylamine reagent. Add 1·5 ml. of diphenylamine (twice recrystallised from 70 per cent. ethanol) and 1·5 ml. concentrated sulphuric acid (reagent grade) to 100 ml. redistilled glacial acetic acid. This reagent can be stored in the refrigerator.

2. Redistilled acetaldehyde (Reagent grade).

3. Standard solution of deoxyribose, containing 20 μg./ml. N perchloric acid.

PROCEDURE.—Prepare the working reagent on the day of use by adding 0·1 ml. acetaldehyde to 20 ml. diphenylamine reagent. If a blue colour develops the diphenylamine reagent must be made up afresh with newly redistilled glacial acetic acid. If the reagent is satisfactory prepare an extract by harvesting and washing the cells and extracting twice with 1 ml. N perchloric acid at 70° C. After each extraction centrifuge and combine the supernatants. To 2 ml. of working reagent in a test-tube add 1 ml. of test solution, containing 50-500 μg. DNA. Incubate at 30° for 16-20 hours and measure the optical density of the blue solutions at 600 mμ. (Note— 20 μg. deoxyribose≡124 μg. DNA.)

Determination of protein

In many biochemical and kinetic studies it is necessary to determine the total protein in a sample. All methods have their difficulties. The most reliable general method is the determination of protein nitrogen, and the easiest way to do this is by Nesslerisation. Unfortunately, the method requires a preliminary digestion and is tedious. For this reason more arbitrary but more convenient methods are often used. The commonest method in current use for tissue culture material is the Lowry method, which is, however, not wholly reliable. The reaction is linear over a small range and depends on an average distribution of aromatic amino acids in the proteins measured. The bromsulphalein method depends on dye-binding by protein and is therefore very empirical. On the other hand it is highly reproducible, very sensitive and very simple to carry out. In the author's opinion it merits more extensive use.

Determination of protein nitrogen by Nessler's reagent

REAGENTS.—

1. Digestion mixture. 1 g. selenium dioxide in 18 N (50 per cent.) sulphuric acid.
2. Nessler's reagent (modified). 4 g. KI and 4 g. HgI_2 are dissolved in 25 ml. water. 3·5 g. gum acacia is dissolved in 750 ml. warm water. The solutions are combined and made up to 1 litre with water.
3. 2 N NaOH.
4. Ammonium sulphate standard, containing 10 µg. N_2/ml.

PROCEDURE.—Add 1 ml. of digestion mixture to the specimen. By simmering gently in a digestion apparatus reduce the volume and then digest with strong heat until the solution is clear. (An anti-bumping device is required.) Dilute the digestion mixture with water so that it contains about 10 µg./ml. N_2. To 2 ml. of this add 2ml. Nessler's reagent and 3 ml. 2 N NaOH. After 15 minutes read the optical density at 490 mµ.

(Note.—Unless protein has been separated from other tissue components this method gives total nitrogen which includes e.g. nucleic acid nitrogen.)

Determination of protein by the Lowry method

REAGENTS.—

1. Mix together 0·5 ml. 1 per cent. $CuSO_4·5H_2O$ and 0·5 ml. 2 per cent. potassium tartrate. Add slowly with stirring to 50 ml. of 2 per cent. Na_2CO_3 in 0·1 N NaOH. (Reagent A.)
2. Folin-Ciocalteau reagent, 4 ml. diluted to 10 ml. with water.
3. Standard crystalline bovine serum albumin, 0·5 mg./ml.

PROCEDURE.—The tissue is taken up in N NaOH and the sample diluted to contain 0·5-1 mg. protein per ml. To 3 ml. reagent A 0·2 ml. of the diluted sample is added. After mixing this is left at room temperature for 10 minutes and 0·3 ml. of diluted Folin-Ciocalteau reagent is added, taking care to ensure good mixing. After one hour the optical intensity of the blue colour is read at 750 mµ.

Determination of protein by bromsulphalein

REAGENTS.—

1. *Bromsulphalein reagent.* 1 ml. 5 per cent. bromsulphalein, 100 ml. N HCl and 50 ml. M citric acid made up to 250 ml. with distilled water.
2. N NaOH.
3. 0·1 N NaOH.

PROCEDURE.—A sample of tissue containing 10 to 100 µg. protein is freed of medium by centrifugation and washed with BSS (not containing phenol red). 0·4 ml. *N* NaOH is added and the sample is incubated for one hour at 37° C. To the extract is added 1 ml. bromsulphalein reagent. After thorough mixing the tube is centrifuged. 0·5 ml. of the supernatant is transferred to a tube containing 7 ml. 0·1 *N* NaOH. After mixing the optical density is read at 580 mµ. The decrease in optical density from the control reading is proportional to the amount of protein.

Determination of cell viability

It is often valuable and sometimes essential to be able to estimate the proportion of cells in a culture that are actually alive. In theory, the best way to do this is to determine the plating efficiency, *i.e.* the proportion of cells able to form colonies. In practice, this method is not completely reliable since many factors besides viability may determine whether cells are capable of forming colonies. For instance, it is difficult to grow colonies from single cells of certain strains and yet it can be shown readily by the incorporation of labelled metabolites and the growth characteristics of the culture that the vast majority of the cells are healthy and viable.

Many other procedures have been suggested, *e.g.* the ability to incorporate radioactive thymidine into DNA as shown by autoradiography, the ability of fixed cells to take up nuclear stains. However, the most convenient techniques are based on the observation that the surface membrane of living cells is able selectively to exclude certain substances whereas dead cells permit these substances to enter easily. By using dyes it becomes very simple to distinguish permeable cells.

In earlier studies involving bacteria, yeasts and later ascites cells, the dyes used were trypan blue, safronin, erythrosin and eosin. In cell cultures Phillips and Terryberry showed that erythrosin B, added to medium or BSS at a concentration of 20 mg. per 100 ml. would stain dead cells but not living ones and would not affect the respiration of the non-staining cells. Hanks and Wallace later showed that eosin Y at a concentration of 150 mg. per 100 ml. could be used similarly and that the cells were capable of growth afterwards.

After investigating a large number of compounds Kaltenbach *et al.* came to the conclusion that the best dye for this purpose was nigrosin, at a concentration of 20-50 mg. in 100 ml. BSS or medium. They developed this technique for use with ascites tumour cells but it is equally useful for cultured cells. A satisfactory system is as follows.

A stock solution of 50 mg. nigrosin in 100 ml. BSS is used. A suspension of cells is diluted 1/10 with the counting fluid in a white-cell blood pipette. A drop of this stained suspension is placed on a slide and covered with a coverslip (it is desirable to use a haemocytometer chamber). After 5-10 minutes the total number of cells and the number of dead (staining) ones are counted in several fields. The viability is calculated by the formula:

$$\frac{(\text{Total cells} - \text{dead cells})}{\text{Total cells}} \times 100\%$$

Metabolic studies

Metabolic parameters have sometimes been used as general criteria of viability in a cell population. In particular the respiratory rate, rate of glucose utilisation, rate of uptake of metabolites and rate of synthesis of proteins and nucleic acids have all been proposed as measurements of 'growth'. It is abundantly clear that neither the growth rate nor the viability of cells need be related directly to any of these and should not be used except as a crude index (as in the metabolic inhibition test, p. 352). On the other hand, many exceedingly valuable studies have been made of metabolic processes in cultured cells, in which questions of a different nature have been asked. These involve some special technical considerations which it is appropriate to mention here.

Harvesting cells for metabolic studies

In terminating metabolic experiments two objectives have usually to be kept in mind. (1) The metabolic process should be stopped as quickly as possible, so that timing can be precise. (2) Terminating the process should not introduce any artefact *e.g.* by removing or altering the products. In many cell culture experiments there is some difficulty in meeting these requirements. For example, if cells are dispersed in a large volume of protein-containing medium it sometimes presents a problem to stop a reaction precisely since centrifugation and cooling both take time while additions to the medium may introduce artefacts. For this reason it is sometimes preferable, despite the obvious advantages of suspension cultures, to use cells grown on a surface from which the medium can be removed immediately by decantation.

Nevertheless, suspension cultures are of great advantage in many studies, especially when the cells are to be analysed. Two methods of fairly rapid harvesting can be used. Most commonly cells are separated from their medium by centrifugation. If balanced, cooled tubes are prepared in advance this can be done very quickly since only two or three minutes centrifugation at 1,000 to 2,000 g. are required. Occasionally, if a small number of cells is to be harvested from suspension filtration may be effective. Millipore filters are used but they quickly become clogged by cells and therefore this technique is rather limited in its application.

When cells are grown as monolayers part of the chemical fractionation procedure may sometimes be carried out *in situ*. For example, after pouring off the medium and washing quickly with BSS, a protein precipitant, such as trichloroacetic acid may be added directly to the cell layer. This will extract the ' acid-soluble ' material. Other extractions can be carried out similarly and this technique is sometimes useful although it has the disadvantage that rather large volumes are required. In many experiments, where the medium and easily extractable tissue components are required for analysis a procedure of this kind is most convenient. In a great many experiments, however, it is necessary to harvest the cells. This is usually done either by scraping or trypsinisation. Both of these procedures obviously involve the hazard of leaching material from the cells. The technique we have found most generally useful is as follows. At the termination of the experiment the medium is poured off and the vessel is immediately placed on crushed ice. A suitable volume of ice-cold BSS is added to the vessel, gently swirled around and poured off. This washing can be repeated as often as desired. Finally a rather small amount of BSS is added to the vessel and the cell sheet is scraped off with a ' policeman ' (which can be made by fitting a piece of rubber or silicone tubing tightly over a glass rod bent in such a way that a large part of it can be drawn flat across the surface of the sheet). The suspended cells are transferred to a centrifuge tube by pipette, a little more BSS is added to the vessel and this washing is added to the suspension. A protein precipitant may be added before or after centrifugation. It is difficult to obtain a quantitative yield by this procedure. This is often unimportant but if a quantitative yield (*e.g.* for cell counting or DNA determination) is required it is usually necessary to resort to trypsinisation, which is carried out in exactly the way described in Chapter XV. Apart from the time involved in the process trypsinisation carries the risk of elution of material, particularly proteins and small molecules, from the cells. The method of choice will clearly depend on the information sought.

EXPERIMENTAL DESIGN

The object of designing an experiment should be to provide an answer to a specific question. Thus, much of the work of designing experiments consists in posing the correct questions in the correct manner. Questions are usually posed so as to test a ' null hypothesis '. That is to say, one assumes that if two test objects are treated differently they will respond in the same way (the null hypothesis—nothing will happen). If they respond differently then the null hypothesis is void and the observation is significant.

The design of the experiment depends on the information sought, the material available and the reproducibility of experimental conditions. Assuming that experimental conditions are perfectly controlled and the response to be elicited is very great, then the simplest experimental design of all involves the use of only two samples, one of which is subjected to the test stimulus and the other of which is not, other factors remaining constant. Then any change observed in the test specimen which does not occur in the control can be attributed to the test stimulus. In planning an experiment based on such a principle, it is essential that the samples should behave in an identical fashion. Attempts to obtain such conditions have been made with the simplest primary explant techniques by using two halves of the same explant as test and control respectively. In practice, cultures are first set up in roller tubes and when they have grown well they are harvested and halved. The two halves are transplanted to coverslips and one is subsequently used as a control specimen, the other being used for the test.

It is immediately obvious that in no tissue culture experiment could one rely on a single experiment of this sort even if the control explant were seen to flourish while the test explant died. Therefore one must perform more experiments, either at successive dates or simultaneously. It is not always practicable to perform many complicated experiments simultaneously but where this can be done it is desirable since it then becomes possible to determine statistically the amount of the random variation between tests and controls and whether the differences between the two groups are significant. The standard error is derived from a simple formula $(s = \sqrt{\frac{\Sigma x^2}{(n-1)}}$ where $x =$ deviations from the mean and $n =$ number of observations) and the two groups are readily compared by applying Student's t test. In performing an experiment of this kind it is necessary to include as many cultures in the control group as in the test group and in giving the results it is essential to mention the number of observations on which the conclusion is based. Frequently one wishes to investigate several concentrations of one factor rather than a single concentration. This again could conceivably be done, one concentration at a time, over a period. But it is much more reliable and much more economical to investigate as many concentrations as possible at one time.

At this point the question arises: how many cultures should there be within a group. The answer is simply that there should be sufficient cultures to give a positive answer to the question being asked. Obviously (except in rare cases) a single determination has little value by itself since we do not know to what extent experimental error affects the results. Duplicates are not much more useful except that when they agree they reinforce each other. Errors are, however, not recognisable. Three samples provide us with rather more evidence of the true result since there is a definite tendency to weight out errors. The factors which will dictate the numbers of determinations needed in a group are the reproducibility of results and the magnitude of the effect being measured. There is no convenient rule of thumb.

The above considerations lead us to the simplest type of titration experiment which will be illustrated by describing the determination of the toxicity of an antibiotic for a cell strain.

Titration of toxicity by serial dilution

This type of experiment is one of the most commonly used. It will be illustrated by an experiment to determine the toxicity

22

of chloramphenicol for HeLa cells but the same general principle is used for titrating viruses and all kinds of physiological and pharmacological effects.

1. Materials required:

HeLa cells (at least 3×10^6).

150 ml. Eagle's medium containing 5 per cent. calf serum (medium A).

Sterile test-tubes and stoppers ($6'' \times \frac{5}{8}''$).

Sterile graduated pipettes, bottles and universal containers.

Chloramphenicol.

2. Test media. Make up a sterile stock solution containing 10 mg. chloramphenicol/ml. medium A. Add 9 ml. of medium A to each of seven sterile test tubes. To the first tube add 1 ml. of chloramphenicol stock solution (to give a solution containing 1 mg./ml.) and mix. Remove 1 ml. of this solution and add it to the second tube (to give a solution of 0·1 mg./ml.) and mix. Transfer 1 ml. from this tube to the third tube and so on, repeating these 1/10 dilutions down to the last tube so that the seven tubes will then contain respectively 1, 10^{-1}, 10^{-2}, 10^{-3}, 10^{-4}, 10^{-5}, 10^{-6} mg./ml. chloramphenicol dissolved in medium. Add 10 ml. or so of medium to an eighth tube (to be used for control cultures).

3. Experiment. Day 1. Trypsinise and count the stock HeLa cells. Suspend $3·5 \times 10^6$ cells in 70 ml. medium A. With care to maintain an even suspension of cells throughout, transfer 2 ml. of this suspension to each of 30 test-tubes. Stopper and incubate as stationary cultures at an angle of about 10° in a 37° C. incubator. (30 replicate cultures, each with 10^5 cells in 2 ml. medium are thus obtained.)

Day 2. Examine the cultures with the inverted microscope. If any are clearly unsuitable reject them. If more than three are unsuitable repeat the experiment. Number the remaining cultures. Nos. 1-24 will be used for the remainder of the experiment. Numbers above 24 are used as initial samples and are harvested now and analysed.

Unstopper all the cultures. Remove the medium (by pipetting or decantation). Replace with the test media, adding 2 ml. of each medium to each of three tubes as follows:

Tube Nos.	1-3	4-6	7-9	10-12	13-15	16-18	19-21	22-24
Chloram-phenicol concn. (mg./ml.)	0	1	10^{-1}	10^{-2}	10^{-3}	10^{-4}	10^{-5}	10^{-6}

Day 5. Harvest and analyse the cultures.

4. Analysis. (a) In many experiments of this kind it is adequate to examine the test-tubes microscopically. Two values can be determined—the lowest concentration of chloramphenicol at which damage first becomes apparent and the lowest concentration at which cells are killed. Assessment of both these points is facilitated by using a viability stain (p. 353).

(b) A more precise assessment can be obtained by determining the amount of cell growth. The medium is decanted from the cultures. They are washed twice with BSS and 0·5 ml. of trypsin in citrate (p. 228) is added. The cells may then be counted directly in a Coulter counter after adding diluting fluid or they may be centrifuged down and the DNA or protein content of the tubes determined by one of the methods described. Whichever method is employed the increment is calculated by the formula

$$\frac{T-I}{I}$$

Where T is the value for the test culture and I is the mean value for the initial cultures. The levels of the drug initiating depression of growth and also those causing complete inhibition can be determined as before. Alternatively the concentration causing a 50 per cent. depression of growth may be calculated by the method of Reed and Muench (p. 352).

This type of experiment can be modified in many ways. One commonly used variation is the metabolic inhibition test for the titration of viruses. The principle of the test is exactly the same as above except that the criterion of cell survival or cell death is simply whether the pH of the medium has changed as shown by the colour of the phenol red indicator. If cells are not killed acid metabolites are produced and the medium turns yellow. If cells are killed the medium remains pink. As in most virus titrations two- or three-fold serial dilutions of virus are usually made. In practice special plastic plates are used for this test, having a large number of small wells with a capacity of about 2 ml. Each well is inoculated with

0·5 ml. of a suspension containing about 3×10^5 cells per ml. in a suitable medium. Serial dilutions of virus are prepared in Hanks' BSS and 0·5 ml. of each dilution is added to a well. The cultures are then sealed by layering 0·5 ml. of sterile liquid paraffin on top of each. The plates can be read in 5-8 days. Appropriate controls, from which cells or virus have been omitted should, of course, be included. The results are usually assessed by the method of Reed and Muench as described in the next chapter.

Clearly this type of experimental design can be adapted to many other techniques and, for instance, it is particularly suitable to use the plating efficiency of a cell strain as the criterion of survival. The migration of cells from primary cultures, the appearance of altered cell colonies or alteration of a metabolic parameter can all be measured against factors titrated in this way.

Another point may have become apparent on considering the above experimental design. The response of tissues to test materials frequently follows a definite mathematical relationship in that very often the response is proportional to the logarithm of the dose applied (log. dose response curve). Where experimental observations can fit into a linear relationship of this sort, it is obvious that fewer replicates at a given concentration of test substance are required since the general trend of the line acts as a check on the accuracy of the individual results. Thus, in the experiment described above, better precision in defining this relationship might have been obtained by using single estimates at 24 different concentrations of chloramphenicol provided that the correct statistical analysis was applied to the results. The treatment for the analysis of regression of this sort can be found in any statistical textbook.

Yet another conclusion can be drawn from this type of experimental design. Instead of using the same drug at a number of different concentrations along with the same controls, one could have used the same controls and a number of tests on different drugs. This would have had the advantage that they were all tested in identical conditions and therefore a comparison of the effects of this basis would have more weight.

A particularly interesting example of the use of a linear relationship between response and treatment is commonly used in radiobiological studies. It has applications in other fields also. In this test the proportion of surviving individuals is determined after an experimental treatment and this is plotted on a logarithmic scale against the dose on an arithmetic scale.

Determination of the absorbed mean lethal dose of X-rays for HeLa cells

The absorbed mean lethal dose of irradiation means that dose of absorbed radiation which permits the survival of 37 per cent. (logarithmic mean, $1/e$) of irradiated cells. The criterion of survival is the capacity to form colonies from single cells.

1. Materials. A rapidly growing culture of HeLa S3 cells (or other cells with known high plating efficiency).

   One hundred ml. medium (*e.g.* medium 109 with 10 per cent. calf serum).

   Sixteen 50 mm. polystyrene tissue culture Petri dishes.

   CO_2 incubator.

   X-irradiation source.

2. Procedure. Trypsinise the cells as described on page 228 and add 5,000 cells to 100 ml. medium (to give 50 cells per ml.). Distribute 5 ml. of cell suspension to each dish (*i.e.* 250 cells per dish). Irradiate as follows:

Dish No.	1,2	3,4	5,6	7,8	9,10	11,12	13,14	15,16
rads	0	25	50	100	200	300	400	600

   Immediately place the cultures in the CO_2 incubator and leave to incubate. (During irradiation precautions may have to be taken to prevent the medium from becoming too alkaline.)

3. Analysis. After 7-10 days remove the cultures. Fix and stain (Jenner-Giemsa). Count the colonies in each dish and in each case calculate the ratio n/n_0, where n is the actual number of colonies found and n_0 is the number of colonies expected in the absence of irradiation (*i.e.* the number found in the control cultures). A colony is disregarded if it has less than ten cells. Using semilogarithmic paper plot the values for n/n_0 on the logarithmic scale on the ordinate and the values for D (dosage in rads) on the arithmetic scale on the abscissa. As shown in Figure 56 a straight line is obtained which deviates as it approaches the ordinate. When the line is extrapolated in a straight line it intercepts the ordinate at a value in excess of 1. The dose corresponding to a value of $n/n_0 = 0.37$ is the absorbed mean lethal dose (D_0). For most mammalian cells irradiated in air the value is about 130 rads.

(A radiobiologist should be consulted about the calculation of irradiation dosage.)

Further complications in experimental design beyond this extremely simple treatment do not have a place in this textbook but mention must be made of the value of factorial design. It is sometimes stated that there should be only one variable in an

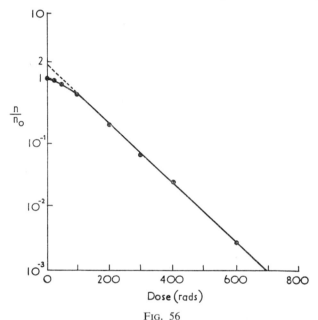

Fig. 56

The surviving fraction of a cell population plotted against the dose of X-irradiation.

experiment at any one time. However, frequently much more information can be obtained by introducing several variables simultaneously since, in this way, information can be obtained not only about the action of the individual test substances but about interaction between them.

In all the experimental designs discussed so far it has been assumed that the experimental treatment is to be applied for the same time in all cases. Sometimes, however, it is desirable to follow the course of a reaction over a period of time. Thus one might wish to follow the course of a metabolic reaction in cells at periods of time after exposure to a high temperature. In design-ing such an experiment, the following considerations have to be kept in mind. In the first place, control specimens must be removed at the same times as test specimens. In effect, this means that as many controls as tests are required (unless there are several differently treated groups within each time group, when one group of controls will suffice for each of the latter). The other point is similar to one which was mentioned before. In constructing regression relationships with time, better results will be obtained by taking single samples at short intervals than by taking several samples at longer intervals.

There are many other ways of designing experiments to give meaningful results. Those which have been outlined, along with some described in the next chapter, are the ones which have been most commonly used. Before embarking on an experimental problem involving these considerations it is well worth while consulting a statistician.

BIBLIOGRAPHY

BASES, R. E. (1959). Some applications of tissue culture methods to radiation research. *Cancer Res.* **19**, 311.

BONTING, S. L. & JONES, M. (1957). Determination of microgram quantities of deoxyribonucleic acid and protein in tissues grown *in vitro*. *Arch. Biochem.* **66**, 340.

BOOTSMA, D., BUDKE, L. & VOS, O. (1964). Studies on synchronous division of tissue culture cells initiated by excess thymidine. *Exp. Cell Res.* **33**, 301.

BRUES, A. M. & STROUD, A. N. (1951). Action of physical agents on living cells. Radioactive tracers in tissue culture. In *Methods in Medical Research*. Ed. Visscher, M. B. Chicago: Year Book Publishers.

CERIOTTI, G. (1955). A microchemical determination of DNA. *J. biol. Chem.* **195**, 297.

DANES, BETTY S., CHRISTIANSEN, G. S. & LEINFELDER, P. J. (1953). A Cartesian diver balance-capillary respirometer for metabolic studies of tissue cultures. *Exp. Cell Res.* **5**, 234.

DAVIDSON, J. N., LESLIE, I. & WAYMOUTH, CHARITY (1949). The nucleoprotein content of fibroblasts growing *in vitro*. 4. Changes in the ribonucleic acid phosphorus (RNAP) and deoxyribonucleic acid phosphorus (DNAP) content. *Biochem. J.* **44**, 5.

EARLE, W. R., SANFORD, K. K. & EVANS, V. J. (1951). General methods for quantitative studies on cells in tissue culture. In *Methods in Medical Research*. Chicago: Year Book Publishers, Inc.

EHRMANN, R. L. & GEY, G. O. (1953). The use of cell colonies on glass for evaluating nutrition and growth in roller tube cultures. *J. nat. Cancer Inst.* **13**, 1099.

ENGELBERG, J. (1961). A method of measuring the degree of synchronization of cell populations. *Exp. Cell Res.* **23**, 218.

EVANS, VIRGINIA K., EARLE, W. R., SANFORD, KATHERINE K., SHANNON, J. E. & WALTZ, HELEN K. (1951). The preparation and handling of replicate tissue cultures for quantitative studies. *J. nat. Cancer Inst.* **11**, 907.

FISHER, R. A. (1951). *The Design of Experiments,* 6th ed. Edinburgh: Oliver & Boyd.

HANKS, J. H. & WALLACE, J. H. (1958). Determination of cell viability. *Proc. Soc. Exp. Biol. (N.Y.).* **98,** 188.

HARRIS, H. (1955). Some quantitative studies on the multiplication of connective tissue cells *in vitro. Brit. J. exp. Path.* **36,** 115.

HARRIS, M. (1957). Quantitative growth studies with chick myoblasts in glass substrate cultures. *Growth* **21,** 149.

HARRIS, M. (1959). Growth measurements on monolayer cultures with an electronic cell counter. *Cancer Res.* **19,** 1020.

HEALY, G. M., FISHER, DOROTHY C. & PARKER, R. C. (1954). Nutrition of animal cells in tissue culture. VIII. Desoxyribonucleic acid phosphorus as a measure of cell multiplication in replicate cultures. *Canad. J. Biochem.* **32,** 319.

HILL, R. B., BENSCH, K. G., SIMBONIS, S. & KING, D. W. (1959). Variability of content of deoxyribonucleic acid in L-strain fibroblasts. *Nature (Lond.)* **183,** 1818.

HULLIN, R. P. & NOBLE, R. L. (1953). The determination of lactic acid in microgram quantities. *Biochem. J.* **55,** 289.

JACQUEZ, J. A. (1962). Tissue culture screening. *Cancer Res.* **22,** 81.

JACQUEZ, J. & MOTTRAM, F. (1953). Tissue culture screening of amino acid analogs for selective damage to mouse sarcoma cells. *Cancer Res.* **13,** 605.

KALTENBACH, J. P., KALTENBACH, M. H. & LYONS, W. B. (1958). Nigrosin as a dye for differentiating live and dead ascites cells. *Exp. Cell Res.* **15,** 112.

KATSUTA, H. & TAKAOKA, T. (1962). Synchronous cultivation of a substrain of L cells (mouse fibroblasts) in a protein-free medium. *Jap. J. exp. Med.* **32,** 279.

LEVINE, S. (1960). Effect of manipulation on ^{32}P loss from tissue culture cells. *Exp. Cell Res.* **19,** 220.

LITTLEFIELD, J. W. (1962). DNA synthesis in partially synchronized L cells. *Exp. Cell Res.* **26,** 318.

MAGEE, W. E., SHEEK, M. R. & SAGIK, B. P. (1958). Methods of harvesting mammalian cells grown in tissue culture. *Proc. Soc. exp. Biol. (N.Y.)* **99,** 390.

NEWTON, A. A. & WILDY, P. (1959). Parasynchronous division of HcLa cells. *Exp. Cell Res.* **16,** 624.

OYAMA, V. I. & EAGLE, H. (1956). Measurement of cell growth in tissue culture with a phenol reagent (Folin-Ciocalteau). *Proc. Soc. exp. Biol. (N.Y.)* **91,** 305.

PARKER, R. C., HEALY, G. & FISHER, DOROTHY (1954). Nutrition of animal cells in tissue culture. VII. Use of replicate cell culture in the evaluation of synthetic media. *Canad. J. biochem. Physiol.* **32,** 306.

PAUL, J. (1956). The chemical determination of deoxyribonucleic acid in tissue culture. *J. biophys. biochem. Cytol.* **2,** 797.

PAUL, J. (1958). Determination of the major constituents of small amounts of tissue. *Analyst* **83,** 37.

PAUL, J. & HAGIWARA, A. (1962). A kinetic study of the action of 5-fluoro-2'-deoxyuridine on synthetic processes in mammalian cells. *Biochim. biophys. Acta* **61,** 243.

PHILLIPS, H. J. & TERRYBERRY, J. E. (1957). Counting actively metabolizing tissue cultured cells. *Exp. Cell Res.* **13,** 341.

POMERAT, C. M., DRAGER, G. A. & PAINTER, J. T. (1946). Effect of some barbiturates on tissues *in vitro. Proc. Soc. exp. Biol. (N.Y.)* **63,** 322.

POMERAT, C. M. & LEAKE, C. D. (1954). Short term cultures for drug assays: general considerations. *Ann. N.Y. Acad. Sci.* **58**, 1110.

PUCK, T. T. (1958). Action of radiation on mammalian cells. III. Relationship between reproductive death and induction of chromosome anomalies by X-irradiation of euploid human cells in vitro. *Proc. nat. Acad. Sci. (Wash.)* **44**, 772.

PUCK, T. T. (1959). Quantitative studies on mammalian cells *in vitro*. *Rev. mod. Physiol.* **31**, 433.

PUCK, T. T. (1960). The action of radiation on mammalian cells. *Amer. Nat.* **94**, 95.

PUCK, T. T. & MARCUS, P. I. (1955). A rapid method for viable cell titration and clone production with HeLa cells in tissue culture. The use of X-irradiated cells to supply conditioning factors. *Proc. nat. Acad. Sci. (Wash.)* **41**, 432.

PUCK, T. T., MARCUS, P. I., & CIECIURA, S. J. (1956). Clonal growth of mammalian cells *in vitro. J. exp. Med.* **103**, 273.

SANFORD, KATHERINE K. (1951). General methods for quantitative studies on cells in tissue culture. Measurement of proliferation in tissue culture by enumeration of cell nuclei. In *Methods in Medical Research,* Ed. Visscher, M. B. Chicago: Year Book Publishers.

SANFORD, KATHERINE K., EARLE, W. R., EVANS, VIRGINIA J., WALTZ, HELEN K. & SHANNON, J. E. (1951). The measurement of proliferation in tissue culture by enumeration of cell nuclei. *J. nat. Cancer Inst.* **11**, 773.

SCHMIDT, G. & THANNHAUSER, S. J. (1945). A method for the determination of desoxyribonucleic acid, ribonucleic acid, and phosphoproteins in animal tissues. *J. biol. Chem.* **161**, 83.

SISKEN, J. E. (1962). Induction of partial synchrony in mammalian cells by sub-culturing procedures. *Nature (Lond.)* **197**, 104.

SNEDECOR, G. W. (1956). Statistical methods. Iowa State College Press. Ames, Iowa.

SZYBALSKI, W. (1959). Genetics of human cell lines. II. Method for determination of mutation rates to drug resistance. *Exper. Cell Res.* **18**, 588.

SZYBALSKI, W. & SMITH, M. J. (1959). Genetics of human cell lines. 1. 8-Azaguanine resistance, a selective 'single-step' marker. *Proc. Soc. exp. Biol. (N.Y.)* **101**, 662.

SZYBALSKI, W., SZYBALSKA, E. H. & RAGNI, G. (1962). Genetics studies with human cell lines. *Nat. Cancer Inst. Monograph No.* **7**, 75.

TERASIMA, T. & TOLMACH, L. J. (1963). Growth and nucleic acid synthesis in synchronously dividing populations of HeLa cells. *Exp. Cell Res.* **30**, 344.

TREVELYAN, W. E. & HARRISON, J. S. (1952). Microdetermination of yeast carbohydrates. *Biochem. J.* **50**, 299.

WAYMOUTH, CHARITY (1951). General methods for quantitative studies on cells in tissue culture. Measurement of growth by nucleic acid determination. In *Methods in Medical Research.* Ed. Visscher, M. B. Chicago: Year Book Publishers.

WAYMOUTH, CHARITY (1956). A rapid quantitative hematocrit method for measuring increase in cell population of strain L (Earle) cells cultivated in serum-free nutrient solutions. *J. nat. Cancer Inst.* **17**, 305.

XEROS, N. (1962). Deoxyriboside control and synchronization of mitosis. *Nature (Lond.)* **194**, 682.

CHAPTER XXI

VIROLOGY AND HOST-PARASITE RELATIONSHIPS

TISSUE CULTURE IN VIROLOGY

ALTHOUGH viruses had been grown in tissue cultures for many years and indeed some vaccines had been produced in this manner, it was not until the late 1940s that the tissue culture method became widely used among virologists. Its widespread application was initiated by the observation of Enders and his associates in 1949 that poliomyelitis virus would grow in human tissues of non-nervous origin in tissue culture. Up till that time it had been believed that if the poliomyelitis virus could be cultivated *in vitro* it would be necessary to grow it in nervous tissue because of the very high degree of tissue specificity exhibited *in vivo*. It has now been shown that many human viruses will grow readily in almost all cells of human origin and also in cells of monkey origin. The poliomyelitis virus is an example of one which will grow in a somewhat restricted range of cells. By contrast, some viruses will grow in cells from very different species. For instance, the vaccinia virus can be readily grown in tissue cultures made from chick embryos.

The tissue culture materials used in virology are very varied and practically all the methods described in earlier parts of this book have been used. Even organ culture techniques are producing some very interesting results in the study of host-parasite relationships and there is no doubt that this method will be more widely used in such investigations. The most commonly employed technique using primary explants is the Maitland culture (Chapter XII). This consists essentially of a suspension of chopped tissue in a nutrient medium. It is used almost entirely for the production of large amounts of virus and particularly for the production of poliomyelitis virus for the manufacture of vaccine.

Freshly trypsinised cells are very commonly used in virus work. One of the earliest types of tissue culture material to be employed in virological studies was trypsinised mixed embryonic cells, but the most commonly used cells at the present time are monkey kidney cells and human amnion cells, the preparation of which has been fully described in Chapter XIII.

Finally, great use is made of established cell strains in virology. The one most frequently used is the HeLa strain, but many others are in routine use, *e.g.* the Detroit 6 strain, many of Chang's human strains, and transformed strains of amnion cells. Almost all known cell strains have been tested for viral susceptibility and many of them support adequate viral growth.

While it is very difficult to classify tissue culture cells on the basis of morphology, it is possible in general to separate them into cells of epithelial type and cells of fibroblast type. Some viruses will attack both but others will preferentially attack the epithelial type of cell, leaving the fibroblastic type almost untouched. This is particularly evident in the case of adeno-viruses. Amnion cells resemble epithelial cells rather than fibroblast cells in morphology but in many respects differ from both. They are attacked by almost all kinds of viruses and demonstrate a rather specific type of cytopathology. However, if amnion cells undergo transformation to form a continuously growing strain they are liable to show the cytopathology typical of other cell strains.

Some specificity in the infectivity of different cell types has also been shown in organ culture by Bang. When small organised rudiments of tissue are infected with viruses *in vitro* it appears that the lesions are frequently confined to one particular type of cell within the tissue.

The effects produced by virus infection of cells vary. Some cells show no change whatsoever with certain viruses and the presence of an infection can only be demonstrated by other techniques, for example, haemadsorption. On the other hand, in many cells changes in both morphology and metabolism are produced. The morphological changes have been thoroughly described and are sufficiently typical to enable a provisional identification of the virus to be made. The metabolic changes have not yet been thoroughly investigated although inhibition of metabolism due to death of cells is often used as a test for the presence of virus.

Brief mention may be made here of the types of cytopathic effect (CPE) produced in tissue culture. The most severe effect, *total destruction* of cells, is produced by some of the common viruses such as the poliomyelitis virus and some of the Coxsackie viruses. Both epithelial and fibroblastic cells of susceptible strains are affected.

A somewhat less severe type of injury is produced by some of the encephalitis viruses. It is called *sub-total cellular degeneration* and consists of death of some cells and pyknosis of the nuclei of others.

In a third group of viruses the characteristic lesion is *focal degeneration*. This is produced by the herpes-B-pseudorabies group and consists of the development of intranuclear inclusion bodies commencing in a focus and progressing centrifugally in plaques. In the case of the vaccinia virus, a similar lesion is produced except that the inclusion bodies occur in the cytoplasm rather than in the nucleus.

A still lesser degree of degeneration is produced by some of the adenoviruses. In these cases *morphological changes occur without any cessation of cellular metabolism*. These consist of swelling of cells which form clumps and become granular and degenerate. Epithelial cells die quite quickly but fibroblastic cells survive much longer.

Yet another type of degeneration is known as *foamy degeneration* and has been described as being produced by the measles virus and some of the simian orphan viruses.

Some viruses of the influenza and para-influenza groups may infect cells without causing obvious cytopathic effect. These viruses have strong haemagglutinating activity and the presence of virus in a culture may be recognised by haemadsorption—the adsorption of washed erythrocytes to infected cells. A 0·5 per cent. suspension of washed guinea-pig or chicken erythrocytes is added to the culture (*e.g.* 0·2 ml. suspension per 5 ml. culture medium). The culture is incubated at 4° C. for 20 minutes and examined microscopically for adsorption of erythrocytes to the cell sheet.

This ability of tissue cultures to support the growth of viruses and to reveal their presence by lesions which are in some cases specific has been applied in virology for three main purposes : (1) the study of host-parasite relationships, (2) the detection and identification of viruses, and (3) the production of viruses for vaccine manufacture.

The study of the relationship between the virus and the cell on which it grows promises to be greatly aided by use of the tissue culture method. The techniques employed are varied and specialised and depend on the actual problems being investigated, but on the whole they employ methods of tissue culture already described in this book, along with some of the analytical techniques of virology which have been developed in connection with the study of bacteriophage.

Probably the most important single development in virology in recent years has been the use of tissue culture for the detection and identification of viruses. As a rule, the method is used for the identification of known viruses isolated from individuals suspected to be suffering from the diseases caused by them. In the course of these investigations, however, a large number of other viruses have been discovered. Many of these have been called the ' orphan ' viruses because, as Duran-Reynals has pointed out, they are viruses in search of a disease.

Tumour viruses

Since Rous demonstrated the infective nature of the fowl sarcoma bearing his name, many other infective cancer-producing agents have been recognised.

Some years ago, Carrel demonstrated that the Rous sarcoma virus could be propagated in chick embryo tissue cultures and subsequently intermittent reports of the same nature appeared from Halberstaedter and Doljanski in 1939 and from Manaker and Groupe in 1956. This particular problem has been reinvestigated by Rubin and Temin (1958, 1959) using Dulbecco's method for plating viruses on monolayers of trypsinised chick embryonic tissue. Proliferative or degenerative foci indicate loci of virus infection and in this way the virus can be studied quantitatively.

Much of the present interest in this problem has stemmed from the observations of Stewart and Eddy that the polyoma virus of mice can be propagated serially in cultures of mouse cells, in which it produces typical necrotic foci. This virus is easy to handle and is remarkable for the extraordinary variety of tumours it can produce in the mouse.

Other tumour viruses have been shown to be capable of producing destructive foci in cultured cells, particularly Friend's leukaemia virus of mice and the virus of avian lymphoma.

It is surprising perhaps that viruses which cause tumours in the animal should cause rapid death *in vitro*. This may not be a general property of tumour viruses, however, although it is obviously a feature which makes recognition of the presence of an infective agent easier. By inoculating cell populations during cloning it has now been recognised that tumour viruses, such as the polyoma virus, can cause cellular transformation without causing cell death. At the time of writing transformation of baby hamster kidney cells by polyoma virus has been most thoroughly studied. Transformation of human cell cultures by the simian virus SV40 has also been investigated. Suggestive evidence concerning other viruses of this kind are the report by Coman of passage of the Shope papilloma virus through cultures of rabbit skin and also the reports by Lasfargues of growth of the Bittner agent in cultures of mouse mammary tissue.

Isolation and identification of viruses

The isolation, identification and titration of the normal pathogenic viruses is carried out by standard techniques, the three most important of which will be described in detail. They are respectively, simple titration of virus ; titration by observation of metabolic inhibition (the metabolic inhibition test) ; and titration by means of the Dulbecco plaque technique.

Viruses are isolated simply by preparing a bacteria-free suspension of infected material and exposing susceptible cells to it. As an example the isolation of poliomyelitis virus from faeces will be described.

A 1/10 suspension of a faeces specimen is prepared by stirring it in BSS with a glass rod until all lumps have disappeared. The solid matter is then removed by centrifugation at 3,000 r.p.m. or faster for 15 - 20 minutes. The clear supernatant is removed for testing. With careful preparation it will probably be already free of bacteria but to minimise the risk of contamination a mixture of antibiotics (penicillin, streptomycin and mycostatin) is added (the mixture is kept as a X 100 stock solution).

Static test-tube cultures should have been prepared in advance with about 150,000 cells (HeLa or monkey kidney) in 1 ml. of medium. Without removing the medium 1 ml. of the faecal extract is added to a pair of tubes. After 1 hour the medium is removed from the cells and replaced with fresh medium. The specimens are examined daily for the appearance of typical cytopathogenic effects.

By the time this has been done a provisional diagnosis will have been made on the following criteria : (1) The source of the specimen. (2) The rate of appearance of cell lesions. (3) The cytopathogenic effect observed. A final diagnosis may be reached with the aid of specific antisera.

A 1/8 dilution of antiserum is used in routine work. Three sets of cultures are set up, one with cells and antiserum, a second with cells and virus, and a third with cells, virus and antiserum. Survival of the cells in the first and third groups, but not in the second, indicates protection by the antiserum and hence the identity of the virus.

Titration of virus

Before proceeding to examine sera for the presence of anti-bodies, it is desirable to titrate the virus to obtain a suitable dose. This can be done very simply by an extension of the methods described above.

Serial tenfold dilutions of virus with medium are first made. 1 ml. of each dilution is added to several stationary test-tube cultures each containing about 150,000 cells of a susceptible strain. After an hour the medium is removed from the cells and replaced with fresh medium. The cultures are re-examined after a few days (sufficient to produce typical CPE). The dilution of virus at which half of the cultures are infected is called the $TCID_{50}$ (50 per cent. Tissue Culture Infective Dose) and is used for reference in all future work.

Calculation of the $TCID_{50}$

Not all virus particles are infective and titration methods only recognise infective particles. If a culture is inoculated with at least one infectious unit (IU) it will be killed. There is, of course, a random distribution of infectious particles in aliquots of a suspension. When this has been diluted to the point where, on the average, one half of the aliquots of one ml. contain at least one infectious unit then the suspension is said to contain one $TCID_{50}$ per ml.

Only rarely, and by chance, will it be found that, at one particular dilution of virus, exactly half of the inoculated cultures are infected. More usually results of the following type are obtained (in a titration in which 12 cultures were inoculated at each dilution).

Reciprocal log diln.	Infected cultures	Uninfected cultures	Cumulative infected	Cumulative uninfected	Fraction infected	Percentage infected
5	12	0	48	0	48/48	100
6	12	0	36	0	36/36	100
7	10	2	24	2	24/26	92·5
8	8	4	14	6	14/20	90
9	4	8	6	14	6/20	30
10	2	10	2	24	2/26	7·5
11	0	12	0	36	0/36	0

Clearly the 50 per cent. endpoint lies between 10^{-8} and 10^{-9}. Several methods are used for interpolating between the observed values to give a nearer approximation. The most commonly used method is that of Reed and Muench. The data are set out as shown and the following formula is then used. The numbers from the above example are included in parentheses.

$$\frac{\text{Number above } 50\% \ (90) - 50}{\text{Number above } 50\% \ (90) - \text{Number below } 50\% \ (30)}$$

In this example this becomes $\dfrac{40}{60} = 0.67$. The 50 per cent. endpoint is then $10^{-8.67}$. Hence the original solution contained $10^{8.67}$ $TCID_{50}$/ml.

Relationship between infectious units (IU) and the $TCID_{50}$

When a suspension has been diluted to the point where half of a large number of 1 ml. fractions contain at least one infectious unit it will be obvious that the distribution of these infectious units is random. Thus, while 50 per cent. of the samples contain no infectious units, the remaining 50 per cent. will include many tubes which contain only one IU, some of which contain two IU and a few which contain more. The distribution of the units will follow a pure Poisson distribution. Hence, one $TCID_{50}$ will actually contain more than an average of 0·5 IU. From the Poisson distribution one $TCID_{50}$ is equivalent to 0·693 IU. The two values can be interconverted by the use of this factor.

Antiserum titration by the metabolic inhibition test

In addition to their use in isolating and identifying viruses, tissue cultures can be used for the titration of antisera. In particular, they can be used to determine the titre of antibodies against viruses in blood. For this purpose it is rather tedious to employ the method previously described. Since known viruses are used in the test, a study of the CPE is unimportant and the only information required is whether the serum protects cells from damage by virus or not. The metabolic inhibition test is therefore used. The principle is very simple. Cells are grown in a medium containing phenol red. As they accumulate acidic metabolites, the phenol red turns yellow, indicating that the cells are alive. If the cells are killed by the virus the medium remains red. Thus, cell survival (indicating protection by antiserum) can be recognised at a glance. A typical simple titration of this sort will be described.

A virus dilution equivalent to 100-200 $TCID_{50}$ is usually employed. The serum is first inactivated by heating at 56° for half an hour and doubling dilutions are prepared. Controls with serum and no virus must be set up in case the serum is itself toxic. The titrations can be carried out either in small test-tubes or in specially made plastic trays with multiple depressions which are used as small test-tubes. If the latter are used they are sterilised by ultraviolet light or by 95 per cent. alcohol.

PROCEDURE.—

1. Prepare a dilution of virus in medium equivalent to 100-200 $TCID_{50}$ per 0·25 ml.
2. Prepare 2-fold serial dilutions of serum (say 1/8, 1/16, 1/32) in medium.
3. Set up tubes as follows:

Tube No.	Cell Control	Serum Control	1	2	3
Virus dilution .	0	0	0·25 ml.	0·25 ml.	0·25 ml.
1/8 serum dilution .	0	0·25 ml.	0·25 ml.	0	0
1/16 serum dilution .	0	0	0	0·25 ml.	0
1/32 serum dilution .	0	0	0	0	0·25 ml.
Medium .	0·5 ml.	0·25 ml.	0	0	0

4. Leave these tubes at room temperature for 1 hour.
5. To each add 0·25 ml. of a suspension of HeLa cells (150,000 cells per ml.).
6. Layer on top of each 0·5 ml. liquid paraffin.

23

7. Incubate the tubes for 5 - 7 days.

8. Examine. Complete cell survival is indicated by a yellow colour in the medium. Death of the cells is indicated by a purple-red colour. Partial survival is indicated by intermediate tints.

In order to obtain good results by this technique, it is essential that absolute uniformity of conditions should be maintained throughout.

Plaque technique

Sometimes it is desirable to quantitate even more accurately, and this can be achieved by using the plaque-counting technique originated by Dulbecco and developed by Dulbecco and Vogt and Hsiung and Melnick. The principle of the technique is simple. Monolayer cultures of cells are exposed to very dilute suspensions of virus. The cells are then covered with a thin overlay of agar. Loci of viral infection can be recognised after some days as plaques of dead cells. Theoretically each virus produces a plaque, but for a variety of reasons the efficiency is rarely as high as 100 per cent.

The number of plaques gives the number of plaque-forming units (PFU) in the inoculum. One PFU is, in general, equivalent to one IU.

To get the best results, it is necessary to take very great care in preparing the monolayers of cells. They can be grown in any kind of vessel. Petri dishes were originally used, but prescription bottles are most commonly employed.

METHOD.—

1. Decant the growth medium from confluent cultures of healthy cells in 3 oz. prescription bottles. Wash three times with 2 ml. BSS to remove serum.

2. Prepared serial tenfold dilutions of virus in BSS to cover the range considered appropriate and overlay the cells with 0·5 ml. of this virus suspension. Allow the bottle to incubate for 1 hour.

3. Mix 15 ml. of medium (20 per cent. equine serum in BSS or maintenance solution containing 0·004 per cent. neutral red) with an equal volume of 3 per cent. molten agar in BSS. (Melt the agar by heating to 100° and then cool to 43° before mixing.)

4. Quickly cover each cell monolayer with 4 ml. of the agar mixture and place aside to solidify.

5. Invert the bottles and incubate at 37° C.

6. Observe the bottles daily in oblique light, preferably with the bottle resting on a white or pale green surface.

Agar suspension plaque technique

This modification of the Dulbecco plaque technique is particularly valuable when the cells used grow in suspension and do not adhere to glass. It can also be used readily with ascites tumour cells and freshly trypsinised cell suspensions. An additional advantage is that no adsorption period is required. The main limitation is that it requires more cells than the monolayer technique described above.

1. Plates are prepared by mixing 3 ml. of double-strength medium with 3 ml. molten 1·8 per cent. agar at 44° and pouring into 100 mm. Petri dishes. The agar is allowed to set.

2. To 10 ml. test-tubes are added 0·5 ml. of cell suspension containing $1-1·5 \times 10^8$ cells per ml.: 0·1 ml. of a virus suspension containing 100-1,000 plaque-forming units (PFU) per ml. are added, followed by 2 ml. molten agar medium (prepared as in 1) at 44°.

3. Immediately the cell-agar suspension is rapidly mixed and poured on top of a prepared plate, being spread by rotation before it sets. The tube is allowed to drain as completely as possible, the final drop being removed by touching it to the agar surface.

4. After setting the plates are incubated at 37° for about 40 hours in a CO_2 incubator. To stain they are flooded with Earle's saline containing 1/20,000 neutral red for about 2 hours.

The use of a CO_2 incubator may be eliminated by using prescription bottles as above or by incorporating a 0·3 per cent. tris(hydroxymethyl)amino-methane buffer in the medium.

These plaque methods are not only more precise than titration methods in which killing of a whole culture is determined, they are less time-consuming and require less material and fewer replicates. Hence, they are the methods which should receive first consideration.

THE USE OF TISSUE CULTURE FOR
VACCINE MANUFACTURE

Of very great importance in recent years has been the development of vaccines against poliomyelitis and these are made from virus grown in tissue culture. The virus can either be grown in chopped tissue fragments, *i.e.* the Maitland culture, or in monolayers of cells. A general outline of the technique follows.

Suitable monkeys are tuberculin tested and carefully examined to exclude disease. They are anaesthetised by means of thiopentone and bilateral nephrectomy is performed aseptically. The kidneys are immediately decapsulated and chopped up into small pieces in medium 199, by means of long scissors. The kidney fragments are then trypsinised in the manner described in Chapter XIII. When the cells have been counted, medium (consisting of 2 per cent. calf serum in medium 199) is added to give a cell count of approximately 300,000 cells per ml. 400 ml. of this suspension are inoculated into 5 litre diphtheria toxin bottles, or 80 ml. each into one litre Roux bottles. After the cells have become established, the fluid is removed and the cells are washed with BSS. Then 150 ml. of medium 199 are added per 1 litre bottle, followed by 0·5 ml. of a stock virus preparation. The cultures are replaced in the incubator and degeneration due to the virus becomes apparent within two to three days. All contaminated cultures are discarded at this point. All the material from the flasks is pooled and the cell débris is allowed to settle in the cold. The supernatant is carefully decanted off and filtered. It contains the crude virus preparation. In the case of the Salk vaccine formalin is then added to give a final concentration of 1/4,000 and this is left for about 12 days at 37°. Samples are then dialysed free of formalin and tested in tissue culture for living virus. This testing must be carried out very thoroughly indeed and it is usual to grow the cells for a period of 30 days after inoculation with the vaccine.

The general form of preparation of other vaccines is similar although, of course, when living vaccines containing attenuated strains of virus are used, the killing stage is omitted.

BIBLIOGRAPHY

ACKERMANN, W. W., ISHIDA, N. & MAASSAB, H. F. (1955). Growth characteristics of influenza virus concerning the binding of virus by host cells. *J. exp. Med.* **102**, 545.

ANDREWES, C. H. (1929). Virus III in tissue cultures. II. Further observations on the formation of inclusion bodies. III. Experiments bearing on immunity. *Brit. J. Path.* **10**, 273.

ANDREWES, C. H. (1942). Interference by one virus with the growth of another in tissue-culture. *Brit. J. exp. Path.* **23**, 214.

ANDREWES, C. H., BURNET, F. M., ENDERS, J. F., GARD, S., HIRST, G. K., KAPLAN, M. M. & ZHDANOV, V. M. (1961). Taxonomy of viruses infecting vertebrates: Present knowledge and ignorance. *Virology* **15**, 52.

ANDREWES, C. H., CHAPRONNIERE, D. M., GOMPELS, A. E. H., PEREIRA, H. G. & RODEN, A. T. (1953). Propagation of common-cold virus in tissue cultures. *Lancet* **365**, 546.

BANG, F. B. (1955). Pathology of cells infected with viruses—morphological and biochemical aspects. *Fed. Proc.* **14**, 619.

BANG, F. B. & GEY, G. O. (1951). Viruses and Cells. A study in tissue culture applications. I. Cells involved—availability and susceptibility. II. Effect of several viruses on cell types and the amount of virus produced. *Trans. N.Y. Acad. Sci.* **14**, 15.

BERGMANN, L. (1959). Plant viruses in tissue culture. *Trans. N.Y. Acad. Sci.* **21**, 227.

BERGMANN, L. & MELCHERS, G. (1959). Infektionsversuche an submers kultivierten Geweben mit Tabakmosaikvirus. *Z. Naturforsch.* **14**, 73.

BLACK, P. H. & ROWE, W. P. (1963). An analysis of SV40-induced transformation of hamster kidney tissue *in vitro*. I. General characteristics. *Proc. nat. Acad. Sci. (Wash.)* **50**, 606.

BLACK, P. H. & ROWE, W. P. (1963). SV-40 induced proliferation of tissue culture cells of rabbit, mouse, and porcine origin. *Proc. Soc. exp. Biol. (N.Y.)* **114**, 721.

BLACK, P. H., HARTLEY, J. W., ROWE, W. P. & HUEBNER, R. J. (1963). Transformation of bovine tissue culture cells by bovine papilloma virus. *Nature (Lond.)* **199**, 1016.

BLACK, F. L., REISSIG, M. & MELNICK, J. L. (1956). Propagation of measles virus in a strain of human epidermoid cancer cells (Hep 2). *Proc. Soc. exp. Biol. (N.Y.)* **93**, 107.

BLAND, J. O. W. & CANTI, R. G. (1935). The growth and development of psittacosis virus in tissue cultures. *J. Path. Bact.* **40**, 231.

BLAND, J. O. W. & ROBINOW, C. F. (1939). The inclusion bodies of vaccinia and their relationship to the elementary bodies studied in cultures of the rabbit's cornea. *J. Path. Bact.* **48**, 381.

BROADHURST, J., CAMERON, GLADYS & SAURINO, V. (1938). Measles inclusion bodies in blood and tissue cultures. *J. infect. Dis.* **62**, 6.

CAPSTICK, P. B., TELLING, R. C., CHAPMAN, W. G. & STEWART, D. L. (1962). Growth of a cloned strain of hamster kidney cells in suspended cultures and their susceptibility to the virus of foot and mouth disease. *Nature (Lond.)* **195**, 1163.

CARREL, A. (1924). Action de l'extrait filtré du sarcome de Rous sur les macrophages du sang. *C.R. Soc. Biol. (Paris)* **91**, 1069.

CARREL, A. (1926). Some conditions of the reproduction *in vitro* of the Rous virus. *J. exp. Med.* **43**, 647.

CHANG, S. L., BERG, G., BUSCH, K. A., STEVENSON, R. E., CLARKE, N. A. & KABLER, P. W. (1958). Application of the 'most probable number' method for estimating concentrations of animal viruses by the tissue culture technique. *Virology* **6**, 27.

CIECIURA, S. J., MARCUS, P. I. & PUCK, T. T. (1957). The use of X-irradiated HeLa cell giants to detect latent virus in mammalian cells. *Virology*, **3**, 426-428.

COMAN, D. R. (1946). Induction of neoplasia *in vitro* with a virus. Experiments with rabbit skin grown in tissue culture and treated with shope papilloma virus. *Cancer Res.* **6**, 602.

COOPER, P. D. (1955). A method for producing plaques in agar suspensions of animal cells. *Virology*, **1**, 397.

COOPER, P. D. (1961). An improved agar cell-suspension plaque assay for poliovirus: some factors affecting efficiency of plating. *Virology* **13**, 153.

DALLDORF, G., ENDERS, J. F., HAMMON, W. M., SABIN, A. B., SYVERTON, J. T. & MELNICK, J. L. (1955). Enteric cytopathogenic human orphan (ECHO) viruses. *Science* **122**, 1187.

DARNELL, J. E. & SAWYER, T. K. (1960). The basis for variation in susceptibility to poliovirus in HeLa cells. *Virology* **11**, 665.

DAVIS, O. S. & GUSTAFSON, D. P. (1959). Tissue culture of avian visceral lymphoid tumors and *in vitro* serial passage of the virus. *Amer. J. vet. Res.* **20**, 119.

DULBECCO, R. (1955). Interaction of viruses and animal cells. A study of facts and interpretations. *Physiol. Rev.* **35**, 301.

DULBECCO, R. (1961). Viral carcinogenesis. *Cancer Res.* **21**, 975.

DULBECCO, R. & VOGT, M. (1954). Plaque formation and isolation of pure lines with poliomyelitis viruses. *J. exp. Med.* **99**, 167.

DULBECCO, R. & VOGT, M. (1955). Biological properties of poliomyelitis viruses as studied by the plaque technique. *Ann. N.Y. Acad. Sci.* **61**, 790.

DULBECCO, R. & VOGT, M. (1960). Significance of continued virus production in tissue cultures rendered neoplastic by polyoma virus. *Proc. nat. Acad. Sci. (Wash.)* **46**, 1617.

DULBECCO, R., VOGT, M. & STRICKLAND, A. G. R. (1956). A study of the basic aspects of neutralization of two animal viruses, western equine encephalitis virus and poliomyelitis virus. *Virology* **2**, 162.

DUNNEBACKE, THELMA, H. (1956). Cytopathic changes associated with poliomyelitis infections in human amnion cells. *Virology* **2**, 811.

DUNNEBACKE, THELMA H. (1956). Correlation of the stage of cytopathic change with the release of poliomyelitis virus. *Virology* **2**, 399.

EAGLE, H. & HABEL, K. (1956). The nutritional requirements for the propagation of poliomyelitis virus by the HeLa cell. *J. exp. Med.* **104**, 271.

EDDY, B. E. & STEWART, S. E (1959). Characteristics of the SE polyoma virus. *Amer. J. publ. Hlth* **49**, 1486.

EDDY, B. E., STEWART, S. E., YOUNG, R. & MIDER, G. B. (1958). Neoplasms in hamsters induced by mouse tumor agent passed in tissue culture. *J. nat. Cancer Inst.* **20**, 747.

ENDERS, J. F. (1948). Propagation of viruses and Rickettsiae in tissue cultures. In *Viral and Rickettsiae Infections of Man*, ed. T. M. Rivers. Philadelphia: Lippincott.

ENDERS, J. F. (1954). Tissue culture in the study of immunity—restrospection and anticipation. *J. Immunol.* **73**, 62.

ENDERS, J. F. & PEEBLES, T. C. (1954). Propagation in tissue cultures of cytopathogenic agents from patients with measles. *Proc. Soc. exp. Biol. (N.Y.)* **86**, 277.

ENDERS, J. F., WELLER, T. H. & ROBBINS, F. C. (1949). Cultivation of Lansing strain of poliomyelitis virus in cultures in various human embryonic tissues. *Science* **109**, 85.

FAULKNER, G. H. & ANDREWS, C. H. (1935). Propagation of strains of rabbit fibroma virus in tissue culture. *Brit. J. exp. Path.* **16**, 271.

FELLER, A. E., ENDERS, J. F. & WELLER, T. H. (1940). The prolonged coexistence of vaccinia virus in high titre and living cells in roller tube cultures of chick embryonic tissues. *J. exp. Med.* **72**, 367.

FOGH, J. & LUND, R. O. (1955). Plaque formation of poliomyelitis viruses on human amnion cell cultures. *Proc. Soc. exp. Biol. (N.Y.)* **90**, 80.

FINDLAY, G. M. (1928). A note on the cultivation of the virus of fowl-pox. *Brit. J. exp. Path.* **9**, 28.

GEY, G. O. & BANG, F. (1951). Viruses and cells—a study in tissue culture applications. I. Cells involved, availability and susceptibility. II. Effect of several viruses on cell types and the amount of virus produced. *Trans. N.Y. Acad. Sci.* **14**, 15.

GRANOFF, A. (1955). Plaque formation with influenza strains. *Virology* **1**, 252.

HAAGEN, E. (1934). Yellow fever virus in tissue culture. *Arch. exp. Zellforsch.* **15**, 405.

HALBERSTAEDTER, L. & DOLJANSKI, L. (1939). Transformation *in vitro* of cultures of normal cells treated with Rous sarcoma agent into sarcoma cells. *Nature (Lond.)* **143**, 288.

HARDING, C. V., HARDING, D., McLIMANS, W. Γ. & RAKE, G. (1956). Cytological changes accompanying the growth of poliomyclitis virus in cells of human origin (strain HeLa). *Virology* **2**, 109.

HARTLEY, J. W., HEUBNER, R. J. & ROWE, W. P. (1956). Serial propagation of adeno-viruses (APC) in monkey kidney tissue culture. *Proc. Soc. exp. Biol. (N.Y.)* **92**, 667.

HEINE, U., BEAUDREAU, G. S., BECKER, C., BEARD, D. & BEARD, J. W. (1961). Virus of avian erythroblastosis. VIII. Ultrastructure of erythroblasts from the chicken and from tissue culture. *J. nat. Cancer Inst.* **26**, 359.

HENLE, G. & DEINHARDT, F. (1955). Propagation and primary isolation of mumps virus in tissue culture. *Proc. Soc. exp. Biol. (N.Y.)* **89**, 556.

HIRST, G. K. (1959). Virus-host cell relation. *Viral and rickettsial infections of man*, chap. 3, pp. 111-112.

HOLLAND, J. J. & McLAREN, L. C. (1959). The mammalian cell-virus relationship. II. Adsorption, reception, and eclipse of poliovirus by HeLa cells. *J. exp. Med.* **109**, 487.

HOWES, D. W. & MELNICK, J. L. (1957). The growth cycle of poliovirus in monkey kidney cells. I. Maturation and release of virus in monolayer cultures. *Virology* **4**, 97.

HOYLE, L. & FRISCH-NIGGEMEYER, W. (1955). The disintegration of influenza virus particles on entry into the host cell; studies with virus labelled with radiophosphorus. *J. Hyg. (Lond.)* **53**, 474.

HSIUNG, G. D. & MELNICK, J. L. (1955). Plaque formation with poliomyelitis, Coxsackie, and orphan viruses in bottle cultures of monkey epithelial cells. *Virology* **1**, 533.

HSIUNG, G. D. & MELNICK, J. L. (1957). Morphologic characteristics of plaques produced in monkey kidney monolayer cultures by enteric viruses (poliomyelitis, Coxsackie and Echo groups). *J. Immunol.* **78**, 128.

HUANG, C. H. (1943). A visible method for titration and neutralization of viruses on the basis of pH changes in tissue culture. *Proc. Soc. exp. Biol. (N.Y.)* **54**, 160.

HULL, R. N., MINNER, J. R. & SMITH, J. W. (1956). New viral agents recovered from tissue cultures of monkey kidney cells. I. Origin and properties of cytopathogenic agents S.V.$_{1, 2, 4, 5, 6, 11, 12, 15}$. *Amer. J. Hyg.* **63**, 204.

KAPLAN, A. S. (1955). The susceptibility of monkey kidney cells to polio virus in vivo and in vitro. *Virology* **1**, 377.

KASSANIS, B. (1957). The multiplication of tobacco mosaic virus in cultures of tumorous tobacco tissues. *Virology* **4**, 5.

LASFARGUES, E. Y., MOORE, D. H. & MURRAY, M. R. (1958). Maintenance of the milk factor in cultures of mouse mammary epithelium. *Cancer Res.* **18**, 1281.

LENNETTE, E. H. & KOPROWSKI, H. (1946). Interference between viruses in tissue culture. *J. exp. Med.* **83**, 195.

LI, C. P. & RIVERS, T. M. (1930). Cultivation of vaccine virus. *J. exp. Med.* **52**, 465.

LIPTON, M. M. & STEIGMAN, A. J. (1955). A simplified colorimetric test for poliomyelitis virus and antibody. *Proc. Soc. exp. Biol. (N.Y.)* **88**, 114.

LLOYD, W., THEILER, M. & RICCI, N. I. (1936). Modification of the virulence of yellow fever virus by cultivation in tissues *in vitro. Trans. roy. Soc. trop. Med. Hyg.* **29**, 481.

LWOFF, A., DULBECCO, R., VOGT, MARGUERITE & LWOFF, MARGUERITE (1955). Kinetics of the release of poliomeyelitis virus from single cells. *Virology* **1**, 128.

MACPHERSON, I. (1963). Characteristics of a hamster cell clone transformed by polyoma virus. *J. nat. Cancer Inst.* **30**, 795.

MACPHERSON, I. & STOKER, M. (1962). Polyoma transformation of hamster cell clones—an investigation of genetic factors affecting cell competence. *Virology* **16**, 147.

MAITLAND, M. C. & MAITLAND, H. B. (1931). Cultivation of foot-and-mouth disease virus. *J. comp. Path.* **44**, 106.

MAITLAND, H. B. & MAITLAND, M. C. (1928). Cultivation of vaccinia virus without tissue culture. *Lancet* **2**, 596.

MANAKER, R. A. & GROUPÉ, V. (1956). Discrete foci of altered chick embryo cells associated with Rous sarcoma virus in tissue culture. *Virology* **2**, 838.

MARCUS, P. I. & PUCK, T. T. (1958). Host-cell interaction of animal viruses. I. Titration of cell-killing by viruses. *Virology* **6**, 405-423.

MARCUS, P. I. & TOLMACH, L. J. (1958). Virus synthesis in giant cells produced by X-irradiation of mammalian cells. *Radiat. Res.* **9**, 149.

MATA, L. J. & WELLER, T. H. (1962). A cell culture system on agar permitting direct investigation of viral antigens by immunodiffusion. *Proc. Soc. exp. Biol. (N.Y.)* **109**, 705.

MELNICK, J. L. & OPTON, E. M. (1956). Assay of poliomyelitis neutralizing antibody in disposable plastic panels. *Bull. Wld Hlth Org.* **14**, 129.

MURPHY, W. H. & LANDAU, B. J. (1962). Clonal variation and interaction of cells with viruses. *Nat. Cancer Inst. Monograph No.* **7**, 249.

NOYES, W. F. (1953). A simple technic for demonstrating plaque formation with virus of vaccinia. *Proc. Soc. exp. Biol. (N.Y.)* **83**, 426.

PARKER, F., JR. & NYE, R. N. (1925). Studies on filtrable viruses. I. Cultivation of vaccine virus. *Amer. J. Path.* **1**, 325.

PARSONS, R. & TYRRELL, D. (1961) A plaque method for assaying some viruses isolated from common cold. *Nature (Lond.)* **189**, 640.

PAYNE, F. E., KURTZ, H. & ACKERMANN, W. W. (1958). Initial stages of the interaction of HeLa cells with poliovirus. *Arch Virusforschung,* **8**, 1-15.

PORTERFIELD, J. S. (1959). A simple plaque-inhibition test for antiviral agents: application to assay of interferon. *Lancet* **2**, 326.

PORTERFIELD, J. S. (1959). A plaque technique for the titration of yellow fever virus and antisera. *Trans. R. Soc. trop. Med. Hyg.* **53**, 458.

RAPPAPORT, C. (1955). Monolayer cultures of trypsinized monkey kidney cells in synthetic medium. Application to polio virus synthesis. *Proc. Soc. exp. Biol. (N.Y.)* **91**, 484.

REED, L. J. & MUENCH, H. (1938). A simple method of estimating 50 per cent. endpoints. *Amer. J. Hyg.* **37**, 493.

REISSIG, M., BLACK, F. L. & MELNICK, J. L. (1956). Formation of multi-nucleated giant cells in measles virus infected cultures deprived of glutamine. *Virology* 2, 836.

RIVERS, T. M., HAAGEN, E. & MUCKENFUSS, R. S. (1929). Development in tissue cultures of the intracellular changes characteristic of vaccinal and herpetic infections. *J. exp. Med.* 50, 665.

RIVERS, T. M. & WARD, S. M. (1933). Further observations on the cultivation of vaccine virus for Jennerian prophylaxis in man. *J. exp. Med.* 58, 635.

RIVERS, T. M. & WARD, S. M. (1935). Jennerian prophylaxis by means of intradermal injections of culture vaccine virus. *J. exp. Med.* 62, 549.

ROBBINS, F. C. & ENDERS, J. F. (1950). Tissue culture techniques in study of animal viruses. *Amer. J. med. Sci.* 220, 316.

ROBBINS, F. C., ENDERS, J. F. & WELLER, T. H. (1950). Cytopathogenic effect of poliomyelitis viruses *in vitro* on human embryonic tissues *Proc. Soc. exp. Biol. (N.Y.)* 75, 370.

ROBERTSON, H. E., BAUMER, K. T. & SYVERTON, J. T. (1955). Propagation *in vitro* of poliomyelitis viruses. VII. pH changes of HeLa cell cultures for assay. *Proc. Soc. exp. Biol. (N.Y.)* 88, 119.

ROGER, N. G., BANKHEAD, A. S., CRAWFORD, I. P. & MEYER, H. M. (1957). Serodiagnosis of group B Coxsackie virus infections by a metabolic inhibition test. *Bact. Proc.* p. 74.

RUBIN, H. & TEMIN, H. M. (1959). A radiological study of cell-virus interaction in the Rous sarcoma. *Virology* 7, 75.

RUBIN, H., FRANKLIN, R. M. & BALUDA, M. (1957). Infection and growth of Newcastle disease virus (NDV) in cultures of chick embryo lung epithelium. *Virology* 3, 587.

SABIN, A. B. & OLITSKY, P. K. (1936). Cultivation of poliomyelitis virus *in vitro* in human embryonic nervous tissue. *Proc. Soc. exp. Biol. (N.Y.)* 34, 357.

SALK, J. E., YOUNGNER, J. S. & WARD, E. N. (1954). Use of colour change of phenol red as the indicator of titrating poliomyelitis virus or its antibody in a tissue culture system. *Amer. J. Hyg.* 60, 214.

SCHERER, W. F., SYVERTON, J. T. & GEY, G. O. (1953). Studies on the propagation *in vitro* of poliomyelitis virus. IV. Viral multiplication in a stable strain of human malignant epithelial cells (strain HeLa) derived from an epidermoid carcinoma of the cervix. *J exp. Med.* 97, 695.

SEGRETAIN, G. (1943). Culture d'un virus et son inoculation sur fragments de tige de tabac cultives in vitro. *Ann. inst. Pasteur* 69, 61.

STEINHARDT, E., ISRAELI, C. & LAMBERT, R. A. (1913). Studies on the cultivation of the virus of vaccinia. *J. infect. Dis.* 13, 294.

STEWART, S. E., EDDY, B. E., GOCHENOUR, A. M., BORGESE, N. G. & GRUBBS, G. E. (1957). The induction of neoplasms with a substance released from mouse tumors by tissue culture. *Virology* 3, 380.

STEWART, S. E., EDDY, B. E. & BORGESE, N. (1958). Neoplasms in mice inoculated with a tumor agent carried in tissue culture. *J. nat. Cancer Inst.* 20, 1223.

STOKER, M. (1962). Characteristics of normal and transformed clones arising from BHK21 cells exposed to polyoma virus. *Virology* 18, 649.

STOKER, M. & MACPHERSON, I. (1961). Studies on transformation of hamster cells by polyoma virus *in vitro*. *Virology* 14, 359.

SYVERTON, J. T. (1957). Host-parasite relationships in living cells. In *Cytopathology*. Springfield: Thomas.

SYVERTON, J. T. (1957). The response of mammalian cells in culture to virus infection. *J. nat. Cancer Inst.* **19**, 687.

TAYLOR, J. & GRAHAM, A. F. (1961). Analysis of a plaque assay method for purified poliovirus MEF-1. *Virology* **13**, 427.

TEMIN, H. M. & RUBIN, H. (1958). Characteristics of an assay for Rous sarcoma virus and Rous sarcoma cells in tissue culture. *Virology* **6**, 669-688.

THEILER, M. & SMITH, H. H. (1937). The effect of prolonged cultivation *in vitro* upon pathogenicity of yellow fever virus. *J. exp. Med.* **65**, 767.

THEILER, M. & SMITH, H. H. (1937). The use of yellow fever virus modified by *in vitro* cultivation for human immunization. *J. exp. Med.* **65**, 787.

TODARO, G. J., WOLMAN, S. R. & GREEN, H. (1963). Rapid transformation of human fibroblasts with low growth potential into established cell lines by SV_{40}. *J. cell. comp. Physiol.* **62**, 257.

VOGT, M. & DULBECCO, R. (1960). Virus-cell interaction with a tumor producing virus. *Proc. nat. Acad. Sci.* (*Wash.*) **46**, 365.

WELLER, T. T. (1953). The application of tissue culture methods to the study of poliomyelitis. *New Engl. J. Med.* **249**, 186.

WELLER, T. H. & ENDERS, J. F. (1948). Production of hemagglutinin by mumps and influenza A viruses in suspended cell tissue cultures. *Proc. Soc. exp. Biol.* (*N.Y.*) **69**, 124.

WELLER, T. H., ENDERS, J. F., ROBBINS, F. C. & STODDARD, M. B. (1952). Studies on cultivation of poliomyelitis viruses in tissue culture. I. Propagation of poliomyelitis viruses in suspended cell cultures of various human tissues. *J. Immunol.* **69**, 645.

WHITE, P. R. (1928). Multiplication of the viruses of tobacco and aucuba mosaic in growing excised tomato root tips. *Phytopath. Class.* **24**, 1003.

HOST-PARASITE STUDIES WITH ORGANISMS OTHER THAN VIRUSES

By far the greatest volume of work in the study of host-parasite relationships with tissue culture has been done with viruses. However, a number of other intracellular organisms have also been investigated. The Rickettsiae in particular have been the subject of intensive study, mainly by the group at the Walter Reed Army Hospital. This group has managed to grow these organisms in several cell-types, especially the MB III cell which can be readily cultured in suspension. By this method data have been collected on the growth, life-cycle and metabolism of Rickettsiae.

A considerable amount of work has also been done with mycobacteria, especially the tubercle and leprosy bacilli. Macrophages have been used in a great many studies but recently cell-strains have been used and, for instance, lepraemurium has been grown successfully in the strain L cell.

Many parasitic protozoa have been cultured successfully in tissue culture cells, including the parasites of several tropical diseases.

The pleuropneuomonia organisms also promise to form an interesting subject of study since they have been found as chronic contaminants of cell strains (see Chapter VIII).

The above organisms are all either slow-growing or else dependent wholly or in part on the presence of living cells. Consequently, it is feasible to study them by the tissue culture method, even with buffy coat macrophages which grow very slowly, if at all. More rapidly-growing organisms quickly overwhelm these cells. However, the introduction of fast-growing cell strains has made it feasible to study their interaction with some of the more rapidly growing pathogenic bacteria. Shepard, in particular, has studied a number of rapidly growing mycobacteria and other organisms in this way. Undoubtedly, a great deal remains to be done in this field, especially with regard to facultatively intracellular pathogenic organisms.

BIBLIOGRAPHY

BLAND, J. O. W. (1933). Cultivation of a protozoon (Toxoplasma) in tissue culture. *Arch. exp. Zellforsch.* **14,** 345.

BOZEMAN, F. M., HOPPS, H. E., DANAUSKAS, J. X., JACKSON, E. B. & SMADEL, J. E. (1956). Study on the growth of rickettsiae. I. A tissue culture system for quantitative estimations of Rickettsia tsutsugamushi. *J. Immunol.* **76,** 475.

FELL, HONOR B. & BRIEGER, E. M. (1947). The effect of phagocytosis on the growth and survival of avian tubercle bacilli in embryonic chicken tissues cultivated *in vitro. J. Hyg. (Lond.)* **45,** 359.

FELL, HONOR B. & BRIEGER, E. M. (1951). A comparative study of the reaction *in vivo* and *in vitro* of rabbit tissues to infection with bovine tubercle bacilli. I. Observations of rabbit spleen infected *in vitro. J. Hyg. (Lond.)* **49,** 181.

FJELDE, AUDREY (1957). The growth pattern of human cancer cells in tissue culture with Mycobacterium tuberculosis. *Exp. Cell Res.* **12,** 35.

FJELDE, AUDREY & ENGBAEK, H. C. (1957). The relationship of mycobacteria and mammalian cells in tissue culture. *Amer. Rev. Tuberc.* **75,** 347.

GARBUTT, ELIZABETH W., REES, R. J. W. & BARR, YVONNE M. (1958). Multiplication of rat-leprosy bacilli in cultures of rat fibroblasts. *Lancet* **2,** 127.

GAVRILOV, W., LESNERET, S. & COWEZ, S. (1940). Emploi de la methode des cultures de tissus dans l'étude de protozoaires. Les Trypanosomes. *Riv. Parassit.* **4,** 148.

GEIMAN, Q. M., ANFINSEN, C. B., MCKEE, R. W., ORMSBEE, R. A. & BALL, E. G. (1946). Studies on malarial parasites. VII. Methods and techniques for cultivation. *J. exp. Med.* **84,** 583.

HANKS, J. H. (1947). The fate of leprosy bacilli in fibroblasts cultivated from lepromatous lesions. *Int. J. Leprosy* **15,** 48.

HANKS, D. P. & THIMANN, K. (1947). A study of the bacilli in tissue culture of lepromata in serum media. *Int. J. Leprosy* **15,** 21.

HAWKING, F. (1945). Growth of protozoa in tissue culture. I. *Plasmodium gallinaceum*, exo-erythrocytic forms. *Trans. R. Soc. trop. Med. Hyg.* **39**, 245.

HAWKING, F. (1946). Growth of protozoa in tissue culture. II. *Plasmodium relictum*, exo-erythrocytic forms. *Trans. R. Soc. trop. Med. Hyg.* **40**, 183.

HAWKING, F. (1946). Growth of protozoa in tissue culture. III. *Trypanosoma cruzi*. *Trans. R. Soc. trop. Med. Hyg.* **40**, 345.

HAWKING, F. (1947). Growth of protozoa in tissue culture. V. *Leishmania donovani*. *Trans. R. Soc. trop. Med. Hyg.* **41**, 545.

JAHNES, W. G., FULLMER, H. M. & LI, C. P. (1957). Free living amoebae as contaminants in monkey kidney tissue culture. *Proc. Soc. exp. Biol. (N.Y.)* **96**, 484.

LOCK, J. A. (1953). Cultivation of *Toxoplasma gondii* in tissue culture in mammalian cells. *Lancet* **1**, 324.

MEYER, H. (1949). *The cultivation of Protozoa in Tissue Culture*, Inst. do Biofisica, Univ. do Brasil, Rio de Janeiro.

REES, R. J. W. & GARBUTT, E. W. (1962). Studies on Mycobacterium lepraemurium in tissue culture. I. Multiplication and growth characteristics in cultures of rat fibroblasts. *Brit. J. exp. Path.* **43**, 221.

REES, R. J. W. & WONG, P. C. (1958). Limited multiplication of M. lepraemurium in tissue culture. *Nature (Lond.)* **181**, 359.

SCHAECHTER, M., BOZEMAN, F. M. & SMADEL, J. E. (1957). Study on the growth of rickettsiae. II. Morphologic observations of living rickettsiae on tissue culture cells. *Virology* **3**, 160.

SHAFFER, J. M., KUCERA, C. & SPINK, W. (1953). The protection of intracellular Brucella against therapeutic agents and the bactericidal action of serum. *J. exp. Med.* **97**, 77.

SEGS, W. & BLOCH, H. (1957). Pathogenic and immunogenic differentiation of M. tuberculosis grown *in vitro* and *in vivo*. *Amer. Rev. Tuberc.* **75**, 495.

SHEPARD, C. C. (1957). Use of HeLa cells infected with tubercle bacilli for the study of antituberculous drugs. *J. Bact.* **73**, 494.

SHEPARD, C. C. (1957). Growth characteristics in HeLa cells of the rapidly-growing acid fast bacteria. Mycobacterium fortuitum, Mycobacterium phlei and Mycobacterium smegmatis. *J. Bact.* **73**, 722.

STAHELIN, H., KARNOVSKY, M. L. & SUTER, E. (1956). Studies on the interaction between phagocytes and tubercle bacilli. The action of phagocytes upon C^{14}-labelled tubercle bacilli. *J. exp. Med.* **104**, 137.

SUTER, E. (1952). The multiplication of tubercle bacilli within normal phagocytes in tissue culture. *J. exp. Med.* **96**, 137.

SUTER, E. (1954). Some aspects of intracellular parasitism of pathogenic microorganisms. *Int. J. Leprosy* **22**, 1.

SUTER, E. (1956). Interaction between phagocytes and pathogenic microorganisms. *Bacteriol. Rev.* **20**, 95.

VISCHER, W. A. & SUTER, E. (1954). Intracellular multiplication of Toxoplasma gondii in adult mammalian macrophages cultivated *in vitro*. *Proc. Soc. exp. Biol. (N.Y.)* **86**, 413.

WISSEMAN, C. L., JR., HAHN, F. E., JACKSON, E. B. BOZEMAN, F. M. & SMADEL, J. E. (1952). Metabolic studies of rickettsiae. II. Studies on the pathway of glutamate oxidation by purified suspensions of Rickettsia mooseri. *J. Immunol.* **68**, 251.

INDEX

Printed by The Central Press (Aberdeen) Ltd.